ENCYCLOPEDIA
SCIENCE
SUPPLEMENT

A Modern Science Anthology for the Family

1981

ISBN 0-7172-1511-3
Library of Congress Catalog Card Number 64-7603

ACKNOWLEDGMENTS

Sources of articles appear below, indicating those reprinted with the kind permission of publications and organizations.

THE SUN-GRAZERS, Page 6: *Astronomy,* August 1979. Reproduced by permission of publisher. Copyright © 1979 by AstroMedia Corp., Milwaukee, WI. All rights reserved.

THE MULTIPLE-MIRROR TELESCOPE, Page 11: Copyright 1979 Smithsonian Institution, from SMITHSONIAN magazine, May 1979.

AN AMAZING GALAXY IS FOUND, Page 17: Reprinted from the Special Winter 1979 issue of *Science Digest* by permission of the authors.

SS 433: A PECULIAR STAR, Page 23: © Copyright 1979, Astronomical Society of the Pacific. Reprinted by permission from *Mercury* magazine, 1290–24th Avenue, San Francisco, CA 94122.

SATURN, Page 26: Reprinted from *Sky and Telescope,* November 1979.

ARIANE: EUROPE'S SPACE LAUNCHER, Page 31: Reprinted with permission from *Science News,* the weekly news magazine of science, copyright 1979 by Science Service, Inc.

BIOFEEDBACK AS BEHAVIORAL THERAPY, Page 38: Copyright 1979 Smithsonian Institution, from SMITHSONIAN magazine, December 1979.

ANIMAL BEHAVIOR, Page 44: Copyright 1979 by the National Wildlife Federation. Reprinted from the September-October issue of *International Wildlife.*

DRUGS AND THE MIND, Page 53: Copyright © 1979, American Chemical Society, reprinted by permission of the author.

SMOKING ADDICTION, Page 57: Reprinted from *Medical World News.* Copyright © 1979, McGraw-Hill, Inc.

THE AMERICAN CHESTNUT, Page 72: This article first appeared in *Horticulture* magazine, published by the Massachusetts Horticultural Society, May 1978.

THE LEAF'S PLUMBING, Page 80: Reprinted from *Garden* magazine, May/June 1979. Published by the New York Botanical Garden, © 1979.

TALKING TO COMPUTERS, Page 92: Reprinted from *Science,* Volume 203, pages 634–635, 16 February 1979. Copyright 1979 by the American Association for the Advancement of Science.

PROBLEMS TOO HARD FOR COMPUTERS, Page 98: Copyright 1979 Smithsonian Institution, from SMITHSONIAN magazine, October 1979.

BASIC, Page 104: Adapted from "Problem-Solving With the Computer" by Edwin R. Sage (Portsmouth, NH) ENTELEK 1968.

EL NIÑO, Page 120: Reprinted with permission of *Science 80,* copyright American Association for the Advancement of Science, from the March/April 1980 issue of *Science 80.*

MEXICAN OIL, Page 127: Reprinted from *Science,* Volume 202, pages 1261–1265, 22 December 1978. Copyright 1978 by the American Association for the Advancement of Science.

DINOSAUR HEAD HUNT, Page 132: Reprinted with permission from *Science News,* the weekly news magazine of science, copyright 1979 by Science Service, Inc.

JOVE'S THUNDERBOLTS, Page 140: Copyright © 1979 *Harvard* magazine. Reprinted by permission, from the July/August 1979 issue.

AMBER, Page 152: This article first appeared in *Horticulture* magazine, published by The Massachusetts Horticultural Society, February 1980.

SOLAR PHOTOVOLTAIC ENERGY, Page 160: Reprinted by permission from *Fortune* magazine; © 1979 Time Inc.

FUEL FROM PLANTS, Page 170: Reprinted from *Ecolibrium,* Fall 1978, by permission of the authors.

THE ESKIMO AND THE BOWHEAD, Page 186: Reprinted by permission from *National Parks & Conservation* magazine, September 1978. Copyright © 1978 by National Parks & Conservation Association.

CLEANLY FLOWS THE THAMES, Page 192: Copyright 1978 by the National Wildlife Federation. Adapted from the January/February 1978 issue of *International Wildlife.*

CANCER AND THE DIESEL CAR, Page 196: Reprinted by permission from *Fortune* magazine; © 1979 Time Inc.

ORV'S THREATEN A WILD CANYON, Page 203: Reprinted by permission from *The Living Wilderness,* September, 1979. Copyright 1979 by The Wilderness Society.

THE AIR: UNSAFE AT ANY SITE, Page 208: © 1978/79 by The New York Times Company. Reprinted by permission.

ASPIRIN, Page 220: © 1979 by The New York Times Company. Reprinted by permission.

CONTENTS

EARTH SCIENCE

ENERGY

THE ENVIRONMENT

HEALTH & DISEASE

MAN & HIS WORLD

PHYSICAL SCIENCES

TECHNOLOGY

WILDLIFE

STAFF

EDITORIAL

HERBERT KONDO	Editor-in-Chief
LANSING WAGNER	Editor
BARBARA TCHABOVSKY	Editor
LINDA TRIEGEL	Editorial Assistant
SUZANNE SCHUTZ	Proofreader
JILL SCHULER	Chief Indexer
SUSAN DEROMEDI	Indexer

ART

PATRICIA BYERS	Art and Production Director
MICHÉLE A. MᶜLEAN	Layout Artist
FRANK H. SENYK	Art Consultant
JAN BRAUNLE	Photo Researcher
JANET FILLING	Photo Researcher
DEDE GRACE	Photo Researcher

GROLIER INCORPORATED

HOWARD B. GRAHAM	Senior Vice-President—Publishing
WALLACE S. MURRAY	Vice-President—Editorial Director

COVER: A new generation of astronomical telescopes was born May 9, 1979, with the dedication of the Multiple-Mirror Telescope at the Mt. Hopkins Observatory in Arizona. The unconventional MMT's six 1.80-meter primary mirrors are linked together by a cat's cradle of metal struts and electronic nerve ends. Light from distant celestial objects is captured by the individual mirrors and brought to a common focus.

photo by Gary Ladd

These six Mission Specialist/Astronaut candidates are the first women to be named by the National Aeronautics and Space Administration to its astronaut program.

ASTRONOMY & SPACE SCIENCE

ASTRONOMY & SPACE SCIENCE
REVIEW OF THE YEAR

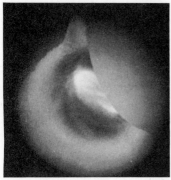

NASA

Pioneer revealed a roughly crescent-shaped, dense cloud collar around the north pole (center) of Venus. This collar, some 15 kilometers above the planet's main cloud deck, is probably produced by a disturbance caused by solar heating.

Significant developments in astronomy during 1979 touched several areas. Space probes revealed much about the solar system, particularly Venus, Jupiter, and Saturn, while orbiting satellites and ground-based research continued to provide a wealth of data about the rest of the universe. Space also became more of a home for humans—with record-setting manned space flights and continuing work on space vehicles.

The Solar System. Current theories about the sun may be in for some revision. Recent observations suggest that vibrations deep inside the sun may cause it to vibrate every 2 hours, 40 minutes. A team of U.S.–Soviet astronomers suggest that present theories cannot account for the energy needed for these pulsations.

The U.S. Pioneer probes of 1978–79, Soviet Venera probes, and ground-based radar observations have at long last provided a closeup picture of Venus. It is in many ways a view of Hades—a planet with extremely high temperatures subject to horrendous thunder and lightning. There are mountains, the highest so far observed rising about 10 kilometers above the surface, and at least one canyon of continental dimensions, about 1,400 kilometers long, 4.6 kilometers deep, and 280 kilometers wide. Winds on Venus blow westward about one meter per second near the surface but increase with altitude, rising to perhaps some 200 kilometers per second.

Scientists still don't know what forces or substances cut the characteristic channels on the surface of Mars, but some believe that nearly two thirds of the surface has been reworked from its pristine state by volcanic activity. ■ The planet's polar caps are better understood. Hugh H. Kieffer of the U.S. Geological Survey reports that the north polar cap is composed mostly of water ice, the south polar cap of frozen carbon dioxide. ■ Meanwhile a lander on the Martian surface continues to transmit photographs and weather reports to a Viking craft that has been orbiting the planet for three years.

Asteroids seem to be getting more complex. In 1978 astronomers reported that asteroid 532 Herculina may have a moon. In 1979 they reported that asteroid 18 Melpomene may be double and that two asteroids—128 Nemesis and 393 Lampetia—rotate very, very slowly, in 39 hours and 38.7 hours respectively.

Callisto, its bright spots revealing numerous impact craters, may be the only pristine surface in the solar system.

NASA

Perhaps the most startling discoveries in astronomy in 1979 concerned Jupiter and its moons. The first high-resolution pictures of Jupiter and five of its satellites—Amalthea, Io, Europa, Ganymede, and Callisto—were received from U.S. Voyager 1 and 2 space probes in March and July 1979. Jupiter, multicolored with red, yellow, brown, orange, and blue mottlings, was found to be surrounded by a ring and by a doughnut-shaped flux tube of charged sulfur particles. The ring, about 30 kilometers thick and 9,000 kilometers wide, extends out to about 57,000 kilometers from the Jovian cloud tops. ■ The photographed satellites revealed much data. Amalthea is reddish and nearly twice as long as it is wide. Europa is orange with surface streaks, possibly fault lines indicating earthquake activity. Ganymede, the largest of Jupiter's satellites, appears brown and gray, like dirty ice, but may have a heat-producing radioactive interior. Callisto, a white-speckled bronze color, is heavily cratered and, suggests one astronomer, may be the only pristine surface in the solar system. But it was Io that held the most surprises. About the size of earth's moon, Io has a red and yellow craterless surface that may be less than 10,000,000 years old. Voyager scientists found a volcanic eruption in progress on Io, ejecting material at one kilometer per second, about twice as fast as volcanoes on earth. Io is the most volcanically active body yet discovered in the solar system. ■ The Voyager probes also discovered a 14th moon for Jupiter—1979J1—and possibly a 15th. 1979J1 is the fastest moving satellite in the solar system, orbiting Jupiter every 7 hours 8 minutes at a speed of 108,000 kilometers per hour.

In September 1979 Pioneer 11, still active after seven years in space, conducted the first spacecraft reconnaissance of Saturn. Voyagers 1 and 2 are en route to Saturn for more detailed observations in November 1980 and August 1981 respectively. (For a discussion of Pioneer findings about Saturn see "Saturn," starting on page 26.)

The rings of Uranus—discovered only in 1977—do not appear like those of Saturn. They seem to be narrower and more sharp-edged. Peter Goldreich of the California Institute of Technology and Scott Tremaine of the Institute of Astronomy at Cambridge University have observed that four of the rings are elliptical while five appear circular. The ring shapes may be caused by a number of small undiscovered satellites.

Neptune is also beginning to reveal its secrets. A team of scientists headed by H. J. Reitsema of the University of Arizona has observed clouds around the planet. Two bright regions are separated by a dark equatorial band. Scientists suggest that the clouds are made of methane ice crystals. ■ Pluto's eccentric orbit took it inside Neptune's orbit in early 1979 and until 1999 Neptune, not Pluto, will be the outermost known planet in our solar system.

The Milky Way. An unusual object in the Milky Way with a remarkable spectrum was the subject of intensive study during 1979. Bruce Margon of the University of California at Los Angeles and astronomers throughout the world analyzed the object, a strong radio and X-ray source named SS 433, seeking to determine exactly what it is. (For a more detailed discussion, see "SS 433: A Peculiar Star," starting on page 23.)

Do some pulsars have planets? Probably yes. Radio observations of the pulsar PSRO329+54 analyzed by M. Demiánski and M. Prószyński of the Warsaw University Institute of Physics in Poland suggest that the pulsar may have a planetary companion. PSRO329+54 has a cycle that could occur if it is orbited once every three years by a planet about 0.10 to 0.60 as large as earth. Ten other pulsars seem to have similar properties that could be related to the presence of planets.

Fewer stars may have habitable planets than was previously thought. A reanalysis of statistical theories by Michael H. Hart of Systems and Applied Sciences Corporation in Maryland has narrowed the zone near a star where life can form and organic evolution occur.

The Universe. A new galaxy in the direction of Orion has been discovered by Riccardo Giovanelli of the National Astronomy and Ionosphere Center at Arecibo, Puerto Rico. Heavily obscured by dust, the new galaxy was found through radio observations and is probably not a member of the Local Group, the group of about 20 galaxies including and closest to the Milky Way. ■ Meanwhile F. Schweizer of the Cerro Tololo Inter-

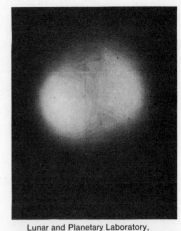

Lunar and Planetary Laboratory, University of Arizona

Neptune is beginning to reveal its secrets. Its bright regions are thought to be methane ice-crystal clouds overlying methane gas.

Japan is accelerating its space activities. Here is an artist's conception of the ionosphere around one of the Japanese-launched satellites.

NASDA

Skylab debris lit up the skies over northwestern Australia as the space station plunged through the earth's atmosphere.

An Australian boy holds a piece of Skylab debris that fell in his backyard. There was concern that the debris might cause injuries and damage, but none were reported.

American Observatory in Chile suggests that galaxies form as multiples. He cites as evidence radio galaxy NGC 1316 (Fornax A) with a cloud of ionized hydrogen that rotates independently of the galaxy and may represent the remains of a companion galaxy.

Quasars, those starlike objects that pose so many questions for astronomers, were once again the subject of much study during 1979. An ongoing survey by Patrick Osmer of Cerro Tololo and Alan Stockton of the University of Hawaii suggests that quasars may be galactic nuclei that never formed into galaxies. Several other observations related quasars and galaxies, including the discovery, by Halton C. Arp of the California Institute of Technology, that two galaxies have multiple quasar companions—NGC 2859 with four and NGC 2639 with ten.

The first observation of antiprotons in cosmic rays was made during 1979—and it raised a fundamental question in physics. R. L. Golden and colleagues at New Mexico State University, Las Cruces, and at the Johnson Space Center in Houston, Texas, found 2,000 times as many protons as antiprotons in cosmic rays detected by balloon-borne instruments. This difference may indicate that the long-held concept of balance in physics is invalid.

And finally, some age-old questions about the universe itself: How old is it? Is it open or closed? It may be younger than previously thought. New measurements of distant clusters of galaxies made by John P. Huchra of the Center for Astrophysics in Cambridge, Massachusetts, with colleagues at the University of Arizona and Kitt Peak National Observatory indicate that distant galaxies may be traveling twice as fast as previously thought and thus are only one-half as distant as supposed. This implies that the universe may be less than 10,000,000,000 years old. Such a young universe would require changes to theories of stellar and galactic evolution. ▪ Meanwhile, Arno Penzias of Bell Telephone Laboratories in New Jersey, co-winner of the 1978 Nobel Prize in physics for his discovery of residual radiation that helped confirm that the universe began in a gigantic explosion, or "big bang," presented evidence to support the idea of an open universe. He has observed more primordial and ancient deuterium near the edge of the galaxy than at the center—an observation considered evidence that the universe is expanding and is not closed.

Katherine Haramundanis

U.S. Space Activities. In addition to space probes to several planets, the results of which have already been discussed, U.S. space efforts concentrated on the development of the space shuttle, the loss of Skylab, and the deployment of scientific and other satellites.

At one time the U.S. National Aeronautics and Space Administration (NASA) had hoped to get the space shuttle off the ground in 1979, but repeated setbacks with engine testing and the installation of a thermal protection coating have forced one postponement after another. The shuttle is a winged vehicle to be launched like a rocket, flown in orbit like a spacecraft, and steered to a runway landing like a glider. It was developed to provide a reusable—and thus economical—vehicle for launching satellites. Both the U.S. Congress and the White House have criticized the project's cost overruns and management problems, but the Carter Administration did pledge additional funds to expedite the deployment of four shuttles. The first manned orbital test flight is not now expected to occur before late 1980 or early 1981.

The loss of Skylab, the 78.5-ton space station that had been the workplace of three U.S. crews in 1973 and 1974, was one of the most spectacular space happenings in 1979. Launched May 14, 1973, Skylab made 38,981 orbits of the earth and had long been abandoned before it reentered the earth's atmosphere July 11. There was worldwide concern that debris might cause injuries and damage, but the burning and breaking-apart craft scattered debris only over the Indian Ocean and sparsely populated areas of southwestern Australia. There were no injuries.

Other NASA activities during 1979 included the launching in September of the High Energy Astronomy Observatory (HEAO) 3 to examine cosmic rays and gamma rays and in October of Magsat to study earth's magnetism and to assist in the search for mineral resources on earth. Several communication satellites were also launched. One, Satcom 3, an RCA satellite for cable-television transmission, had a mysterious fate: it disappeared in orbit without a trace on December 10, perhaps the victim of an explosion.

Soviet Space Activities. Long-duration manned flights highlighted space activities for the Soviet Union during 1979. On August 20, 1979 Vladimir Lyakhov and Valery Ryumin ended history's longest manned space flight when they landed safely in Soviet Central Asia after orbiting earth in the Salyut 6 space station for 175 days. This was 35 days more than their predecessors and 91 days more than the longest U.S. mission in Skylab. The Soviet cosmonauts had travelled 115,840,000 kilometers, equivalent to a round-trip to Mars. During the mission, they were resupplied three times by unmanned Progress spacecraft. Another crew, Nikolai Rukashnikov and Georgi Ivanov, attempted to visit the Salyut record-setters on April 10, but the docking mechanism on their Soyuz spacecraft failed and they had to return to earth on April 12. Salyut 6 remains in orbit and may be visited again by other cosmonauts.

Other Space Activities. The European Space Agency, an organization of eleven Western European nations, took an important step toward developing an independent launching capability in 1979. They had previously depended on NASA to launch their satellites. On December 24, 1979 the prototype of Europe's Ariane rocket was successfully launched from the Kourou Space Center in French Guiana on South America's Atlantic coast. It placed a small dummy satellite in orbit. A conventional three-stage rocket, Ariane was designed primarily to launch communications and scientific satellites into earth orbit. After at least three more test flights, Ariane is expected to launch four or five vehicles a year—for European nations and for commercial operators. (For a more complete discussion of Ariane, see "Ariane: Europe's Space Launcher," starting on page 31.)

China, Japan, and India also accelerated their space activities during 1979. Visitors to China reported that China is building its own communications and weather satellites and is developing rocket systems. The Chinese also reported that they had recovered dogs and mice after suborbital test flights. This is considered preliminary to manned space flights. ■ Japan, which has now launched 19 satellites, successfully tested a new rocket in a February 1980 launching and announced plans to mount its first interplanetary mission—a 1985 mission to study Venus and Halley's comet. ■ India completed its own space rocket and, though its first test flight in 1979 was a failure, is expected to join the launching club soon.

John Noble Wilford

Tass from Sovfoto
Cosmonauts Vladimir Lyakhov and Valery Ryumin orbited earth in the Salyut 6 space station for 175 days—history's longest manned space flight.

The European Space Agency now has its own launch capability—Ariane, shown here at the Kourou Space Center launch pad.
A. Nouges/Sygma

THE SUN-GRAZERS

by Joel Davis

FROM a place so distant that the sun's light takes over a year to reach it, they come. The trip takes uncounted thousands of years, and for most of it, they are unnoticed by the sky watchers of the third planet.

During the last months of their journey, they are indeed noticed. The show they put on is spectacular.

They are called sun-grazers. They are comets. They are the most awesome of those heavenly objects that have terrified, inspired, and baffled humans for all of history.

Most people think of comets as huge objects with tails millions of kilometers long. But they're actually about as close to nothing as something can get. The *nucleus* of a comet is a chunk of rock, dust, and ices no more than 80 kilometers in diameter. As this "dirty iceberg"—so called by astronomer Fred Whipple—gets closer to the sun, it develops a *coma.* A coma is a spherical cloud of dust and gas that can extend more than 150,000 kilometers out from the nucleus. The coma forms as material is blown off the nucleus' surface by the sun's heat and the solar wind.

THE CHANGING TAIL

Only if the comet crosses the orbit of Mars will a tail begin to develop. As the sun's heat and the solar wind become stronger, material from the coma begins to stream away from the sun. Sometimes two tails develop—one of dust and one of ionized gases—but stars shine clearly through both.

As the comet swings around the sun at its closest approach (perihelion), the tail swings with it. As the visitor from afar heads back into the depths of space, its tail precedes it, still being blown away from the sun by the force of the solar wind.

Do comets come from interstellar space? Are they captured by the sun's gravity only to escape back to the void between suns? Apparently not. If they were, a sizable number of them would travel in hyperbolic orbits resembling a hairpin bent wide apart. Such an orbit is open, and the comets would never return. No comet has ever been observed that had an original orbit proven to be open.

THE OORT CLOUD

Instead, comets probably originate in the *Oort cloud,* a vast halo of material weakly bound to the sun by gravity. Named after astronomer Jan Oort who originally proposed the idea, the Oort cloud extends from 5 to 16,000,000,000,000 kilometers from the sun. That is nearly half the distance to the nearest star. And so the solar system assumes an almost mind-boggling size.

The Oort cloud itself, and the comets that compose it, may have been formed by the sun capturing matter from between the stars. The cloud, though, may have been formed along with the rest of the solar system, some 5,000,000,000 years ago. Icy and rocky material from the region of Uranus and Neptune could have been pulled out by the gravitational forces of those two planets to form the cloud. Still another theory proposes that the Oort cloud formed just where it is. The comets would be the frozen leftovers of the solar system's creation.

The theory that comets come from the Oort cloud isn't in dispute. Most likely the dirty icebergs are wobbled out of their creeping orbits by the gravitational actions of passing stars. Slowly, the fragile conglomerates of dust and ice deviate from their age-old paths. Some head out and are lost forever; some head in toward the sun.

Most comets visible to the naked eye travel in extremely stretched-out orbits that look like elongated cigars. The outer end of the orbit lies in the Oort cloud. The *long-period comets* take several thousand to several million years to complete one turnaround on their highly elliptical paths. *Short-period comets,* with orbital periods similar to those of the planets, are simply long-period comets that have been "captured" by a giant planet such as Jupiter or Saturn.

Halley's Comet, with a period of 76 years, is one such short-period comet. That great disappointment of 1974, comet Kohoutek, was a long-period comet. It will be millions of years before Kohoutek again approaches the sun. Perhaps our distant descendants will have a better show than we did.

KINDS OF COMETS

Where do the sun-grazers fit into the scheme of things?

Sun-grazers are comets that come within a sun's diameter of the solar surface at their closest approach. There are at least a dozen comets that would fit this category, but the ones usually referred to as the sun-grazers belong to a curious entity called a *comet group*.

Comet groups shouldn't be confused with comet families. A *comet family* is a collection of comets whose aphelia, or farthest distance from the sun, center on the orbit of a particular planet. They have, in effect, been captured by the gravitational influence of Jupiter, Saturn, Uranus, or Neptune. Jupiter has the largest comet family; the others each have their own retinue, also.

A comet group is different. It is a collection of comets that all travel in the same orbit. As an imaginary comparison, one might speak of a "planet group" as two or more planets that occupy the same orbit. If more than one planet traveled in earth's orbit, we could speak of an "earth group" of planets.

Planet groups don't exist. The 5,000,-000,000 or more years of the solar system's existence has been plenty of time for the planets to sweep their orbits clean of any po-

Halley's Comet is a short-period comet, next due to be visible from earth in 1986.

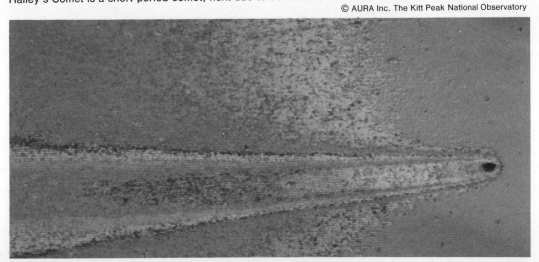

The nucleus of a comet, such as that of comet Bennet 1970 shown here, has been likened to a dirty iceberg. It is a chunk of rock, dust, and ice that probably originated in a cloud of material far distant from the sun.

tential rivals. Not so for comets. New ones constantly plunge in from the Oort cloud. While each one has its own orbit, sometimes a catastrophe happens.

There are several possibilities how this happens. It could be a collision with some piece of matter. Or during its approach to the sun, the nucleus may heat up unevenly. Or while it's spitting out dust and gas under the influence of the sun's wind, one jet of matter may become unusually strong. Whatever the cause, the nucleus splits into several different pieces. Each piece would follow almost the same path in the future, each arriving back at the sun at a slightly different time. The result: a comet group.

Fifteen comet groups are well-known, and are named A through Q. The sun-grazers are group M.

THE SUN-GRAZERS GROUP

The eight known members of group M deserve the name sun-grazers. With one exception, they have all had approaches to the sun of less than 800,000 kilometers. They dive in closer to the sun than any other object in the solar system. Comet 1843 I and comet 1880 I came within 126,000 kilometers of the sun's surface. (The I means that they were the first comet to pass perihelion in that year.) Comet 1882 II (the "Great Comet of 1882") approached to 453,000 kilometers, while 1887 I and 1945 VII reached close-in distances of 794,000 kilometers and 249,000 kilometers respectively. Comet Ikeya-Seki (1965 VIII) came within 491,000 kilometers. The record holder is comet Pereyra (1963 V): it came within 96,000 kilometers of the solar surface at its closest approach.

Only the comet of 1668 at its closest approach to the sun was more than 800,000 kilometers away from the sun's visible surface. Its perihelion distance was about 9,600,-000 kilometers—still well within the orbit of Mercury, the closest planet to the sun. The others all came so close that they streaked through the sun's corona during their closest passage.

SIMILAR ORBITS

Not only did the sun-grazers all come perilously close to the sun, but they all followed almost exactly the same orbit in their journeys. Comet 1668, along with comet 1843 I and comet 1880 I, had an orbit inclined at about 144° from the plane of the earth's orbit around the sun. The others all have orbits with practically the same inclination. All eight sun-grazers approach the sun from below earth's orbital plane, and they all follow a clockwise direction as they come around and fly away.

Suppose we could sit in a space vehicle high above the sun's north pole and somehow speed time up while looking down on the solar system. The planets would appear to speed around the sun in a counterclockwise direction. Every planet but Pluto would lie very close to an imaginary plane passing through earth's orbit. But the sun-grazers would appear to come from a point below the plane, climbing up toward the sun.

The approach of the sun-grazers is very direct. They are seemingly aimed right at the heart of the sun. But in the last instant they flash through the corona and whip around the sun at a blurring speed. Then the tail becomes spectacular as the sun-grazer heads back out beyond Pluto. Its orbit will take it so far out from the sun that it will be at least a thousand years before it returns.

HOW FORMED

It's not too difficult to guess how the sun-grazer group, group M, was formed. At some time in the past a single large comet came perilously close to the sun. Whether this was its first brush with the sun, or whether it had survived previous encounters is not important. This time it didn't make it.

The gravitational stresses were too much. The nucleus was heating up unevenly and huge cracks developed in the conglomerate of ices and rock. Fountains of gases erupted. The gases, acting like rocket exhausts, set the nucleus spinning. The spinning set up still more stresses in the dirty iceberg. At some point, it broke apart, and pieces drifted away from each other.

A SPECTACULAR EXAMPLE

Eight of this comet group have appeared in the last 300 years. One appeared in 1668, then a cluster of four between 1843 and 1887, and three more in this century.

The most recent sun-grazer to blaze across our skies was Ikeya-Seki (1965 VIII). A classic example of a sun-grazer, Ikeya-Seki could well have been called "The Great Comet of 1965" if such nomenclature were still in use. Like the Great Comet of 1882, lucky observers had a chance to see it in broad daylight. It shone brighter than the full moon. People in the southwestern United States were the lucky ones. Observers in the rest of the United States were less lucky—cloudy skies blocked the view.

The daylight view was just the beginning. Its surface boiling from the close brush with the sun, Ikeya-Seki swept down to 491,-000 kilometers above the solar surface and whipped around the sun in just six hours. Then the comet began to develop a spectacular tail as it headed back out. It twisted and turned like a lace curtain in the solar wind. In the morning sky, the tail stretched up like a searchlight, covering a full 25° of arc. Its 120,000,000-kilometer length was almost as great as the distance from the sun to earth. Only three other comets have had longer

As a comet approaches the sun, the veil-like coma surrounding the nucleus changes into defined layers, called envelopes, and nebulous matter streams from the head.

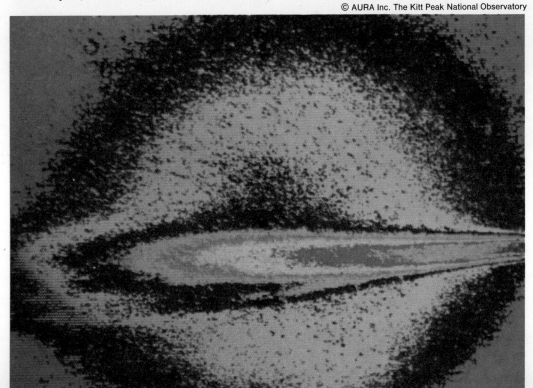

© AURA Inc. The Kitt Peak National Observatory

Ikeya-Seki (1965 VIII) was the most recent sun grazer to cross our skies, developing a spectacular tail.

when it was 32,000,000 kilometers away.

Some surprising things were learned about the composition of Ikeya-Seki, too. Shortly after the comet's closest approach to the sun, the Lick Observatory's 305-centimeter telescope was used to take emission spectra of a region within the comet's head. The ultraviolet spectrum showed the presence of iron, nickel, chromium, and calcium. The visible spectrum strongly showed the presence of sodium. The ultraviolet spectra also indicated the possible presence of copper, potassium, and a cyanogen compound.

Perhaps the most interesting development was also the least surprising—after all, Ikeya-Seki was obviously a near twin of 1882 II. Fifteen days after its closest approach to the sun, the nucleus of Ikeya-Seki broke apart. A second distinct nucleus appeared in photos taken at the U.S. Geological Survey's station in Flagstaff, Arizona. As the distance between the two increased, the brightness of that second nucleus faded. By working backward in time, astronomers estimated that the comet's nucleus probably began to split only three days after its swift passage above the solar surface. The Great Comet of 1882 had done exactly the same thing.

NEXT BULL'S EYE?

What does the future hold for the sun-grazers, and those who watch them? Ikeya-Seki, or its two fragments, will not return for at least another thousand years. But will we have to wait that long for another sun-grazer to light up the skies?

It's hard to say. The number of observed sun-grazers is in dispute. And it is not known for sure how many fragments resulted when the proto-sun-grazer broke apart. No one will know until the next sun-grazer bears down in a near bull's eye on the sun □

tails. (The all-time record for tail length, 320,000,000 kilometers, is held by comet 1843 I—another sun-grazer.)

GOLD MINE OF INFORMATION

Ikeya-Seki was a gold mine for astronomers. For the first time, a comet's temperature was taken. From a temperature of 370° Celsius, when it was 62,000,000 kilometers from the sun, it heated up to 650° Celsius

 SELECTED READINGS

Comets: An Illustrated Introduction by Patrick Moore. Scribners, New York, 1978.

Comets, Meteorites, and Men by Peter L. Brown. Taplinger, New York, 1974.

"Exploration of comets" by M. Neugebauer and R. Newburn. *Technology Review,* March 1978.

Gary Ladd

THE MULTIPLE-MIRROR TELESCOPE

by James Cornell

FIRST, the MMT doesn't look like an observatory. Rather it squats, blocky and fat, on an Arizona mountain peak like a misplaced Miami condominium exiled to the wilderness.

Second, the MMT doesn't behave as a building should. The entire four-and-one-half-story structure, from rooftop to ground level, rotates.

And, third, the instrument inside this revolving barn isn't a conventional instrument, either. Instead of a single great glass disk, the MMT's six primary mirrors are linked together by a cat's cradle of metal struts and electronic nerve ends.

Astronomers see the odd features of the MMT, or Multiple-Mirror Telescope, as portents of astronomy's future. Indeed, when the MMT was officially dedicated at the Smithsonian's Mt. Hopkins Observatory on May 9, 1979, it marked the birth of a new generation of large astronomical telescopes.

LIGHT FROM SIX MIRRORS

A joint effort of the Smithsonian Institution and the University of Arizona, the MMT represents a major departure from traditional telescope design. Instead of using a single mirror, the MMT uses six primary mirrors, each 1.80 meters in diameter. These create the light-gathering power equivalent to a conventional telescope with an aperture of about 4.4 meters.

The light from distant celestial objects captured by the individual mirrors is brought to a common focus. Then, through an electronic-control system using smaller movable mirrors, lasers, and on-line computers, the focus is maintained as a single image.

The MMT is the world's third largest optical telescope, exceeded only by the 5-meter Hale reflector on Mt. Palomar and the 5.8-meter Soviet telescope in the Caucasus. It is also the prototype for even larger—perhaps much larger—telescopes of similar design in the future.

In a very real sense, the MMT is a response to a problem that has plagued astronomers for years. To extend the boundaries of the known universe, ever larger telescopes are needed to reveal ever fainter and more distant objects. But simply scaling up the size of existing instruments is not practical. Mirrors and their support systems eventually reach a point where they collapse under their own weight.

Faced with the demand for a design that did not depend on sheer brute strength to maintain sharp images, Smithsonian and University of Arizona astronomers began nearly a decade ago to explore the more radical approach of creating a telescope with multiple mirrors.

The technique of using two separated mirrors to detect minute differences in the arrival times of light from a distant star had been used with some success. This technique is called interferometry. The less exacting concept that similarly shaped, but separated, mirror surfaces could bring light to a common focus had also been attempted. But the sticky and nearly insurmountable problem of keeping the images superimposed remained.

The solution to the imaging problem

The MMT uses six primary mirrors to create the light-gathering power of a large telescope.

Gary Ladd

came in part from the space program. Advances in laser and superminiature-computer technology finally made it possible. With these devices scientists could build instruments in which high-image quality could be maintained by automatic electronic sensing and control systems rather than by mechanical devices.

In the final design six independent reflecting telescopes work in concert to produce a common image. Starlight enters each telescope individually and travels down to the primary mirror. Then it bounces to the secondary mirror near the open upper end and then bounces back again to a third mirror at the center of the primary. From this third mirror, the light from each telescope is relayed into the center of the array, producing a pattern like the spokes of a wheel. A pyramid of mirrors at the center combines the beams and redirects the light, now as a single image. The image finally enters recording instruments located at the focal point behind the telescope.

KEEPING A STABLE IMAGE

A major problem was to devise a way to keep a stable image. The solution was an active-guidance optics system. The guidance system sends light from an "artificial star"—actually, a laser beam—speeding through the entire optical system until it is intercepted at the back of the MMT by electronic detectors. Those detectors, together with the small on-line computer, position the secondary mirrors to correct any disturbances or misalignments so that the six "artificial stars" become one. Simultaneously, the six images of true starlight are also brought into common focus, becoming a single, much stronger, image.

The MMT's active optics system might be compared to human eyes. Each eye focuses independently, and two separate images are transmitted to the brain. Our cerebral computer does a quick calculation and signals back through the nerve to the muscles controlling the eyeballs. These muscles make minute adjustments so that the individual eyes are realigned and refocused. The two separate images thus become one back in the brain. All this happens instantaneously, of course, as we turn our heads or move toward or away from objects. The computer in our head helps maintain a clear, precise visual picture of the world. And so does the computer-laser system in the MMT maintain a steady, well-focused optical view of the heavens.

A REVOLVING BLOCKHOUSE

The use of separate reflectors, each folding its light path several times over, means the MMT is extremely compact. Its focal length is no longer than that of any one of its six components. Moreover, the 20-odd optical elements and associated electronic hardware are carried on a simple altitude-azimuth mount. It turns like a naval gun, around the compass points in azimuth and up and down in altitude. Thus the support structure holding the telescope optics experiences little stress and can be of a relatively lightweight construction.

Astronomers traditionally have resisted such mounts because star tracking requires rotation around both axes simultaneously, with continuously varying tracking speeds. Again, however, the MMT's on-line computer control allows rapid and automatic calculations of the correct rates.

The MMT, like other large telescopes, is very dependent on electronics for both operations and observations. For that reason these systems were placed near the instrument. Because at least the top half of the building had to turn with the telescope in the azimuth direction, the Smithsonian designers suggested that the entire building could rotate. And, by giving up the traditional dome shape and giving the MMT building a square-shouldered barnlike configuration, more control-room space was made available.

Thus, the entire 500-ton facility—offices, labs, workshops, and lunchrooms—turns slowly on steel wheels riding on a circular track. The telescope itself, standing on an independent pier anchored in bedrock, turns simultaneously on its own bearing. Together, building and telescope have become a single, giant instrument.

Actually, even when the facility turns at top speed, the motion is hardly perceptible to

Gary Ladd

Not dome-shaped, the MMT building is square, has ample control-room space, and rotates.

anyone inside, unless one happens to glance out the window and see the other peaks of the Santa Rita Range gliding by. However, its engineer notes, "Pool is the traditional cloudy night pastime of astronomers, and it will require special skill if played in the MMT building."

PROGRAMMED OBJECTIVES

The MMT is more than just a test model for larger instruments of the future. It is a working scientific instrument. Appropriately, today's technology—particularly advances in computers and transistor electronics—will significantly shape the investigations of this generation of telescopes.

The computer-control system that automatically realigns the eyes of the MMT may also help to remove much of the drudgery from observing. According to Herbert Gursky, a Smithsonian specialist in X-ray astronomy: "A scientist may come to the MMT with lists of objects to be observed, punch in a set of numbers at the computer console, and then sit back while the telescope automatically and accurately proceeds from object to object with little or no human intervention. For certain observations, the scientist might not even be present, because the data can be taken and stored for later analysis elsewhere."

Indeed, under the proposed operations plan, lists of objects from several scientists at different institutions can be sent to the telescope in advance. Then the computer will develop a plan that minimizes the time required to move from object to object. Because the MMT is certain to be oversubscribed, this feature should ensure access for many more users.

THE RED-SHIFT MACHINE

A dramatic and far-reaching change in observing techniques may come from the application of new devices known as "self-scanning diode arrays." The diode arrays are by-products of transistor technology that allow cramming thousands of electronic circuits into fingernail-size wafers composed of 10,000 to 100,000 individual light-sensitive elements. The most common material used is silicon, which records more than half of the photons of light falling on its surface. (By contrast, even specially-treated photographic film can capture only about four of every hundred photons.)

Two diode-array instruments will be operated on the MMT. One of these will be used with the "red-shift machine," a high-gain spectrometer developed by colleagues at the Harvard College Observatory. The other will be used with the CCD (charge-coupled device) camera, a solid-state optical detector.

The red-shift machine measures the shift toward longer—or red—wavelengths in the light that reaches us from distant galaxies. This measurement is vital to determining the size of the universe, because galaxies appear to be receding from us at speeds in proportion to their distances.

The CCD camera can be used exactly like a television camera to produce images of very faint objects, either for immediate viewing or for storage. The red-shift machine's data show the spectra of celestial objects.

MAPPING DEEP SPACE

Both instruments are being used to study the most distant galaxies in both optical and infrared light. This is being done to produce better "maps" of the universe. In one sense, we have already mapped out our immediate neighborhood, or more properly, our "time zone." To produce an atlas of those areas beyond this zone, we must look farther into space, a task that requires better light collecting.

Because the incredible distances of space are measured not in kilometers but in light years, to look deeper in space is also to look far backward in time. The light from the most distant objects reaching telescopes on earth actually originated billions of years ago. Suppose, theoretically, one could look beyond the edge of the now-known universe, or some 15 million years into the past. One might see light from those stars formed by the first primordial explosion. Perhaps one

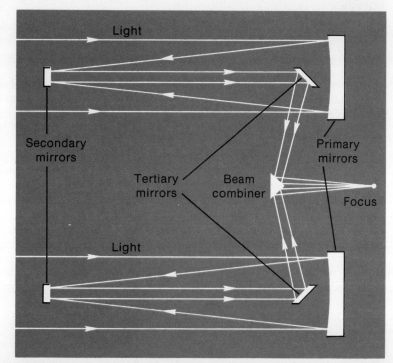

An electronically controlled system of mirrors, lasers, and computers brings the light from six "artificial stars" to a common focus.

could even see that explosion, or "Big Bang," itself.

Naturally, light traveling so long and far through space is extremely faint. By increasing a telescope's light-collecting ability, either through greater size or by improved instrumentation, more of this light can be collected and, more important, analyzed. Its faint spectrum can be dissected, and its components classified. This information would reveal the chemical and physical properties of the bodies that emitted light so long ago.

Most important are the measurements of distance made possible by the spectra obtained on the red-shift machine. At the very limits of current telescopes are seen strange, powerful sources of light, radio, and X-ray emission known as quasi-stellar objects, or quasars. Although they look like stars, their red shifts indicate they are receding from us at velocities almost 90 per cent that of the speed of light. Translated into time, that means the light has been traveling more than ten billion years before it reaches us.

To be seen at such distances, quasars must be extremely powerful, perhaps more energetic than a billion stars combined. The MMT astronomers, working in cooperation with astronomers using radio telescopes and satellite observatories, hope to learn more about these objects.

LOOKING AT HOW STARS ARE BORN

The MMT is especially well-suited for infrared observations and is the largest telescope ever constructed specifically for this purpose. Infrared astronomy is a growing field that has gained impetus in the past two decades. Among the interesting objects to be studied in infrared are "cool" stars, many times larger than our sun but only about one-third its temperature. Other objects are celestial newcomers. These are so young they have hardly begun to use their internal fuel supplies and are still shrouded in clouds of the dust and gas out of which they are forming. Also intriguing are suspected "proto-stars." These are even newer objects evolving from dust-gas. Still other objects emit abnormal amounts of both radio and infrared radiation, but are virtually invisible to optical telescopes.

By looking in the infrared region of the spectrum, the MMT is expected to reveal new information about the birth of stars. And infrared analysis may better define conditions at the heart of our own Milky Way. Furthermore, it might explain the inordinate amounts of infrared radiation discovered from the cores of more active galaxies.

In the end, however, no scientist can predict exactly what the MMT may do. This attitude is hard to explain to efficiency experts who demand immediate payoffs for dollars expended, but as Neville Woolf, the British-born Steward Observatory astronomer who has served as the MMT's Acting Director, explains it: "The research programs of large telescopes are seldom confined to any preconceived plans. Each time the MMT points at a new object, it may reveal something never before known to science."

Throughout the history of astronomy, the introduction of new instruments has inevitably led to new discoveries affecting both astronomy and philosophy. The first observations made by Galileo in 1609 with a crude telescope revealed that the earth was a vassal of the sun and that the sun itself was only one among millions of suns in the Milky Way. The great reflectors of the early 20th century showed that the Milky Way was itself only one among untold millions of other galaxies, all aswim in a universe that stretched beyond sight. The ground-based radio telescopes and space telescopes of the last two decades, in turn, have shown this universe to be populated throughout by mysterious and violent objects such as black holes, pulsars, and cosmic bursters.

The universe is no longer seen as a static void dotted with immutable objects. Instead, it is seen as a dynamic place as the stars play out an evolutionary scheme on a scale far vaster than anyone can conceive. Perhaps, like the innovative astronomical tools that preceded it, the Multiple-Mirror Telescope will also reveal new visions of the cosmos □

 SELECTED READINGS

"MMT dedicated." *Astronomy,* July 1979.

"New breed of telescope born in Arizona" by F. F. Hartline. *Science,* May 25, 1979.

Images derived from the radio emissions of distant objects in the heavens are computer-enhanced and color-coded to help astronomers unravel their secrets.

AN AMAZING GALAXY IS FOUND

by Mark R. Chartrand III and Trudy E. Bell

BEHOLD the universe, strewn with galaxies like so much luminous dust—somewhere between one and 10,000,000,000 of them, fading off into infinity. Suppose you were able to view them from a cosmic vantage point in the isolated depths of space. The myriads of galaxies would appear as so many motionless swarms of glowing fireflies. They would appear to be clustered in groups ranging from fewer than a dozen members to rich superclusters of a thousand or more.

Then suppose you were also able to speed up time, so a million seconds passed in one. You would see that the swarms of galaxies are not motionless at all. Rather, they are engaged in an endless celestial ballet—revolving, merging, gliding closely past one another. Their mutual gravity pulls out wisps of stars and gas that trail behind. And all the while they are receding from one another as the entire universe expands.

Seen more closely, each galaxy appears as a seething system of billions of stars, planets, and magnetic fields pirouetting on its own axis. Inside each galaxy, luminous gas and dust is coalescing into fresh, hot, young stars. And old stars are fading into obscurity or exploding for a cosmic moment of grandeur.

SCALING THE MILKY WAY GALAXY

Imagine that our entire solar system, 12,-000,000,000 kilometers across, is shrunk to the size of a grain of talcum powder. If you drew a circle with a diameter of 160 meters, not quite two football fields, and spread in that circle 265 grams of talc, you'd have the scale of the Milky Way galaxy, the home galaxy for our solar system.

Scattered within a distance of a few kilometers from our galaxy would be about two dozen other galaxies, our *Local Group* of galaxies. Clusters of galaxies outside this would be scattered in all directions. These clusters would each contain a few spiral galaxies, many small ellipsoidal galaxies, and a few irregular and peculiarly shaped blobs.

Every galaxy is a swirling maelstrom of stars, gas, and dust. Our solar system travels around the Milky Way at 250 kilometers per second, taking about 246,000,000 years to make one circuit. All galaxies move together, but each also has a slight motion within the group. Once we get very far out of the Local Group, the cosmic effects of the expansion of the universe are stronger than the random motions of the individual galaxies this means that every distant galaxy is moving away from us.

TYPES OF GALAXIES

Examining the individual galaxies reveals their differences. Perhaps a third are shaped like fat lozenges, spheres, or ellipsoids. These are composed mainly of older reddish stars. Others, nearly half, are graceful celestial whirlpools, trailing lacy arms of gas and stars. The remainder seem to be bluish tangles of mainly hot young stars and gas, irregular and shapeless.

As varied as they are in form, galaxies are even less alike in size. They range from dim, dwarf systems to magnificent spirals like the Milky Way some 10,000 times larger. And there are elliptical titans yet 50 times more massive than even the spiral galaxies.

The lacy grandeur of the spiral galaxies intrigued observers well before their true nature was perceived. The spirals are fascinating, beautiful structures. Some have their arms tightly wound around their brilliant nuclei, others have them loosely spread. Some spirals appear to have their arms originating from a bar-shaped nucleus, earning them the name of barred spirals. But spiral galaxies are more than simply breathtaking. Because they account for nearly half of all galaxies in the heavens, they are one of the universe's principal components. They may even be a key to understanding the universe's history and fate.

CRIPPLED GIANT

Recently one spiral galaxy has drawn keen attention. Three astronomers at the Carnegie Institution of Washington and the National Radio Astronomy Observatory announced a discovery about the bizarre-looking spiral galaxy known as NGC 1961. It was found to be the most massive spiral galaxy known. It has perhaps two to three times the diameter of our Milky Way and perhaps 10 times as much mass.

The galaxy is so peculiar that the astronomers describe it as "pathological." Instead of being a lovely pinwheel with gracefully curved lanes of stars and dust, the arms of NGC 1961 are distorted by tangled dusty loops and wisps of flying gas. This makes it look as if something inside the system were exploding.

But its most startling property is its enormous mass. The astronomers—Vera C. Rubin and Kent W. Ford, Jr. of the Department of Terrestrial Magnetism of the Carnegie Institution, and Morton S. Roberts of the National Radio Astronomy Observatory, headquartered in Charlottesville, West Virginia—are quick to point out that NGC 1961 is not the most massive galaxy known in the universe, only the most massive spiral galaxy. More massive ellipticals have been found. Nonetheless, the new knowledge of

Spiral galaxies like this one—M-51—constitute a large part of the universe.

U.S. Naval Observatory

the huge mass of NGC 1961 may force us to revise upwards estimates of the mass of every spiral galaxy, including our own. Such a wholesale cosmological stroke could profoundly alter our theories about spiral galaxies. It might also revise our hypothesis that the universe will expand forever.

The existence of NGC 1961 has been known for almost a century, because as galaxies go it's relatively bright. Through a modest telescope it appears as a dim, starlike smudge in the northern sky. Its very name, NGC 1961, means that it is the 1,961st object listed in the *New General Catalogue of Nebulae and Clusters of Stars.* All told, there are 7,840 objects in the catalogue. NGC 1961 is 250,000,000 light-years away—light reaching our eyes today from it left the galaxy about the time of the first dinosaurs on earth.

Elliptical galaxies, like M-32, often have a smooth structure and contain older, reddish stars.

SEARCHING FOR CLUES

The discovery of the peculiar properties of NGC 1961 is a classic case of serendipity—of looking for one thing and of finding quite another. The account of the search, which reads like a detective story, is a stunning example of how exciting the work of an astronomer can be.

The story really begins more than a decade ago with Vera Rubin's early fascination with the rotation of spiral galaxies. What causes the lovely spiral arms? Are they permanent features or are they winding themselves up tighter as the galaxies turn?

Over the years her curiosity led her to far deeper questions about the nature of the universe. How much mass does the universe contain? Is this mass sufficient, by its gravitational attraction, to retard or eventually to halt the universe's expansion? And what fraction of this mass is contained in galaxies?

Few astronomers have attempted to study the inner workings of galaxies, mainly because most are so faint. But in the mid-1960's Kent Ford was completing a new device known as an image tube, which greatly amplifies even the dimmest light. Ford wanted to test his instrument. The two astronomers teamed up and began planning to observe individual galaxies. That led to a plan to investigate the internal motions of about 40 large and luminous spirals.

Rubin and Ford planned to choose their 40 or so massive, bright galaxies from a list of about 200 spirals that they had previously studied to see if the universe was expanding uniformly in all directions. They had observed all those galaxies with two of the giant radio telescopes at the National Radio Astronomy Observatory in West Virginia. Nestled in a lush, green valley away from electrical interference, the silent telescopes of the observatory stand open, unshielded from the sun and rain. With the giant radio dishes, the astronomers had recorded the faint hiss of hydrogen gas swirling in the spiral arms of each of the 200 galaxies. Hydrogen gas makes up about 10 per cent of the diffuse material in spiral galaxies. For this reason the intensity of its radio waves provides a ballpark idea of each galaxy's mass. The way the gas is moving also gives an idea of the speed of each galaxy's rotation. And, for decades it has been thought that a galaxy's mass is somehow related to its rotational velocity.

Rubin now wondered whether she had left any important galaxies off her list of 200 spirals. As she and Ford were combing through that list, she called up Morton Roberts, Director of the National Radio Astronomy Observatory, and asked if he knew of any exceptionally massive, luminous spirals rotating with velocities near 400 kilometers per second. Over the telephone, Roberts read her a list of 10 galaxies. One of them was NGC 1961.

There was something about NGC 1961 that could not be overlooked. Rubin and Ford were trying to restrict themselves to regular, symmetrical spirals. However, it was undeniable that NGC 1961 was rotating faster than any other spiral galaxy they knew. Rough measurements indicated it was spinning faster than 400 kilometers per second. This speed suggests that it must be very massive indeed. Despite its peculiarities, Rubin and Ford suspected it might lead to something big.

MEASURING MOVEMENT AND MASS OF GALAXIES

Just how does one measure the movements and the mass of something that is perhaps three million million million kilometers across, a good fraction of the universe away, and which requires hundreds of millions of years to revolve just once?

The answer lies in applying a simple

Photographs taken using Kitt Peak's Mayall telescope revealed a surprise about NGC 1961.

Kitt Peak National Observatory

principle from high school physics known as the Doppler effect. If the object emitting the light is moving toward you, the "pitch" or frequency of the light is higher (bluer). If the object is moving away, the frequency of the light is lower (redder). The amount by which the frequency of the light is shifted is a measure of the object's speed toward you or away from you.

Rubin and Ford were able to measure the Doppler effect by attaching a device called a spectrogram to a large telescope. They further amplified the light from the galaxy by Ford's image tube. In this way they were able to detect differences in the movements in galaxies with as much accuracy as three kilometers per second. This is possible because in a rotating object such as a galaxy (seen somewhat edge-on), one edge will be approaching and one edge will be receding.

Therefore, light from the galaxy's approaching edge will be displaced toward the blue wavelengths, while light from the receding edge will be displaced toward the red wavelengths. This kind of direct, powerful technique for learning about something is what scientists call elegant.

Now, studying the motions of stars in a galaxy is a powerful means of "weighing" the galaxy's mass. The elementary physics involved says simply that if a star in a galaxy is not to fly off into space, its outward motion must be balanced by the inward pull of the galaxy's gravity. The gravity is the combined pull of all the stars closer to the galaxy's center than the star you are considering. Thus, by measuring the velocities of stars in a galaxy, an astronomer can infer the galaxy's mass. The faster the stars' velocity, the greater the galaxy's mass.

Armed with their sensitive instruments and their elegant technique, Rubin and Ford reserved telescope time on the second largest telescope in the United States—the 4-meter Mayall reflecting telescope at the Kitt Peak National Observatory in Arizona.

TELESCOPE TIME

Telescope time is precious. At the major observatories, it is parcelled out about a year in advance—two days to this astronomer, a week to that one. Woe to those whose ob-

Analysis of the hydrogen-gas hiss recorded by giant radio dishes such as these confirmed that NGC 1961 is the most massive spiral galaxy known.

serving nights are stormy or overcast. Rubin and Ford managed to get four nights in November 1977.

Because of the tight schedule, they were pressed to make every second count. They would have enough hours to observe only a dozen or so of their 40 luminous spirals. For a tense month before their observing run, they culled their list, rejecting all but the most promising. Firmly, they set aside ones that seemed interesting but less vital to their main objectives. Still NGC 1961, in spite of its "pathological" character, passed muster—its extraordinarily high rotational velocity could not be ignored.

On the first night of their observing run, Rubin and Ford entered the 19-story, dimly-lit dome of the Mayall reflector. Under the dome's open slit, the white telescope towered five stories above their heads. The sky that night was slightly hazy. Uncertain as to how long the weather would hold, they quickly had the assistant point the telescope at the two or three galaxies of prime importance. If the weather soured, they wanted to make sure they got something of value.

Their first night went well. They obtained half a dozen five-centimeter square photographic plates of their highest-priority galaxies. The next night also held. Daring to hope now, and feeling more relaxed, on the third night Rubin and Ford instructed the

assistant to give NGC 1961 a two-hour exposure. On their last night they gave it 45 minutes more.

The next day they flew back to Washington, D.C., and returned to the Department of Terrestrial Magnetism at the Carnegie Institution. There, in their sunny offices in a mansion on the crest of a tree-covered hill, they slipped the tiny photographic plates, called spectrograms, under a measuring microscope. They were then able to determine how the velocity of rotation of a galaxy varies at different distances from its center.

SOME SURPRISES

It used to be assumed that the stars in a galaxy were similar to the planets around the sun. The inner planets revolve faster than the outer ones. Most of the matter in the entire solar system is in the sun itself. Therefore, each sun-planet pair can be considered as a simple system, for most purposes neglecting the effects of the other planets. Physicists call such a simple pair system a two-body problem. In a galaxy, astronomers have an unmanageable 200,000,000,000-body problem. Thus it is extremely difficult to study each star's motion individually. Instead they consider large averages of the motions of many stars.

What Rubin and Ford found was that the stars at the edges of the galaxies were not moving more slowly than the stars closer to the center. In fact they were moving at the same speed. And in some cases they were moving even slightly faster. Other recent studies confirmed this result.

The surprise finding meant that the mass of stars at each distance from the center was about the same instead of falling off—as most everyone had anticipated. Analysis of the spectrograms further showed that NGC 1961 had to have some 10 times the mass of our Milky Way and about three times its size.

Seeking to confirm their observations, they went back to earlier radio observations that had not been fully examined. Thus they could independently check their results from the concentration of hydrogen gas in the galaxy. Sure enough, NGC 1961 was confirmed as the most massive spiral galaxy known.

COLLIDING GALAXIES

By analyzing both the peculiar shape and the colors of NGC 1961, Rubin and Ford deduced that its spiral arms may have been distorted by a recent violent event. The event may have been a collision and merger with another galaxy. Such a merger may have triggered an explosive burst of rapid star formation only some 200,000,000 years ago—very recently on a cosmological scale. Since that time, the galaxy's outer regions may have completed only a small fraction of a revolution. After they have revolved a couple of times, the astronomers suspect that the arms will reattain their symmetrical shape.

Rubin, Ford, and Roberts are now studying spiral galaxies of all sizes. They want to learn whether the constant-velocity profiles are true for all galaxies.

The arms of NGC 1961 are distorted by loops and wisps of gas—possibly the result of a recent violent event.

A National Geographic Society and Palomar Sky Survey

Although NGC 1961 is the largest spiral galaxy, it is not the largest known galaxy. The biggest to date is about eight times larger than the Milky Way—that is, if you believe the commonly accepted estimate of the Milky Way as being 100,000 light years across.

Rubin doesn't believe it. "I think it is a fallacy to say that our solar system is near the edge of our galaxy. If you tell me a spiral galaxy's rotational velocity, I can tell you its probable mass and diameter. The Milky Way rotates at about 250 kilometers per second. Because of that, I would be very surprised if it were smaller than about 300,000 light-years across."

If Rubin is right, that would mean that our solar system is not as close to the edge of the Milky Way as astronomers have generally thought—but in fact, that it is right in the thick of things.

So far the measurements of Rubin, Ford, and Roberts suggest that even very small galaxies have a significant fraction of their mass at large distances from their centers. For some galaxies, the outer regions are rotating even faster than the inner regions. "In essence," Rubin comments, "our observations indicate that spiral galaxies are more massive than originally suspected—by about a factor of five." The finding is an exciting one for astronomers in their quest for the so-called missing mass. They have long known that unless the universe has more matter than we know of, it will continue to expand until the last star goes dead.

Does the additional mass that Rubin and Ford have found mean the universe will stop expanding or reverse itself? No, not by quite a margin. But the work adds one more piece of evidence to our continuing attempt to understand the universe, its fate, and our place in it □

 SELECTED READINGS

"Are galaxies here to stay?" by V. Trimble and M. Rees. *Astronomy,* July 1978.

"Galaxy of new ideas" by M Guillen. *Science News,* August 26, 1978.

"Violently active galaxies: the search for the energy machine" by W. Metz. *Science,* August 25, 1978.

"What makes a spiral galaxy?" by D. Darling. *Astronomy,* July 1979.

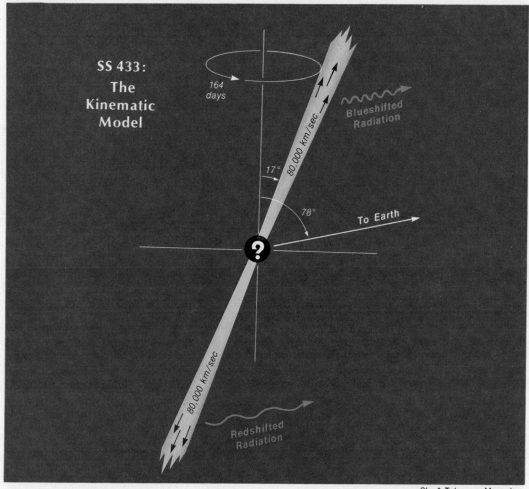

SS 433:
The
Kinematic
Model

164 days

80,000 km/sec

17°

78°

To Earth

Blueshifted Radiation

80,000 km/sec

Redshifted Radiation

The kinematic model of SS 433 holds that two beams of gas are ejected from a central object in opposite directions.

SS 433: A PECULIAR STAR

by Bruce Margon

IT is seldom that an entirely unclassifiable astronomical object is found. However, this is indeed the case with the peculiar star known as SS 433.

Located in the summer Milky Way in the constellation Aquila, the object appears in the Stephenson-Sanduleak catalog of stars whose spectra are peculiar due to the presence of emission lines. This peculiarity is shared by at least a few per cent of all stars. It is often due to a disturbed, thin envelope of hot gas surrounding an otherwise fairly normal star.

Although first noted and cataloged in the mid-1960's, SS 433 was not studied further until the summer of 1978. Three independent groups of researchers noted that it coincides in position with a strong and variable source of radio and X-ray emission. This is again somewhat unusual, as few stars emit detectable quantities of radio or X-radiation, especially at the distance of SS 433, estimated roughly as 10,000 light years. One light year equals approximately 9,600,000,-000,000 kilometers.

Perhaps even more surprising, the position of SS 433 is almost exactly in the center of a prominent, diffuse source of radio emission previously cataloged as W50. This source of radio waves was thought to be the remains of a fairly recently exploded star, or supernova. The central location naturally leads to the speculation that SS 433 and W50 may be physically related, perhaps in the same way that the Crab Nebula pulsar remnant of the supernova of 1054, is located within the diffuse radio and optical nebula in Taurus.

A STRANGE VISIBLE-LIGHT SPECTRUM

The most astonishing property of SS 433, however, emerged only upon a more detailed study of its visible-light spectrum conducted by myself and colleagues at the Lick Observatory, as well as several other groups of observers around the world. The spectrum contains several enormously strong, broad emission lines at unfamiliar wavelengths. The emission lines do not coincide with the signature of any of the common chemical elements, which are always identifiable in other astronomical spectra. Further, these lines are seen to change their wavelengths nightly by very significant amounts. Suppose these wavelength shifts are due to the familiar Doppler effect (caused by the motion of the emitting gas toward or away from the observer). Then the implied velocities and nightly changes in velocities exceed by a factor of 100 the motions previously observed in any stellar object.

Most spectacular of all, we generally see pairs of these extraordinary emission lines in the spectrum of SS 433. One is displaced toward shorter wavelengths, the other toward longer wavelengths from their laboratory values. A Doppler-shift interpretation of these pairs of moving lines then implies that there must be some gas moving towards us while simultaneously some patch of gas moves away, both at enormous speeds.

FAST FLOWING GAS

Recent study of spectra of SS 433 obtained on many different nights, together with related theoretical work, has now proven that the moving lines are originating in a gas flowing at a velocity exceeding one-quarter the speed of light. The emission lines are due simply to hydrogen and helium, the most abundant chemical elements in all stars. The enormous velocity and resulting large Doppler shifts obscured their original interpretation.

We should note that the random motions of all galactic stars that are approaching us are invariably very small—less than 200 kilometers per second—and that almost all external galaxies recede from the Milky Way due to the general expansion of the universe. Therefore, SS 433 gains the distinction as the only observed object in the universe with a significant blueshift in its spectrum—that is, the only object seeming to approach us.

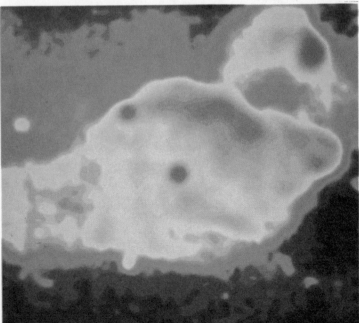

Geldzahler, Pauls, & Salter

SS 433 is located in the center of radio source W50, which is thought to be the remains of a fairly recently exploded star.

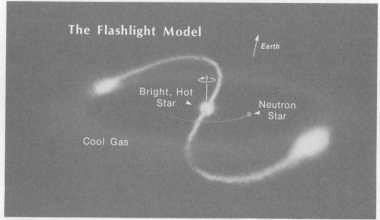

The Flashlight Model

Earth

Bright, Hot Star ▲

Neutron Star ▲

Cool Gas

The flashlight model of SS 433 holds that ionized matter blows out the magnetic poles of a wobbling luminous blue star, forming curving streams.

Sky & Telescope Magazine

A 164-DAY EMISSION CYCLE

A recent tantalizing clue to the nature of the object is our discovery that the moving emission lines cycle through a repeating pattern every 164 days. (See illustration on page 23.) This cyclical change is most easily (although not uniquely) interpreted as follows. The emission lines come from two linear but opposing beams of gas ejected in opposite directions from SS 433 at the fantastic speed of 80,000 kilometers per second, while the axis of these beams rotates once every 164 days. As the inclined axis sweeps through our line of sight, at any given time, we see parts of both beams, one creating redshifted lines from gas receding from us, and one causing blueshifted lines from gas approaching. The change of emission wavelengths is then due not to an actual change in the velocity of the gas, but rather to a change in the orientation of the gas as seen from earth.

To understand this, we must recall that the Doppler effect shows motion only away or towards the observer, not across the line of sight. Thus we see maximum red and blue shifts in the emission lines as one beam points towards earth and the other away, and smaller shifts when the beams are in other orientations. This simple description of the rotating beams is unfortunately compatible with a large variety of different underlying physical models. Therefore, most questions regarding the nature of SS 433 still remain unanswered. The observed ejection velocity is close to that of the escape velocity from the surface of a compact star, suggesting that perhaps a collapsed, evolved object such as a neutron star might be involved.

A NEUTRON STAR COMPANION

Recently, another period of small but significant amplitude has been found in the spectroscopic data, indicating that SS 433 probably circles an as-yet-invisible companion every 13 days. If this periodicity is indeed orbital motion, we may speculate that the system actually consists of a neutron star and a fairly normal but optically faint companion, similar to the famous X-ray binary stars such as Hercules X-1. If this is the case, perhaps rapid radio, X-ray, or visible light pulsations may be found from SS 433, as is observed from the neutron stars which give rise to pulsars.

Numerous other theoretical difficulties remain to be explained in this exotic system. For example, the amount of kinetic energy in the ejected beams is enormous. Probably it is greater than 1,000,000 times the entire light output of our sun. What is the source of this energy? And what is the mechanism that rotates the beams, and keeps them so narrowly aligned? For the observers, perhaps the most tantalizing question is whether a second member of this class of object currently exists in our galaxy, or whether SS 433 is truly unique. Only the accidental discovery of a second such object will tell for certain □

 SELECTED READINGS

"SS 433: a very peculiar star" by Dennis Overbye. *Sky and Telescope,* December 1979.

"Puzzle of SS 433: both a blue shift and a red shift." *Physics Today,* August 1979.

"Something weird in the Milky Way: study of SS 433" by B. Margon. *Science News,* April 28, 1979.

Pioneer 11 took this somewhat distorted image of Saturn while approaching the planet in August 1979. Rings A, B, and C are visible, as is the satellite Rhea at the lower right.

SATURN

by J. Kelly Beatty

FINALLY, it is Saturn's turn. For nearly two decades, spacecraft have crisscrossed throughout the inner, more accessible portions of the solar system, like so many interplanetary tourists. A flyby here, a landing there, taking in all the sights allowed on the economical package tour. Distant destinations cost extra—not until the 1970's did we manage to reach Jupiter.

For ages Saturn was the known limit of the solar system, shining brightly as it passed among the stars but offering the naked eye no clue to its unique character. Its seemingly crisp ring system glistens even in very small telescopes, as 17th-century astronomers discovered. On September 1, 1979, the aging Pioneer 11 spacecraft swept a mere 3,500 kilometers from the outer edge of Saturn's bright, visible ring system. It passed under the rings and edged to within 21,400 kilometers of the planet itself.

In late 1974, Pioneer 11 had plunged deep into the intense radiation envelope around Jupiter. In coming so near to Jupiter, Pioneer 11 was abruptly swung around by the planet's strong gravity onto a new trajectory bound for Saturn.

WHAT WAS KNOWN

Only a little of what we knew about Saturn prior to Pioneer 11 was firmly established. The planet circles the sun a distant 9.5 astronomical units (1,400,000,000 kilometers) away on the average, taking nearly 30 years to complete one circuit. With an equatorial radius of 60,000 kilometers, it is smaller but comparable in size to Jupiter. Saturn's density is only 0.7—less than that of water. The obvious implication is that it contains material less dense than water. Like Jupiter, Saturn should be composed almost entirely of hydrogen and helium, with traces of other low-density molecules like ammonia, methane, and ethane. (These gases were detected by observations from the earth.)

The rings, however, are different in composition. For example, they are whiter and less yellow than the planet. Their spectroscopic signature is dominated by water ice. This suggests that the rings are orbiting chunks of ice-glazed rock. Three principal rings, termed A, B, and C, lie in the planet's equatorial plane in a sheet reaching from 12,600 to 77,400 kilometers above the cloud tops. A fourth ring, D, was discovered by French astronomers in 1970. Another candidate, E, was identified in 1966 when the ring system was last seen edge-on from the earth. However, ring E has not been detected since.

SATURN—AN AFTERTHOUGHT

What, then, was Pioneer 11's mission at Saturn? The spacecraft was not designed to study anything more than Jupiter and its exotic electromagnetic environment. Saturn was an afterthought. Yet the planet tantalized investigators with certain questions: Does Saturn envelop itself with a strong magnetic field and belts of radiation? What is the true character of the rings? What of Titan, its massive satellite that is larger than Mercury and known to have a substantial atmosphere?

On board the spacecraft are instruments for detecting various kinds of charged particles and magnetic fields. One experiment monitors infrared wavelengths; another is tuned to the ultraviolet emissions of hydro-gen and helium. Meteoroid sensors and an imaging photopolarimeter round out the hardware. Pioneer's radio signal records gravitational and atmospheric conditions.

Besides the advantage of actually observing Saturn close-up, Pioneer 11 offered scientists their first chance to view the planet from a vantage point other than earth—that is, as other than a fully illuminated disk. To earth-based viewers, Saturn's poles periodically tip toward us. However, this presents us with only a slightly more favorable view of the rings.

During Pioneer's brief visit, Saturn was poised with its southern hemisphere slightly tipped toward the sun. This position illuminated the underside of the rings. The spacecraft, meanwhile, approached from above the ring plane, affording views of the rings' "dark" side and of their shadows cast on the planet.

Yet Pioneer 11 came away unscathed. Shortly after the encounter, one of NASA's scientists declared, "We welcome Saturn into our books of knowledge." Since then investigators have been carefully combing through their marvelous trove of data. A number of surprises have turned up.

Backlit by sunlight, this Pioneer photograph of Saturn's rings shows details never before seen, including the presence of material running through Cassini's division. The art insert identifies the rings and divisions and points out the satellite Tethys.

NASA Ames Research Center

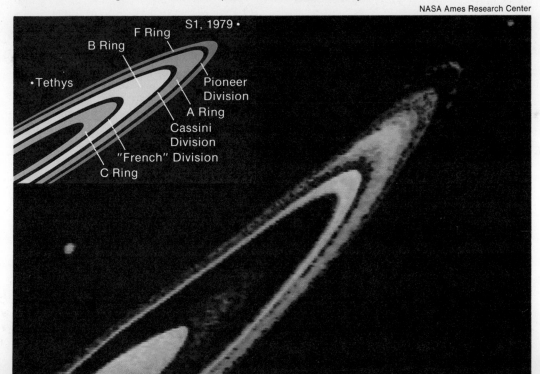

This composite photo of Saturn and its rings was the best available prior to Pioneer's encounter.

MORE RINGS

For many, attention focused on the rings. The images provided by the instruments show that sunlight is transmitted through the rings differently from the way it is reflected by them back toward earth. The illusion of a negative is created: areas normally thought of as dark appear bright.

The brilliant B ring is extremely opaque when viewed this way. "When sunlight passes through the rings," explains Tom Gehrels of the University of Arizona, "you need a certain balance. Enough material must be present to scatter light forward, but not so much that the layer becomes opaque."

Close examination of the images accounts for most known elements of the system. A, B, and C all show clearly, as does Cassini's division, the space separating the A and B rings. There is even a comparably wide gap between B and C, which was tentatively identified in 1943 by the French astronomer B. Lyot. The D ring, however, was not detected.

What the experimenters did find was a new family member, F, centered 3,500 kilometers beyond the visible edge of the A ring. A mere 500 kilometers wide, the thin new ring leaves a gap of some 3,000 kilometers between it and the A ring. Scientists called the new clearing the "Pioneer division."

While the existence of this faint band is certain, that of the elusive E ring is not. It was not seen by Pioneer's instrumentation.

There are other indications, however, of the possible presence of material in Saturn's equatorial plane even farther from the more obvious rings.

"From the point of view of particle concentrations," notes James Trainor of NASA's Goddard Space Flight Center, "things are a little strange" in the region 540,000 to 840,000 kilometers out from the planet. It is here Dr. Trainor believes yet another ring is located. Unlike the others, this one may be made up of relatively few, larger fragments. Additional rings may also exist.

SATURN'S FACE

Even though many of the images obtained by Pioneer 11 exceed the quality of the best earth-based views, the face of Saturn is disappointingly lacking in details. Only faint banding is visible, with hints of turbulent scallops along one or two belt-zone interfaces. One widely accepted explanation is that at Saturn's great distance from the sun, the cloud tops are so cold that ammonia freezes and forms a high-altitude haze over more distinct, Jupiterlike patterns. Yet scientists claim to have identified some spots in the clouds that may yield an accurate determination of Saturn's rotation period. In addition, Dr. Gehrels believes two fast-moving jets of high clouds can be identified: one near the equator and another near the edge of a somewhat brown-and-blue north polar region.

MAGNETOSPHERE

Using estimates based on the Jupiter data, Pioneer scientists expected a relatively strong magnetic field enclosing a volume out to about 3,000,000 kilometers. Yet the actual field strength, according to Edward Smith of Jet Propulsion Laboratory, was three to five times weaker than anticipated. It was calculated to be 0.22 gauss at the planet's equator. By comparison, the earth's equatorial field is 0.3 gauss. However, since Saturn is so much larger, its intrinsic field is still many hundreds of times stronger than earth's.

Saturn's magnetic field is unique among the planets of our solar system. While Jupiter, Earth, and Mercury also possess fields, their magnetic axes are tipped with respect to the rotational axes. At Saturn the magnetic axis has no apparent tilt. Saturn's magnetic source region probably lies deep within its interior. Because of this, higher-order imperfections remain hidden beneath the surface and only a simple dipole field (like that from a classroom bar magnet) is expressed in the Saturnian magnetosphere.

Moreover, Jupiter's magnetic "bottle" is constantly being injected with particles from Io's volcanoes. Such charged particles exist around Saturn, too, but there aren't as many of them. The only potentially large source of particles is Titan. Its orbit, however, is some 1,120,000 kilometers from Saturn, and it lies right at the edge of the magnetosphere, where the field is weak.

In Saturn's well-behaved magnetic environment, several mechanisms apparently clear certain regions of charged particles. The rings, for instance, do this very well—the high-speed ions merely run into a ring particle and are thus removed from circulation. Not surprisingly, then, the Pioneer experiments registered a sharp drop in charged particles when the spacecraft dipped under the rings' outer edge. Even the small amount of matter in Cassini's division and the F ring is enough to absorb the radiation. The existence of the G ring was proposed, not from actually seeing it, but from an analysis of charged-particle data.

Satellites are also effective radiation absorbers. The radiation particles move up and down very quickly but diffuse inward slowly.

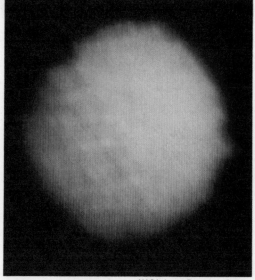

NASA Ames Research Center

Pioneer barely "saw" Titan. The smooth appearance this photo shows is probably due to a global overcast of clouds.

Therefore, once a satellite sweeps an area clean, it remains relatively free of particles until the satellite's next visit. Most of Saturn's satellites orbit within the magnetosphere. Hence the scientists expect to find dips in the particle counts at most locations corresponding to the satellites' orbits.

A third inhibitor, plasma, consists of ions and electrons not moving along the field lines but instead traveling around the planet with them and in random motion. Some satellites and rings have been inferred solely from plasma absorption.

THE ALMOST-NO-TITAN ENCOUNTER

Just after the second crossing of Saturn's ring plane, there remained little doubt that Pioneer 11 had led a charmed life. First, it had survived several days inside Jupiter's lethal radiation environment. Second, it had survived 6½ years of space travel since launch on April 5, 1973. Third, it breezed through a pair of high-risk passages across Saturn's rings. And its radio signal was coming in much stronger than expected.

With such a positive outlook, the scientists turned their instruments toward Titan shortly after the spacecraft passed Saturn. A number of the sensing instruments were poised to observe the satellite. Among them was an infrared radiometer to make two temperature measurements: one each on Titan's day and night sides. By comparing these, it was thought much could be learned about the atmosphere (and even the surface) of this moon. Titan has been subject to such exotic speculations as its perhaps possessing an atmosphere denser than earth's, a surface covered with organic goo or perhaps methane oceans, and a climate conducive to life.

But the good fortune enjoyed by Pioneer 11 seemed to run out as the spacecraft approached Titan. Communications began to deteriorate seriously. Some data were garbled temporarily (to be dredged out later from the noise), but some were lost permanently. Even a Soviet satellite's transmissions nearly got in the way—NASA had failed to notify the Soviet Union of its planned encounter time.

"The good news," intoned a weary Andrew Ingersoll afterward, "is that Titan is there [in the data]. The bad news is that we barely saw it." One infrared reading was salvaged: Titan's globally averaged temperature is about 75° K in the upper atmosphere. He added that there's "not a prayer" of extracting the day-night difference.

But other instruments "saw" Titan. The ultraviolet detector got a peek at Titan, reporting the existence of a hydrogen cloud enshrouding it in an envelope extending along a portion of its orbit. Darryl Judge, from the University of Southern California, comments that Titan is unlikely to contain much hydrogen in its atmosphere. He suggests the cloud probably arises from the breakdown of other suspected components like methane. Other elements like nitrogen may also contribute.

PIONEER 11'S SCOUTING REPORT

Some of the most important information collected by Pioneer 11 concerns Saturn's general characteristics and what the soon-to-arrive Voyager spacecraft can expect. For instance, careful tracking throughout the encounter has produced a new determination of the shapes of the planet and its gravitational field. The centrifugal forces acting on Saturn (a rapidly spinning, fluid object) flatten it by 10 per cent through the poles. This fact was known long before Pioneer 11. Now the exact shape can be refined to within 60 or 70 meters. Moreover, accurate mapping of the overall gravitational field will greatly reduce trajectory errors for the Voyagers.

The radiation environment is much less intense than Jupiter's. The highest-energy particles are found within 540,000 kilometers of the planet. The total accumulated dose of electrons with energies of 3,000,000 electron volts or greater was comparable to what Jupiter dished out in just two minutes. Further analysis should also yield new masses for Saturn, its A and B rings, and its satellites Titan, Iapetus, and Rhea—all useful facts that every Voyager should know ahead of time.

SATURN'S MOONS

What may not be known when Voyager 1 arrives is a complete player roster. Saturn has nine well-documented satellites. A 10th, Janus, was discovered in 1966 and lies some 30,000 kilometers beyond the A ring. Yet some analyses of its sparse sightings conclude the data fit better if a pair of satellites is considered. Thus, there may possibly be other satellites as well.

In addition to Titan, Pioneer 11 glimpsed a number of other satellites. One instrument picked up Iapetus, a strange body that is five or six times brighter on one side than on the other. The instrument picked up Tethys and Mimas as well. The spacecraft has two new and perhaps separate observations to add. One, dubbed Pioneer Rock, orbits just 13,000 kilometers beyond the A ring's outer edge.

Perhaps all this confusion will be resolved soon. Saturn has already entered an extended period with its rings presented edge-on to earth, the ideal situation for satellite searches. The last occasion was in 1966, and instrumentation has been greatly improved since then. Would-be discoverers won't get another chance until 1995, so an all-out effort is planned to take advantage of the present opportunity □

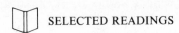

SELECTED READINGS

"Pioneer 11's new Saturn." *Science News,* September 15, 1979.

"Rings around the solar system" by R. Kerr. *Science,* October 5, 1979.

ARIANE: EUROPE'S SPACE LAUNCHER

by Keith Hindley

THE European Space Agency (ESA) is about to have its own vehicle for launching spacecraft into orbit. It is named Ariane, and it stands on its launch pad amidst the swaying palm trees of France's Kourou Space Center in South America. This highly conventional rocket—in contrast to a reusable shuttle design—was born out of a strong political will in France and to a lesser degree in West Germany to be free of dependence on U.S. launchers. It is intended to meet the launch needs of the European states in commercial and scientific satellites. At the same time it is hoped that it will corner a slice of the lucrative and expanding market for orbiting communications and other satellites.

At first sight, Ariane hardly looks like competition for the U.S. National Aeronautics and Space Administration's (NASA's) space shuttle. The shuttle will be able to launch ten times the payload that Ariane can lift into earth orbit. Indeed, the shuttle will launch Spacelab 1, the joint ESA/NASA manned scientific station, in 1981.

The bulk of the bread-and-butter launch business in the 1980's will be to lift at least 200 geostationary satellites into orbit at 35,800 kilometers. There, a satellite's orbital motion exactly counterbalances the earth's rotation. It hangs apparently motionless over a point on the earth's equator. This is the place for communications satellites. There are signs that more and more nations want their own piece of hardware up there.

EXCELLENT LAUNCH SITE

To carry out this kind of satellite-launching mission, the NASA shuttle requires an extra powered stage. This additional stage reduces the payload the shuttle can carry to a point where ESA claims its payload advantage over Ariane falls to a factor of about two rather than ten. (Carrying a manned cabin around is a penalty for any launcher.) Although the shuttle was intended to be able to orbit any type of satellite, it was designed principally for carrying large masses into low earth orbit cheaply.

The top part of Ariane is being lowered into position during construction.

Ariane stands ready to go on the launch pad at the Kourou Space Center.

Ariane can place 1.75 metric tons into geostationary orbit, including a one-ton satellite. ESA claims that Ariane is also suited for placing satellites in polar orbits at 840 kilometers, where they are synchronous with the sun's apparent position. A big bonus is Ariane's launch site in South America, which is within 5½ degrees of the equator. Launches there get the full benefit of the earth's rotational velocity—in effect, get an extra push. This makes the site ideal for geostationary missions. Because less fuel is required to attain the needed velocity, ESA rockets launched from Guiana get a 17 per cent advantage over a similar launch from NASA's Kennedy Space Center in Florida.

FRENCH CONTROL

ESA's Ariane project has progressed relatively smoothly since its inception in 1973. Although much has been said in public about the cooperation of 60 companies in 10 European countries, Ariane owes its success so far to firm French control, and it is France that has footed the major portion of the bill. It is also French industry that has gained the lion's share of the development contracts.

The rocket's total development cost is likely to be about $660,000,000. For this price, ESA gets all the facilities needed to launch the vehicle and an initial five Ariane rockets, four of which will actually be launched.

CONVENTIONAL DESIGN

Ariane is a deliberately conservative design. It is based on European rocket experience, and its lack of major technological innovation has reduced development risk and cost. In addition, the project was designed to make the best use of facilities that already existed in the ESA member states.

Ariane is a conventional three-stage rocket standing 47.5 meters high. It has a dead weight of only 17.5 tons, which rises to 207 tons when fully fueled for liftoff. The first two stages are powered by variants of the Viking motor, a power plant that was already in an advanced state of development when Ariane was planned. A cluster of four motors is used in the first stage and a single motor in the second. Viking uses unsymmetrical dimethyl hydrazine fuel with nitrogen tetroxide oxidizer. In contrast, the third stage is a cryogenic one, using liquid hydrogen and oxygen.

In a typical launch, a first-stage burn of 45 seconds will accelerate the vehicle to a speed of 1.87 kilometers per second and separate at an altitude of 52 kilometers. The second stage will fire for 138 seconds, carrying the payload to 4.78 kilometers per second, and fall away at an altitude of 138 kilometers. The third stage will then burn for 570 seconds, pushing the velocity to 9.76 kilometers per second, and fall away at 213 kilometers, just over 14 minutes after liftoff. The payload will then be en route to geostationary orbit.

FEW PROBLEMS

The testing program has suffered only a few major problems. For example, early firings of the four clustered first-stage Viking engines cracked the graphite liner of the combustion-chamber throat. The noise generated during firing was sufficient to degrade the material, so a silica/phenolic resin replacement was developed.

Some development work has also been necessary on the second stage, which, unlike the first, operates in a near-vacuum. The Viking motor has been modified by extending and thickening its nozzle. In addition, fuel pipes have been relocated to prevent the motor from ingesting pressurized gas when the fuel tanks have almost emptied. Another problem occurred during test-firing of the third-stage motor, when a safety device intended to ignite safely any leaking hydrogen gas failed to operate, and the hydrogen exploded. This did little damage to the third stage but damaged the testing bay.

In general, though, tests have proceeded smoothly and successfully, and the first planned launch date had to be put forward by only a few months during development. Motor trials started in late 1977. The launch and tracking facilities in French Guiana were completed, and the first rocket underwent launch-pad checks in early 1979. This program culminated with full fueling of the rocket and a countdown that was terminated just five seconds before engine ignition.

ESA then had a fully ground-tested launcher with a good reliability record and was ready to make its first qualification launch. It did so on December 24, 1979. The launch was successful and Ariane placed a small dummy satellite in orbit.

ESA is not slow to compare this record with the series of problems and budget overruns that have beset the development of the U.S. space shuttle.

USING ARIANE OR THE SHUTTLE

Certainly some potential users of either Ariane or the space shuttle are delaying before signing a launch contract. NASA enjoys an unrivaled reputation for reliability. Potential users, however, are worried about the technological innovations in the craft's design. Each new spacecraft has suffered early problems that have always taken time to put

A. Nogues/Sygma

The first successful launch of Ariane—in December 1979—was controlled from underground operations centers such as these at the Kourou Space Center.

right. ESA's declared aim is to complete four test launches by the end of 1980, commencing commercial launches by early 1981.

The shuttle schedule is certainly tighter. A failure with one or more of the early Ariane launches would not significantly affect the commercial schedule. Yet one shuttle vehicle (102 Columbia) may be used for NASA's four qualifying flights and up to the first six operational flights. Any problems in flight, even if minor, could further delay the start of commercial shuttle operations.

All these factors have led to a steadily filling launch-book for Ariane. One major coup was the signing in the spring of 1979 of a contract to launch a satellite for the Washington-based Intelsat organization in the face of an offered shuttle launch. The first five Intelsat V's are being lifted by NASA Atlas-Centaur rockets. The Ariane price for the sixth is $25,290,000 with an option for launch of the seventh Intelsat in 1982 at a fixed price of $27,460,000.

These prices are a little cheaper than for a shuttle launch, and the difference could grow. Shuttle launches quoted up to 1983 are being pegged on the cheap side by NASA. From the start of 1984 prices will be adjusted to cover the true flight costs for the first ten-year period. For the first time a NASA project is under external commercial pressure to keep its costs down.

The first four development Ariane rockets either will carry ballast or will launch satellites free of charge on an "owner's risk" basis. In addition, five commercial launches are now firm.

ESA expects further business launching maritime communications satellites and international communications satellites (Intelsats) as well as various earth resources, meteorology, and scientific satellites for countries who would prefer not to be dependent on either the United States or the USSR for launch facilities. The Kourou Space Center can handle about four launches a year, and ESA is looking for between 40 and 50 launches during the 1980's.

IMPROVED VERSIONS COMING

Such is the volume of satellites likely to be orbited that both Ariane and the shuttle should keep a full launch schedule. Most European countries will probably opt for Ariane, and most U.S. satellites will still go to NASA. But the two launch systems operating side by side will give added flexibility. Some organizations will probably choose whichever program can launch to suit a particular date.

ESA is already looking at various economies that could be applied to production rockets. One study has shown that the recovery of the spent first stage from the South Atlantic Ocean for servicing and reuse would save about 15 per cent of the cost of a launcher.

They are also looking beyond the simple initial version of the vehicle. There is work on an improved Ariane 2—with the first-stage thrust increased ten per cent, with two solid propellant boosters, and with the third-stage fuel increased by two tons. This version is scheduled to be ready by 1983. It will add only a few per cent to the development cost so far.

Ariane 2 will be able to launch 2.3 tons into geostationary orbit (including two of the larger satellites) and will be able to use the existing launch pad in Guiana. Plans for even larger Ariane variants, including one that could launch a manned spacecraft, would require a larger launch pad and a further massive investment of funds.

European economic and political unity is slowly gaining momentum through the European Economic Community, but a formal United States of Europe is still a long way off. Yet the European states do have a larger combined economic base than either the United States or the USSR and could certainly finance further space ventures. A major independent European space program is still in the future, but Ariane does mark the first firm steps along that road □

 SELECTED READINGS

"European Space Agency." *Astronomy,* March 1979.

"Jungle space center: Kourou in French Guiana" by M. Morgan. *Americas,* October 1979.

H. S. Terrace

Many chimpanzees, like Nim, have learned to "speak" in sign language, but now scientists wonder if the animals really understand what they are saying, or are just artful imitators.

BEHAVIORAL SCIENCES

BEHAVIORAL SCIENCES
REVIEW OF THE YEAR

NIMH

Scientists have succeeded in transplanting a functioning part of the brain of one rat onto the brain of another—an important step that opens new avenues of possible brain research and disease treatment.

Neurologist Albert Galaburda has found brain-cell abnormalities in some persons afflicted with dyslexia.

Beth Israel Hospital

Brain structure and chemistry. Rapidly expanding knowledge of the brain and its relation to behavior continued to dominate research in the behavioral sciences. The first successful transplant of a functioning part of the brain of one animal onto the damaged brain of another was reported during the year 1979 by an international team of scientists from the U.S. National Institute of Mental Health (NIMH) and from Sweden. The grafts, performed on nine laboratory rats, had survived for several months without rejection by the time the study was reported. Moreover, the transplants had grown into their new brains and even extended their nerve fibers into surrounding brain tissue. Though still in the animal stage, these experiments ultimately may hold promise for victims of Parkinson's disease and other brain disorders. Scientists believe that Parkinson's disease is caused primarily by the loss of cells in the brain's substantia nigra (SN), one of several brain regions that manufactures the chemical dopamine. The research team, headed by NIMH's Richard Jed Wyatt, Mark J. Perlow, and William J. Freed, succeeded in grafting SN cells from healthy rat brains to rats whose own such cells had been destroyed through experimentally induced Parkinson's disease. After the transplants had grown in, most of the rats showed significant improvement in their symptoms. Said Wyatt, "This opens up a new area of investigation, both because of its potential clinical applications and its meaning to basic science."

A different type of brain abnormality—enlarged cerebral ventricles (cavities)—appears to be involved in certain forms of schizophrenia in humans. At one time this and other types of brain-structure problems were believed responsible for much of mental illness, but this explanation has been discounted for decades basically because it could not be proven—at least not with available technology. Now, however, the development of computerized axial tomography (CAT) and other techniques has led to the discovery of subtle structural abnormalities that may indeed contribute to certain disturbances. An NIMH group, headed by Daniel R. Weinberger, used CAT scans to compare the brains of schizophrenics and non-schizophrenics. They found that some of the diagnosed schizophrenics had larger-than-normal cerebral ventricles. ■ In a related study NIMH colleague Daniel J. Luchins found that in a surprising number of schizophrenics, the brain hemispheres seem to be reversed—almost mirror images of normal brain structure. Whereas normal, right-handed individuals tend to have wider right frontal and left occipital (in the rear of the brain) lobes, a significant percentage of right-handed schizophrenics exhibit the opposite of this.

Certain structural abnormalities of the brain, including reversals, have also been linked to certain speech and reading problems, including dyslexia, a reading disability that frequently involves confusion of letter positions and shapes. Neurologist Albert M. Galaburda and colleague Thomas L. Kember of Beth Israel Hospital in Boston have reported that some instances of dyslexia may be caused by abnormalities in certain cells of the brain cortex that are thought to play a critical role in speech and language performance. When they examined the intact brain of a 20-year-old dyslexic who died in an accident, the scientists found a "disorganized cortex . . . the layers were sort of scrambled and whirled [with] primitive, larger cells in [a certain] part of the brain."

"Natural" Drugs. It has been several years since researchers discovered that the human brain makes its own natural morphinelike substances. Called enkephalin and endorphin, these substances are believed to play critical roles in a person's perception of pain and development of emotions. In 1979 evidence of a natural "Valium" in the brain was reported by several researchers. In a November 1979 meeting of the Society for Neuroscience, Danish researcher Claus Braestrup described a substance that, he reports, "binds" to brain receptor cells that also attract Valium, Librium, and other antianxiety drugs. He further reported that the natural substance binds more tightly and powerfully than the synthetic chemicals.

The brain also appears to produce its own version of PCP, commonly known as "angel dust." This substance—an abused drug, primarily by young people—is known to produce schizophrenialike symptoms as well as potentially dangerous physical reactions that may lead to death. However, the drug—or its natural analog—may also be involved in the "regulation of thinking processes [and] perhaps some normal functioning . . . in the sensory system," says Stephen R. Zukin of Mount Sinai School of Medicine and R. Suzanne Zukin of Albert Einstein College of Medicine, both in New York City. This may explain their reported discovery of specific brain sites that bind PCP, an indication that the brain may be manufacturing its own similar substance.

Depression and Genetics. Studies in Denmark and elsewhere have indicated that some forms of emotional depression may be inherited. These studies were based on statistical evidence rather than on any direct, physical proof. Then, in January 1979, medical geneticist David E. Comings of the City of Hope National Medical Center in Duarte, California, reported that he had found "the major gene in depressive disease." The discovery, he said, constituted "the first basis for a biochemical abnormality found in individual psychotic depression." Some scientists called Comings' findings provocative, while others questioned his methodology and techniques in the study of the brains of dead persons in the project and suggested that his report may have been premature and represent an overinterpretation of findings. By the end of 1979 Comings' findings had not been replicated.

Homosexuality. In publishing a new book, *Homosexuality in Perspective,* sex therapists William H. Masters and Virginia E. Johnson revived a controversy that had been simmering for years in the sex-research field. Masters and Johnson said that they achieved a surprising success rate in "converting" or "reversing" homosexual individuals into heterosexuals with just two weeks of sex therapy and psychotherapy at their laboratories in St. Louis, Missouri. Their claims caused an uproar among homosexuals and several other researchers who questioned, respectively, the motivation and scientific validity of the research. Masters and Johnson also confirmed what other scientists had previously reported—namely, that the physical mechanics of sexual functioning in homosexuals is relatively normal.

Joel Greenberg

Einstein College of Medicine

The Drs. Zukin believe that they have found specific brain sites that bind to PCP, leading to the speculation that the brain may produce its own form of PCP or related substance.

Sex researchers William H. Masters and Virginia Johnson have added new data to the controversy concerning homosexuality.

UPI

BIOFEEDBACK AS BEHAVIORAL THERAPY

by Thomas W. Pew Jr.

KEEPING up with Dr. Kenneth Greenspan at the Columbia-Presbyterian Medical Center in New York City turned out to be an unexpected substitute for my morning jog. I followed him down wide corridors and past stretcher-size double doors. I stuck my head inside a closet-size room for a brief meeting with intense researchers and listened to an inquiry about the comfort of a patient propped up in a hospital bed outfitted with some unusual-looking exercise and monitoring devices. And finally I took hasty notes in a computer room that looked more like the control center for operating a Minuteman missile silo than a medical facility.

This is how Dr. Greenspan usually begins his day at Columbia-Presbyterian, where he is assistant attending psychiatrist and director of the Laboratory and Center for Stress-Related Disorders. In his office once again I found the inconspicuous little biological "listening" devices I'd been plugged into from San Francisco to Topeka in my quest for an understanding of biofeedback. Dr. Greenspan introduced me to his own research by flashing a series of slides on the office wall. One was a color picture of himself, stripped to the waist, stretched out on a bed and attached to the exercise equipment and monitoring devices we'd just seen on our tour.

HEALING BY ACTIVE PARTICIPATION

"I try everything on myself first," he explained. "How else can I feel what the patient is feeling?" Using slides of himself and one of his biofeedback trainers working with patients, Dr. Greenspan quickly laid out the ideas he believes underlie the success of biofeedback treatment at the Medical Center. "Patients come to us feeling like victims," he said, "sick and unsure of what to expect, and we try to help them develop an attitude of mastery. We share with them what we know, and we seek their active participation in their own treatment. The goal is self-responsibility for the maintenance of one's own health," he added, "and to assist the doctor within us."

While I was still chewing on these ideas, Dr. Greenspan showed me data on 22 patients whose treatment represents a provocative study of biofeedback's potential benefits. Most of the patients had been referred to Dr. Greenspan by Dr. Arthur B. Voorhees Jr., chief of cardiovascular surgery at the Medical Center. When they first arrived, they could not walk from the hospital parking lot to the stress center—the equivalent of two city blocks—without pain. Their circulatory systems were choked with clots, their legs crippled from lack of proper circulation.

In only three months of intense biofeedback training and behavioral therapy, in which these patients consciously learned to regulate the temperature in their legs, they were able to walk over a kilometer on the laboratory treadmill without pain. Some changes in their cardiovascular systems were similar to those seen during athletic conditioning.

"SEEING" AND "HEARING" THE PROBLEM

These patients were allowed to "see" or "hear" a problem in circulation and to find a natural method for solving the problem.

This hypertension patient is learning how moderate exercise—such as walking on a treadmill—affects his blood pressure.

Both photos: David Attie

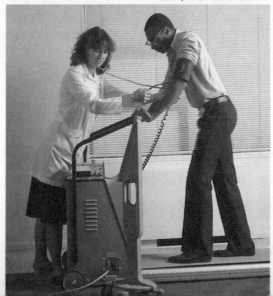

Dr. Judy Green is studying the brain-wave activity and other biological processes of an epileptic.

They were aided in their "seeing" and "hearing" by a rigorous training program using muscle and temperature biofeedback devices on their hands and legs. While the patients relaxed in recliners, temperature information on their blood-starved limbs was monitored, amplified, and displayed to them. By learning to raise the temperature of their limbs (which meant sending more blood to the affected areas), they gradually accelerated the development of collateral blood vessels around the clots. In effect, they developed a natural bypass system to the areas that previously had been cut off by the clots, restoring needed circulation to their crippled limbs. They also achieved deep relaxation and lessened the cardiac stress that often accompanied their efforts at walking.

I have experienced this type of biofeedback training at both the Biofeedback Institute in San Francisco and the Biofeedback and Psychophysiology Center at the Menninger Foundation in Topeka. Watching a large dial thermometer on the biofeedback instrument or listening to electronic beeps indicating temperature changes, I was soon able to raise the temperature of the part of my body to which the sensor was attached. When I saw the temperature start to go up—usually after a few moments of relaxing—I just "went with" the feeling that accompanied it, and the temperature continued to rise. It was quite easy to achieve.

Most of the other participants at a Menninger biofeedback workshop found it the same. Interestingly, for those who insist that no such thing will happen when they are at-tached to temperature trainers, the thermometer will often remain stationary or actually fall when they attempt the training. To biofeedback researchers this only underscores the importance of motivation, and further serves to show that the body tends to do what we visualize—negatively as well as positively.

Dr. Elmer E. Green, founder of the Biofeedback and Psychophysiology Center at Menninger's, says that biofeedback means getting ongoing information about one's own biological processes—such as heart behavior, temperature, brain-wave activity, blood pressure, or muscle tension. Then the information is used to change and control at will the specific process or response being monitored.

Once the signals are heard or seen, an individual is able to influence their direction by willpower. "We don't know how visualization and volition get converted into action," Dr. Green told a workshop of doctors and counselors at Menninger's, "but we don't need to know everything in order to use biofeedback."

YOGIS DO IT NATURALLY

Yogis and similar individuals in many societies learn or seem to possess naturally the same self-regulating abilities the average person can acquire relatively quickly through biofeedback training. In their 20-year study of the mechanisms of biofeedback, Dr. Green, with colleague and wife Alyce M. Green, studied yogis and others with unusual control over their minds and bodies. What they found and documented on a sophisticated array of electronic instruments was that there are people who are in touch with the most subtle workings of what we in the Western world call the autonomic or involuntary nervous system.

Some yogis can alter their heartbeats on command. They can alter their respiration rates, apparently enabling them to enter a kind of hibernation for long periods of time. They can also produce a whole range of brain waves, changing them at will. In addition they can exercise control over the temperatures of their bodies, can stand extremes of environmental temperatures, and seem able to make themselves impervious to pain.

One of the most impressive people ever studied at Menninger's is a Netherlander, Jack Schwarz. Participants in the biofeedback workshops are shown a film made in the laboratory there in which Schwarz runs a large, rusty sailmaker's needle through his upper arm while his body's reactions are closely monitored by a bank of electronic instruments designed to detect the slightest response to this ordeal.

I had heard of this demonstration prior to seeing it at Menninger's, but I had no idea of the size of the needle and had not realized it was run completely through the arm. At the final moment the camera zoomed in to concentrate on the point where the needle was slipping out of Schwarz's arm. As it emerged, the hole could be seen closing instantly, allowing no more than a drop of blood to run down the skin.

Within a matter of hours the wound had completely healed and the flesh exhibited no bruises, needle marks, or signs of internal bleeding. Furthermore, none of the instruments recording Schwarz's heart and respiration rates, galvanic skin response, hand temperature, and brain-wave activity showed he had experienced pain.

One witnessing physician attempted to repeat the Schwarz demonstration himself. He had to halt in the middle, overcome with pain. Then Schwarz coached him through the rest of the way by telling him to close his eyes and "think about the jonquils" blooming outdoors. Unfortunately, the doctor could not control the bleeding and was left with a heavily bruised and sore arm for several days.

BLOOD-PRESSURE CUFF AND THERMOMETER

Almost everyone has at some time in his or her life been hooked up to some of the more obvious biofeedback equipment. A simple blood-pressure cuff can be used for biofeedback training, as can an electrocardiograph, and even, as in Dr. Greenspan's work, a thermometer. In traditional medicine, the information produced by these biofeedback instruments is primarily for the physician's eyes and his use. In biofeedback

training, the diagnostic or feedback instruments are primarily for the patient's information.

It's up to the patient to use the information—whether it tells about heart rate, blood pressure, temperature, muscle contractions, or brain waves—to help restore normal functions to the body. And how does anyone do this?

If you are doing your biofeedback training at Menninger's under the guidance of Dr. Green, he will tell you to "visualize what you want the body to do. Tell the body to do it. Then relax and let it do it." Then something changes in the body, and the biofeedback instruments show that change. With a little practice, when the patient sees the change and realizes that he or she does have an observable physiology, then the patient is on the way to self-regulation.

The remarkable thing that follows the instruction is the rapidity with which many people "get it" and learn to "play" their biofeedback instruments. They advance from being mere observers of the workings of their autonomic nervous systems to being able to exercise their will over it.

GOING WITH THE FEELING

No amount of conscious effort usually works in learning biofeedback. The trick is just to watch or listen to the feedback signal, and when the changes you want begin, "go" with that feeling. "There is another way to say it," advised Dr. Green: "the person visualizes and feels the desired change that will influence the meter, and allows the body to

Various aspects of this patient's respiration are being monitored as she pedals.

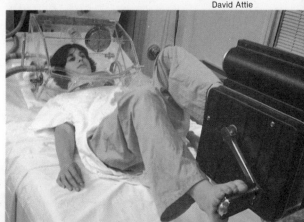

carry out the instruction. The feeling seems to be the instruction.

"This feeling has been reported by many successful performers to be, at least in the early stages of learning, a composite image, emotion and body sensation. After a skill is thoroughly learned, the body sensation can be 'turned on' at will, often with no need for any particular mental image or emotion. Often feedback is not needed for more than a few weeks."

Alan J. Tyler, a counselor and biofeedback trainer with the Associates in Human Development in Tucson, Arizona, believes it is quite possible for patients to become dependent on the biofeedback equipment. He finds it is common for the old symptoms to recur when patients who have successfully used the training no longer get their weekly dose of reassuring feedback from the machinery and fail to practice their daily image-altering exercises.

Dr. Joseph D. Sargent, the chief of internal medicine at Menninger's has confirmed this experience with his migraine patients at Menninger's. "As soon as they withdraw attention from the task—in this case, increasing the blood flow in their hands," he said, "they return to the base line. The migraine headache comes back. They've got to keep repeating the task, repeating, repeating." When boredom with the training sets in, some of his patients rationalize: "Why bother with this when I can take medicine instead?" They aren't willing to stick with the program; they would just as soon take a pill, and they say they don't worry about what the drugs may be doing to them.

BIOFEEDBACK FOR STRESS-RELATED DISEASES

Biofeedback is for people who are highly motivated, or who suffer unbearable side effects from alternative medication. It is not a panacea. "We will need drugs plus biofeedback," said Dr. Sargent. He sees self-regulation being applied most successfully in skeletal muscle control, for stroke victims, and in relaxation techniques for those taking some minor tranquilizers.

He also believes it will be effective in helping treat many psychosomatic diseases caused by or related to stress. Physicians believe that 75 per cent or more of modern disease is related to stress, which makes biofeedback a potential tool for virtually all of the medical and psychological specialities.

A study made in a British factory threatened with a permanent closing illustrates the point. The study showed marked increases in workers' blood pressures. The increase remained even among those employees who were never actually laid off. What had changed in the workers' environment was their sense of security, their image of themselves as valuable members of society. Even when they kept their jobs, their blood pressures did not return to normal.

What happens in cases such as this, according to Dr. Barbara Brown, is that "the problem-solving effort fills all the body's circuits, blocking off any other inputs. The natural, unconscious awareness of how the body is behaving is blocked off by the brain's cortex when the person is under constant stress. Under normal circumstances the cortex would allow tension to relax, but in the context of the social system the cortex doesn't know how to relax. The tension is held and held, and pretty soon physical disease arises."

In the modern vernacular, such a person is "up-tight" to the extent that something has to give. What reacts is blood pressure, lower back, head, stomach, legs, heart, any place in the body where the stress can be converted to disorder-creating tension.

Yoga, golfing, tai chi, running—all body-awareness techniques—are good for relieving stress. However, when a person is ill—when there are actually blood clots in the legs, for example—there isn't time to learn yoga. This is where the accurate and sensitive biofeedback instruments come in.

The individual can see that the hands are too cold, that circulation is being restricted, that muscles are too tight, that brain waves are racing, or that the stomach is too acid. These are typical stress-related symptoms known to almost everyone. If these are allowed to continue without relief, they can be precursors of serious disease. With the use of biofeedback training, many people can learn to alleviate them.

Relaxation and body awareness relieve tension, decrease stress-related diseases, and, for this University of Wisconsin football team, lead to better playing.

Dan McCoy/Rainbow

TEACHING THE DEAF TO SPEAK

Even in instances of disorders that do not arise from stress, biofeedback has found the way to innovative cures. In a program at the University of Alabama Medical Center in Birmingham, deaf children have learned to speak more clearly by using a feedback device called a "palatometer."

This visual biofeedback instrument shows the deaf child the position and shape of his or her tongue alongside that of a hearing person speaking the same sounds. Fifty to 100 sensors imbedded in a custom-designed plastic palate are activated whenever the tongue touches the palate. The positions of the tongue show up as white dots on a television screen, showing the child an outline of where the tongue is located for a specific sound. He can match the position of his own tongue to that of the instructor. To the child who has never heard speech, it is another way of learning to talk.

In still another application, some California schools have achieved dramatic improvements in children with problems of concentration, anxiety, and hyperactive behavior. Often if a child—or an adult for that matter—can just learn to raise the temperature of his or her hands it affects all kinds of other problems. Once an individual sees that it is possible to control one thing, he realizes the potential to control other things—concentration or hyperactivity, for instance. In these cases biofeedback simply gives the individual a sense of self-control and mastery.

What biofeedback seems to be showing is that people have hidden abilities to deal with the kinds of stress they encounter in the modern world. The rapidity with which we can learn to use biofeedback makes this conjunction of individual and machine appear as a natural extension of our own nerves and muscles. Or perhaps biofeedback is just a reminder of something we've had all along but lost the ability to perceive and use.

"In psychology," the Greens have written, "there has been a tendency to look on humans as 'king-size rats,' reflective only of genetics and conditioning. In medicine we have accepted the idea that the doctor must 'cure' us. In order to be made well we must undergo surgery, drug treatment, radiation treatment, or some other kind of manipulation by outside forces. We have not been informed that our bodies tend to do what they are told if we know how to tell them."

If we can have psychosomatic illness, then why can't we have psychosomatic healing? asked Dr. Green. "You meet one of these guys who can do impossible things. It makes you think there is something to be learned about a person's ability not to be programmed solely by his genes and his conditioning. You can make a better life for yourself" □

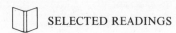 SELECTED READINGS

"Anxiety change through electroencephalographic alpha feedback seen only in high anxiety subjects" by J. V. Hardt and J. Kamiya. *Science*, July 7, 1978.

"Biofeedback: let your body do the talking" by M. E. Earkash and M. I. Rothburd. *USA Today*, March 1979.

"Biofeedback: medicine's newest cure-all?" by L.S. Rubin. *Family Health*, March 1979.

"Tolerable feedback: a mechanism for behavioral change" by A. F. Pring-Mill. *Animal Behavior*, February 1979.

The mannerisms, expressions, games, and battles of animals may look like those of humans, but the reasons behind them are often something else again.

Belinda Wright

ANIMAL BEHAVIOR

by Eugene Walter

WHY do animals do what they do? Until quite recently, people judged animal behavior on the basis of their own emotions and activities—their own behavior. What may look like a smile on a cat's face, however, might have nothing to do with the emotion that causes us to smile.

Behavioral scientists are learning how to look at life through the eyes of the animals they study. They are discovering why non-human species behave as they do. Here are a few examples.

WHY DO MONKEYS MAKE FACES?

It may look like a "yawn" but any primate expert knows the monkey's expression is really a threat. Similarly, when a monkey "grins" or "smiles," it is not in fact expressing pleasure. It is signaling fear or submission. The faces monkeys make are an important part of their communications with each other, but people have traditionally— and wrongly—interpreted those expressions as if they were human. Indeed, this misinterpretation of monkey expressions is a classic example of anthropomorphism.

Scientists, zookeepers, and monkey trainers have long known that, to a primate, a kiss is not a kiss and a sigh is not a sigh. When a monkey puckers up, it is asking another monkey to groom it. When a monkey yawns, it is not necessarily tired. It may be warning another monkey to keep away, or it may be expressing its frustration with a certain situation.

One notable instance of misinterpreting a primate's expression occurred early in the American space program after a chimpanzee named Ham orbited the earth. When Ham landed, someone exclaimed: "He must have enjoyed the trip. Look, he's smiling!" In fact, Ham was terrified.

WHY DO SOME BIRDS MATE FOR LIFE?

Romance has less to do with it than survival. All species of geese mate for life, for example, and scientists believe this bond is crucial to the success of their migration and nesting.

Many of the world's geese—Canada, greylag, and so on—must migrate thousands of kilometers to reach their nesting grounds above the Arctic Circle. This tremendous feat poses special problems. For one thing, the birds can't rush the departure date because the weather up there would make life impossible for early arrivals. Once the migrants arrive, the short arctic summer allows little time for laying eggs, hatching them, and rearing a brood. The youngsters must be able to fly well enough to follow their parents south in time to avoid frigid weather.

Time is so precious for geese that, if they had to seek new mates each year in addition to everything else they must do, they would never make it. Hence, they are programmed by evolution to make permanent "pair-bonds," the zoologists' term for such a union. This enables the geese to save considerable time by performing many of their pre-nesting rituals in southern latitudes, prior to or during migration.

Although some geese don't migrate very far, they still form lifelong pairs. A good example is the néné, or Hawaiian goose. Although it is related to the migratory Canada goose, the néné stays right at home in the tropics. A common ancestor of both species was a "mate-for-lifer" and the trait stuck with the Hawaiian branch.

It is not known exactly why néné don't migrate far or, for that matter, why Canada geese and others do. The choices may have something to do with changes in the world's weather patterns. Eons ago, the arctic climate was milder and more hospitable.

Geese are not the only birds that pair off for life. Some eagles do, too. So do storks, hawks, all cranes, and many others—mostly large species and mostly for the same reasons as geese.

One of these species, the Adelie penguin, is somewhat ambivalent about the whole thing. At nesting time, about 80 per cent of them reunite with their former mates after a seven-month separation. This "bonded" majority demonstrates the wisdom of long-term relationships, because they have much better nesting success than those Adelies that seek new mates each year.

Frank Sladek

V. W. Crich/Photo Researchers

A baboon (left) may appear to be yawning, but experts say this expression is really a threat. Canada geese (right) mate for life—not for romance, but because this bond is crucial to their survival.

Wolfgang Obst

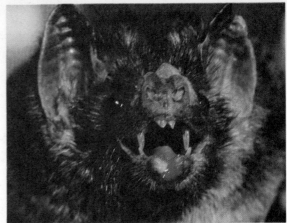
W. A. Wimsatt

WHY DO RACCOONS "WASH" THEIR FOOD?

As a matter of fact, raccoons usually don't wash their food. Their fingerlike paws are as nimble and sensitive as human hands. The animals use them to probe and sift a stream bed with what looks like a scrubbing motion. Once a raccoon locates a crayfish, snail, or mussel, the tidbit is popped directly into its mouth without so much as a rub or a rinse. After a hungry raccoon has separated its supper from the sand or gravel, it doesn't waste time on such niceties as sanitation.

DO ANIMALS REALLY "PLAY"?

Yes, and sometimes it's nothing more than fun and games, as when a monkey swings from a vine and tosses a stick. Or it can be when polar bears amuse themselves with stones, which they sometimes balance on their heads. Often, though, the seemingly frivolous antics we interpret as "play" are serious.

Play can be viewed as a pleasurable way of developing survival skills. The next time you're at a zoo, watch how the lion cubs frolic. One will crouch low against the ground, stalk slowly toward its littermate, and then pounce on the surprised "victim." That usually touches off a knockabout wrestling match, with the cubs cuffing each other harmlessly. Such roughhouse sessions occur frequently among most carnivores such as wolves, tigers, cheetahs, raccoons, and coyotes. As they play, these young develop the abilities they need to become efficient predators.

Among monkeys and apes, playing helps lay the foundation for social order—a requirement for the survival of primate communities. Through play-fighting, a young monkey learns—in a harmless way—where it stands among its peers. The individuals that are most often victorious in the "matches" of infancy are most likely to assume a dominant role when they mature. Others that are lower on the social ladder learn their places early in life. This reduces more violent clashes among the monkeys as adults.

Many hoofed mammals engage in play, too. In herds of Mongolian wild horses, the breeding stallion will play-fight with his offspring, thereby helping the youngsters develop the agility they will need when confronted by predators or other stallions.

It appears that whales play. A calf will perform all sorts of acrobatic gyrations on and around its mother, sliding over her tail, standing on its head or slapping its tail or flipper against the water's surface. It's possible that such play helps cement the bond between mother and offspring.

And what of birds—do they play? Some ornithologists are convinced that a few of the brainier ones do. The subject needs further inquiry. At this point, it's the mammals who appear to dominate the animal playground.

WHY DO VAMPIRE BATS SUCK BLOOD?

Unlike its fictional counterpart, this common flying mammal of the southwestern United States, Central America, and South America is not a ruthless and terrifying man-killer. Nor is it an enormous creature, as it is so often portrayed. It is tiny—only about eight centimeters long. It does not "suck" blood—it laps up the liquid like a kitten with a saucer of milk. It is true that this bat will partake of a little human blood now and then. A foot protruding from beneath a blanket is a tempting target.

But there is no evidence that anyone has ever perished from the bite of a healthy vampire. Only rabid bats have inflicted lethal wounds. In any case, the creature much prefers dining on wild animals or on such domestic substitutes as cows, swine, and goats.

Alighting softly on its victim, the bat slices a shallow cut with its razor-sharp incisors. As blood flows from the wound, the bat licks it up. A chemical in the creature's saliva prevents the blood from coagulating until the bat has had its fill. This usually means about 30 grams of blood a day—an amount rarely missed by the bat's prey unless it is visited by many bats.

Why does the creature eat blood? Nobody knows how it got started, but now its system is so specialized—it has a super-efficient kidney, for instance—that it can't eat anything else. To its benefit, few liquids, if any, are more nourishing than blood.

WHY DO CRANES DANCE?

If cranes didn't dance, there would be no crane chicks every year. For young cranes that have never mated, dancing is a necessary part of choosing a lifetime partner. For older cranes that have already paired off, dancing reinforces the union—it's a sort of annual renewal of "vows." Interestingly enough, there are 15 different species of cranes and they all dance to the same steps.

These courting ballets have a definite physiological effect: They synchronize the male and female sexually. Thus, when the birds arrive at their breeding grounds, the male will have viable sperm ready to fertilize his mate's developing eggs.

Dr. George Archibald, whose International Crane Foundation in Baraboo, Wisconsin, is dedicated to preserving endangered cranes, dances with females all the time. He does this in order to prepare them for artificial insemination. Without the dancing, the female won't be ready to accept the semen when it is injected. Unless the ancient rites are observed, there will be no fertile eggs.

In the wild, cranes go through their dancing ritual in the morning and evening. With wings outstretched, the male and female circle each other, bowing their heads repeatedly, and occasionally flinging twigs or earth into the air with their beaks. Now and then, they leap straight up, then go into a wing-flapping run, side by side. In a furious finale, the birds bring their heads low between their legs and flap their wings wildly. As the wings close, the dancers snap their heads up and back, then quickly resume the normally erect posture. Saturday night fever it may not be, but to the cranes, it is no mere lark.

WHY DO ANIMALS FIGHT?

When one creature challenges another of its own kind, one of two things is probably at stake: food or the right to breed. It's not

Wolves do not howl because they are lonely; rather they do it to keep in touch with other wolves.

surprising that animals fight over these things. What is surprising is how seldom such encounters end in a fatality. This is because killing among members of the same species is biologically wasteful. Over millions of years, animal weapons and ritualized fighting methods have evolved so that one creature can usually escape from another without major injury. This is particularly true of many horned and antlered animals.

North American bighorn sheep, for instance, have a double-layered skull, cross-connected with bone and thick facial hide, that enables them to withstand awesome blows to the head. During mating season, two rams may battle for several hours at a time, constantly banging heads without seriously hurting one another. Similarly, when two wapiti bulls joust over control of a harem, their massive antlers sometimes lock together. The encounter then becomes a relatively harmless test of strength. But when these same antlers are used against a different species, they become lethal weapons.

Aggression is not limited to males, and it is not always harmless. To ensure their own safety, some males must bribe their belligerent female counterparts with gifts before they are allowed to mate. One European spider courts the female by offering her a fly wrapped in silk. There are times, though, when the female spider's aggressiveness is not placated by this ritual. After mating, she bites off the male's head.

WHY DO WOLVES HOWL?

Contrary to popular belief, wolves do not howl at night because they are lonely. These highly social creatures have one of the most complex communication systems in the animal kingdom. The howl is only the most familiar aspect of their rich repertoire of sounds and calls—and body movements.

Howling plays a role in several situations, but its greatest significance probably relates to territory. Because a group of wolves may stake out an area covering many square kilometers, individual pack members often howl just to keep in touch with each other when they are separated. Howling also serves as a mechanism for keeping different packs away from each other. Wolves jea-

Tom McHugh/Photo Researchers

Birds sing to woo their mates, warn away trespassers, and just for the fun of it.

lously protect their territories, but they need all their strength just to survive. Rather than fight with other packs, therefore, they howl. If a neighboring group is nearby, it will know the two packs are too close for comfort.

This same kind of "distancing" is common among many other creatures. It's the major reason why lions roar, howler monkeys howl, and gibbons hoot. Since wolves do most of their hunting at night when visibility is limited, the howl is essential for keeping in touch. They do not, however, bay at the moon. Indeed, they probably howl more when there is no moon.

WHY DO BIRDS SING?

A "song" is a succession of musical tones repeated in a recognizable pattern. Of the world's 8,600 or so bird species, nearly half are songbirds. Some, like the song sparrow family, have a dozen different melodies. Others, like the red-winged blackbird, know only one or two. Birds other than songbirds make various noises—clucks, croaks, peeps, grunts, whistles, hoots, squeaks—but they cannot sing songs.

Usually only the male of a species sings. Scientists believe this activity is closely correlated with nesting and mating. The males sing most effusively when certain hormonal levels increase. They use their melodies to define and defend their nesting territories. Sometimes, singing may substitute for fighting over an area in question—a sort of battle of the singers. Because different kinds of songbirds do not usually have the same food and nesting requirements, several species can coexist peacefully in the same area.

In addition to driving away their rivals, male songbirds employ their musical skills to woo their mates. Once the birds have paired off, singing may reinforce the bond they've established. It is also probably an important factor in reproductive success: Singing may help to synchronize the birds' sexual cycles during the early stages of their "relationship."

Sex is not the only reason birds sing. Some researchers now believe many birds sing for the sheer joy of it. That may help explain why nightingales and European blackbirds combine different notes to, in effect, compose new songs. Other birds seem to enjoy copying melodies they hear around them. Such species as the starling, marsh warbler, robinchat, and lyrebird have no particular songs of their own. But they are expert mimics. It has been suggested that for these birds, singing may have become less of a territorial imperative; it is no longer needed to find a mate. For the highly territorial mockingbird, that is hardly the case, and the reason for its mockery remains a puzzle.

Not long ago, two American scientists found that some songbirds sing not only to announce what species they belong to, but also to proclaim their individual identity. Studying indigo buntings and white-throated sparrows, the researchers learned that conflict between males of the same species is minimized once the birds grow accustomed to each other's distinct melodies.

At times, some songbirds "peep" rather than sing. These sounds are usually made up of one or two "call" notes that have little or nothing to do with mating. Instead, peeps are used to signal members of the same species.

A call may alert a flock that a predator is near, orchestrate migration, or coordinate other group activities.

WHY DOES THE GORILLA BEAT ITS CHEST?

That depends on the gorilla—and on the situation. In some instances, this flamboyant and intimidating gesture may be just what it seems—a warning to keep away. Loosely translated it means, "I'm one tough ape, and you'd better not press your luck, because I'm not scared!"

Chest-beating can also be more of a direct threat than that. When truly aroused, the leader of a gorilla troop, usually a huge silverback male, rises and drums his chest quite rapidly, palms open and slightly cupped. Then he explodes into a charge, which may or may not be a bluff.

Despite all that sound and fury, gorillas are pussycats. The most aggressive charge rarely results in serious physical combat. Scientists who have been charged by gorillas report that the animals almost always stop

Gorillas look fierce, but the threatening thumping of their chests is often just for show.

Tom McHugh/Photo Researchers

Mud wallows are the rhino's favorite place; they feel so good on a hot day.

short of violence—unless the human intruder responds in a hostile manner. Sometimes chest-beating is only an expression of relief after danger has passed.

One thing a gorilla does *not* do is stage a "victory celebration" by drumming a furious tattoo on its chest after cracking an opponent's spine. That sort of thing happens only in "Tarzan" movies.

Since gorillas forage for food over extensive, thickly forested areas, the members of a troop cannot always see each other. Chest-beating is then used to keep in touch. It can also serve to alert other gorillas from different troops who are feeding in the same area, thereby avoiding conflict.

Gorillas, especially young ones, often beat their chests as an expression of high spirits. If, on a sunny summer day, you visit a zoo that has outdoor ape exhibits, you may see a young gorilla tilt its head back and thump its chest in pure exhilaration.

WHY DO RHINOS TAKE MUD BATHS?

Because it feels so good.

All five species of rhinoceros live in the very hot tropical regions of Africa or Asia. All of them seek out areas that are muddy most of the time. They all like to wallow in that mud, rolling and flopping about in the ooze with much satisfaction. This place, which they visit at every opportunity, is called a wallow.

Whether you see them in zoos or in the wild, rhinos always seem to be caked with mud; this is a great comfort to them. It's cooling on a hot day, and it adds a protective layer against the sun. The mud also creates a barrier to at least some biting insects and skin-boring parasites.

Elephants are as fond of mud for essentially the same reasons. If they have access to a wallow large enough to accommodate their bulk, they will plunge in. If not, they pick up

Each of the 1,000 species of firefly has a distinctive flashing light pattern.

Animals groom one another for many reasons: psychological and social, as well as hygienic.

dry earth with their trunks and spray dust all over themselves.

WHY DO FIREFLIES FLASH?

More often than not, it is because they're turned on by sex. Despite their name, fireflies are actually beetles. They produce light with a complex chemical reaction that takes place within their abdominal cells. The cool luminescence is reflected out through their transparent skin. Researchers have learned that almost all of the 1,000 or so species of fireflies found throughout the world have distinctive light patterns. These patterns are used primarily to locate mates, though fireflies sometimes will also light up when they are threatened.

In each species, the signaling is done in a precise code: The blinks must follow a pattern of regular intervals if the message is to be received. The male flies about, flashing and waiting for a female to respond. If she does so at the proper intervals, he recognizes her as one of his own kind.

Sometimes firefly blinks are deceiving. One entomologist discovered that females of the American genus *Photuris* can imitate the code of a different but closely related type of firefly. After luring in the eager males with a few sexy blinks, the alien females devour them, flashing lights and all.

WHY DO ANIMALS GROOM EACH OTHER?

When one creature picks away at another, it usually has more than fleas on its mind. In most cases, grooming provides psychological and social benefits to both the groomer and the one being groomed. It is a particularly important activity for most primates: Survival for them often hinges on the ability of their troop to function as a cohesive unit. Grooming reinforces group bonds, as well as the links between individual animals. Scientists believe this constant picking serves to release tension in the troop.

Whether or not it's their principal aim, grooming does tend to keep monkeys healthier. When one animal rubs and fusses through another one's fur, it is not only soothing its companion, but it is also removing dirt, flecks of dry skin, and annoying ticks as well □

 SELECTED READINGS

"Caring groups and selfish genes" by S. Gould. *Natural History,* December 1977.

"Evolution of behavior" by J. Smith. *Scientific American,* September 1978.

"Life and death at Gombe; violence among chimpanzees" by J. Goodall. *National Geographic,* May 1979.

DRUGS AND THE MIND

by Maya Pines

TWO million Americans suffer from schizophrenia, with its relentless voices and hallucinations. Another 12 million are clinically depressed. One third of these also have cyclical episodes of mania.

In the early 1950's, there was no effective treatment for these people. Hospitals offered little beyond straitjackets, shock, or lobotomies. Shrieking or catatonic patients often spent years in horrible, degrading wards from which they seldom returned.

The discovery that some chemicals could reduce mental illness changed this picture. Since 1952, when chlorpromazine was first used against schizophrenia, the population of mental hospitals has shrunk. Most schizophrenics can now be treated as outpatients. With the help of other drugs most depressed persons, including manic-depressives, can be brought back to serenity.

These achievements are some of the greatest medical miracles of the century. Yet millions of persons remain unable to function normally because of mental illness. And the scientists who study brain function and chemistry are only approaching the point where they may be able to understand why.

A BEGINNING OF UNDERSTANDING

The drugs that exist today were developed mostly by chance, without any solid rationale. Astute clinicians led the way, rather than researchers. To date nobody knows why these drugs work in some cases but not in others. Nor do they know why schizophrenia can be relieved but not cured. Nor do scientists understand what causes mental illness in the first place. (British researchers have recently reported isolating a virus in the cerebrospinal fluid of 18 out of 47 schizophrenics. The same virus was discovered in 8 out of 11 patients with serious neurological disorders.) Despite 25 years of intensive research, they have only begun to decipher the complex codes by which the billions of nerve

Alfred Gescheidt/The Image Bank

cells in the brain act and coordinate their actions.

By piecing together all the available clues, however, researchers have developed a very useful working hypothesis: mental illness results from a chemical imbalance between at least three neurotransmitters in the brain. This hypothesis is being refined and amplified in light of several new findings. One advantage of the hypothesis is that it offers a simple explanation of why drugs such as chlorpromazine work: an effective drug is one that restores a proper balance among the neurotransmitters.

MESSAGE CARRIERS

Neurotransmitters are chemicals that carry messages from one neuron (nerve cell) to the next at lightning speed, telling it to fire or resist firing. While a given neuron can respond to many neurotransmitters, it can produce only one. When researchers squirt acetylcholine into a certain area in a rat's brain, for instance, the rat starts to drink. But when they apply norepinephrine to the same

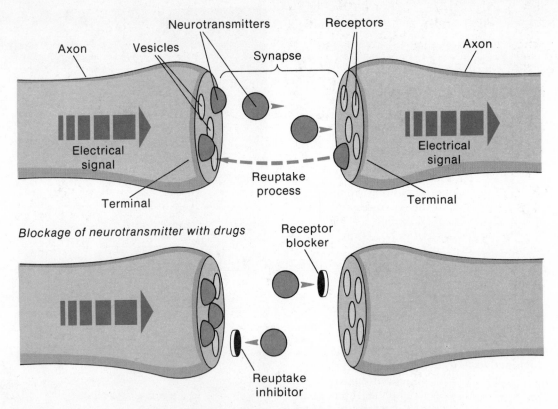

The function of neurotransmitters can be impaired by blocking their passage to a receptor site on the next neuron or by preventing their return to their source neuron.

area, neurons are differently stimulated, and the rat starts to eat.

Over a dozen different neurotransmitters have been identified. The three that have been most carefully studied with respect to mental illness are norepinephrine, dopamine, and serotonin. All three are amines, nitrogen compounds derived from some of the essential amino acids, which are in our food.

These neurotransmitters turn various excitatory or inhibitory cell systems on or off. When this happens, they give rise to a complicated series of actions and reactions. "At a specific instant, any given cell is either turned on or turned off, transmitting or not transmitting," says Dr. Nathan S. Kline of the Rockland Psychiatric Institute in New York. "Always, however, some are transmitting and some not. The ramifications of those 'go-no go' signals reach unimaginable proportions."

The neurons that respond to norepinephrine, dopamine, and serotonin represent only a small fraction of the total number of neurons in the brain. But through their long fibers they interact with every major functional area in the brain. This includes those that regulate emotions.

DEPRESSION AND THE AMINES

The first clue to the role of the amines came in the 1950's. It was shortly after physicians noted that a number of patients who were taking the drug reserpine for hypertension became severely depressed. At about the same time, tubercular patients being treated with the drug iproniazid suddenly began to dance in the halls, as if elated.

Biochemists who were studying the brains of rats then discovered that reserpine depleted the rats' stores of norepinephrine and serotonin. They also found that iproniazid had the opposite effect. It increased the levels of these brain amines by preventing an enzyme, monoamine oxidase (MAO), from metabolizing them. This led physicians to try various MAO inhibitors on depressed patients. It worked. Depression, then, was clearly associated with a lack of norepinephrine or serotonin. Perhaps it could be cured with drugs that restored these brain amines.

This "amine hypothesis" was temporarily threatened by the discovery of the tricyclic antidepressants, which a Swiss psychiatrist developed in the hope of helping schizophrenics. Though they proved useless against schizophrenia, the tricyclics were extremely effective in lifting people out of severe depressions. They did not, however, change the levels of amines in the brains of animals.

The mystery was resolved a few years later by Dr. Julius Axelrod of the National Institute of Mental Health (NIMH), who subsequently won a Nobel prize for his work. His solution described the efficient way in which norepinephrine is turned off after having relayed its message at a nerve synapse (the junction between two nerve cells): it is sucked back into the nerve endings from which it came, to be conserved for future use.

Axelrod called this a "reuptake" process. He showed that the tricyclic antidepressants interfere with this process. This interference increases the amount of norepinephrine that is available to receptors on the next cell. The same soon proved true for serotonin. The amine hypothesis appeared to be saved.

MANIA AND THE AMINES

What about mania—the dramatic spurts of excitement, restlessness, euphoria, or anger which occur cyclically in manic-depression? Does mania come from an over-supply of the same amines whose lack seems to produce depression? Apparently yes, or at least they are related. Lithium, the most effective drug against mania, seems to have exactly the opposite effect from that of tricyclics. Lithium inhibits the release of norepinephrine, serotonin, and perhaps dopamine, and enhances their reuptake. Thus, the amount of these amines available at receptor sites in the brain is reduced.

These findings allow one to visualize a sort of seesaw: on one side of the seesaw low levels of norepinephrine or serotonin produce depression. This can be cured by amine-increasing drugs until a satisfactory balance is reached. On the other side of the seesaw, high levels of amine at particular brain sites produce mania. And that can be prevented by amine-lowering drugs until, once again, a balance is reached.

FLAWS IN THE AMINE HYPOTHESIS

It's neat and attractive—but far from perfect, since many facts do not fit in. For example, the amphetamines increase the level of norepinephrine in the brain. Yet they do not stop severe depression. Conversely, the antidepressants do not make normal persons feel stimulated or happier. And lithium somehow prevents a number of manic-depressives from swinging into either depression or mania.

"The amine hypothesis implies that depression and mania represent opposite poles of a single biochemical continuum," notes Dr. Frederick Goodwin, chief of NIMH's clinical psychobiology branch. "But lithium, a single agent, has therapeutic effects in both depression and mania, suggesting interactions with some underlying processes similar in the two conditions."

SIDE EFFECTS

Both lithium and chlorpromazine, when used for several years, may produce serious side effects. The most disturbing is tardive dyskinesia, in which the arms and legs twitch, and the tongue hangs out of the mouth, all uncontrollably. Recent studies, however, suggest that a simple diet additive, lecithin, may alleviate the symptoms of tardive dyskinesia.

Patients on the MAO inhibitors may develop dangerous high blood pressure, if the drugs are taken with certain foods—such as chicken livers and chocolate.

SCHIZOPHRENIA

Research on schizophrenia has reached the same tantalizing stage. Here, too, important answers seem to be almost within reach. So far this research has focused on the neurotransmitter dopamine. Apparently, chlorpromazine, the first drug to alleviate schizophrenia, blocks the receptor sites for dopamine in animal brains. Other anti-schizophrenia drugs also block these receptors, or actually deplete the stores of dopamine in the brains of animals.

By contrast, drugs that increase dopamine, such as L-dopa (which is used to treat Parkinson's disease) or the amphetamines, may produce schizophrenialike symptoms

National Institute of Mental Health   Johns Hopkins

Drs. Candace Pert and Solomon Snyder have done important research on specific chemical receptor sites in the brain.

in normal persons. These same drugs also aggravate the symptoms of schizophrenia.

It is very tempting, therefore, to conclude that schizophrenics suffer from an excess of dopamine in their brains. Yet dopamine may not be the original culprit at all. As Dr. Solomon Snyder, professor of psychiatry and pharmacology at Johns Hopkins University, points out, "The fact that a dangerous short circuit can be abolished by tripping the appropriate circuit breaker does not mean that the short is in the breaker—it may be anywhere in the circuit."

Existing drugs only relieve symptoms; they do not restore patients to normality. Furthermore, there appear to be several different types of schizophrenia.

"The dopamine hypothesis no longer seems enough," declares Dr. Earl Usdin, chief of NIMH's pharmacology section. "The pendulum is now swinging toward the concept of a balance between dopamine and various other neurotransmitters."

RECEPTOR-SITE THEORY

As amine research continues, various new developments are changing the whole picture of research on mental disturbances.

To begin with, a lot of interest now centers on the receptor sites themselves. Their chemical properties, how these can be changed, and the interaction between receptor sites and neurotransmitters are being studied. "Identification of neurotransmitter receptors is a very young science, dating only from about 1970," says Snyder, who together with Candace Pert made news five years ago by demonstrating the presence of specific receptors for opiates in the human brain. They also developed a new technique that allowed researchers to measure the actual amount of receptors for specific neurotransmitters for the first time.

Using this technique, scientists found some evidence that receptor sites for dopamine and some other neurotransmitters have a surprising ability to lead a double life. Apparently they exist in two completely different, yet interchangeable states. In one state they bind exclusively to dopamine, for instance. In the other state they bind only to dopamine's antagonists, such as haloperidol (an antischizophrenic drug). The problem now is to find out how receptor sites make this switch from one state to the other, what causes it, and its results. New research on lithium antimanic action suggests that it stabilizes this receptor switch.

Meanwhile, the discovery of a whole new class of brain peptides has led to great excitement in the world of neuropharmacology. Some of these brain peptides, such as the endorphins, modify the action of various neurotransmitters. Others act as neurotransmitters themselves. New ones seem to be identified or synthesized every month. Some have already been tried on schizophrenic or depressed patients, with mixed results.

Progress in these areas is advancing so rapidly that it is difficult to absorb. With each new discovery, the brain's chemical machinery appears ever more delicate—and its balance more precarious □

 SELECTED READINGS

"New drugs and the brain" by G. B. Kolata. *Science*, August 24, 1979.

"Norepinephrine in chronic paranoid schizophrenia" by J. Farley et al. *Science*, April 6, 1979.

"Chemical feelings" by J. Gurin. *Science 80*, November/December 1979.

In January 1979 then HEW Secretary Joseph A. Califano Jr. reported that the percentage of adult smokers in the United States had dropped. There were, however, other much less encouraging figures to report.

UPI

SMOKING ADDICTION

by Edward M. Brecher

IN January 1979, in his signed foreword to the 1979 edition of *Smoking and Health: A Report of the Surgeon General,* then U.S. Department of Health, Education, and Welfare (HEW) Secretary Joseph A. Califano, Jr. proudly announced, "Today, more than 30 million Americans are ex-smokers."

A major public-health victory? Hardly. For tucked away in an appendix to the 1,200-page report were some very different statistics.

FIGURES LIE?

Despite those 30,000,000 ex-smokers, the number of smokers in the United States 17-years old or older has, in fact, been rising slowly from 53,300,000 in 1965 to 54,100,000 in 1978. So, though the percentage of adult smokers in the population dropped from about 42 per cent in 1965 to 33 per cent in 1978, going strictly by the numbers, smokers abound.

In addition, the number of cigarettes smoked per year rose 16 per cent during the same period—from 529,000,000,000 in 1965 to 615,000,000,000 in 1978. Moreover, the number of cigarettes smoked per smoker, if HEW's figures are correct, rose 14 per cent.

Knowledgeable observers have long been aware of the tragic underlying fact: anti-cigarette campaigns throughout the 1970's have wholly failed to curtail more than temporarily either the number of smokers or the number of cigarettes smoked. A few observers have explained why.

As far back as 1972, Consumers Union announced in *Licit & Illicit Drugs* that smoking is not just a hard-to-break habit. It is instead a peculiarly stubborn form of drug addiction—addiction to the nicotine molecule. Since then, confirmatory studies have been pouring out of research centers.

AN ADDICTION

Back in 1942, Dr. Lennox M. Johnston reported in the British medical journal *The Lancet* that he had given modest injections of nicotine to 35 volunteers, including himself. "Smokers almost invariably thought the sensation pleasant," he declared, "and, given an adequate dose, were disinclined to smoke for some time thereafter." His findings confirmed his assumption that "smoking tobacco is essentially a means of administering nicotine, just as smoking opium is a means of administering morphine."

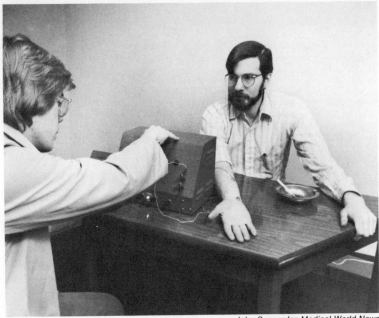

In tests to determine nicotine effects, heavy smokers were able to withstand electric shocks better when smoking high-nicotine cigarettes than when smoking low-nicotine cigarettes. Insufficient nicotine seems to make heavy smokers more irritable and less able to endure stress.

John Senzer for *Medical World News*

Another British researcher, Dr. D. C. Frith of the Institute of Psychiatry at the University of London reported in 1971 that the less nicotine in a cigarette, the shorter the time between one puff and the next. The more puffs taken per cigarette, the less time it took to smoke the cigarette—and the more cigarettes smoked during the day.

In subsequent studies it was found that, upon switching to cigarettes with less nicotine, many smokers smoke a cigarette down to a shorter butt, where proportionately more tar and nicotine is delivered to the lungs, and that many hold smoke longer in their lungs when its nicotine content is low—thus, no doubt, increasing the efficiency of nicotine transfer to the bloodstream.

BOLUS MODEL

Out of such data and a number of similar studies of his own, Dr. Michael A. H. Russell, senior lecturer and honorary consulting psychiatrist at the Addiction Research Unit of Maudsley Hospital's Institute of Psychiatry in London, has evolved the "bolus model" of nicotine addiction. Like each injection of heroin, Dr. Russell explains, each puff of cigarette smoke represents a unit dose of nicotine. The nicotine passes through the lungs to produce a nicotine-laden bolus of blood that reaches the brain within about seven seconds.

By adjusting the puffing pattern, the human body without conscious effort regulates the size of each bolus, the concentration of nicotine in it, the lapse of time between boluses, and the number of boluses per cigarette, per hour, and per day. "At 10 puffs a cigarette, a pack-a-day smoker gets more than 70,000 nicotine shots to his brain in a year," he says.

Nicotine addiction is established more rapidly than addiction to heroin. The bolus model helps explain why: the smoking of just one pack of cigarettes gives some 200 successive nicotine "fixes"—many more than a person first experimenting with heroin is likely to take. An understanding of this phenomenon may prove essential for designing effective programs to end smoking addiction.

NICOTINE AND STRESS

"Almost any smoker can convince you and himself that there are major psychological components to smoking," states Columbia University professor of psychology Dr. Stanley Schachter. "They will convince you that smoking calms them, that it helps them work, that they smoke more at a party, and so on." Dr. Schachter and two of his doctoral students, however, have established that what appears to be smoking to relieve stress is, in fact, smoking to compensate for a physiological idiosyncrasy of nicotine excretion.

In preliminary experiments, the Schachter group first confirmed that seven heavy cigarette smokers smoked an average of 25 per cent more cigarettes per day when shifted to a low-nicotine brand. The group confirmed that smoking seems to help smokers meet stress. When the smokers were compared with non-smokers, however, the apparent tranquilizing effect of cigarettes proved to be an illusion. "Smoking doesn't make a smoker less irritable or vulnerable to annoyance," Dr. Schachter concluded, "not smoking or insufficient nicotine makes him more irritable." He also cites confirmatory evidence showing that on a variety of performance measures smokers while smoking "do neither better nor worse than non-smokers but do markedly better than deprived smokers."

The Schachter group next studied the curious phenomenon that "when the urine is alkaline, only one-fourth as much nicotine is excreted as when the urine is acid; this is explained by the fact that nicotine base is reabsorbed from an alkaline urine."

If smokers smoke to maintain their nicotine levels, Dr. Schachter reasoned, they must have to smoke more when their urine is acidic. This inference proved correct: 13 smokers smoked 20 per cent more cigarettes on days they received ascorbic acid or glutamic acid than on days they received a cornstarch placebo. Next Dr. Schachter and several Columbia students, with a grant from Philip Morris, Incorporated, investigated whether increased smoking during stress is a physiological effect of altered urinary acidity levels.

In one series of experiments involving graduate students, they found that the students' urine was significantly more acidic on high-stress occasions than it was on low-stress occasions. The students were then given either sodium bicarbonate or a placebo and their smoking behavior was observed in both high-stress and stress-free situations. Smokers receiving the placebo took twice as many puffs from a cigarette in the high-stress situation. In contrast, smokers with their urine alkalinized by ingestion of sodium bicarbonate actually took somewhat fewer puffs when subjected to stress. In fact, puff frequency proved wholly unrelated to stress—but tightly linked to urinary acidity. The reason smokers smoke more when they are drinking, reasons Dr. Schachter, is no doubt the same, since alcoholic beverages, like stress, acidify the urine.

WITHDRAWAL SYMPTOMS AND TOLERANCE

The original *Report of the Surgeon General's Advisory Committee on Smoking and Health* back in 1964 alleged that smoking is not an addiction because there are no withdrawal symptoms, no tolerance is developed, and no antisocial behavior is elicited. All three of these allegations have now been decisively refuted.

The Royal College of Physicians in London in its 1977 report, *Smoking or Health?*, says there is evidence of a "nicotine-withdrawal syndrome" composed of "intense craving, tension, irritability, restlessness, depression, and difficulty with concentration" plus objective physical effects, "including a fall in pulse rate and blood pressure, gastrointestinal changes such as constipation, disturbance of sleep, impaired performance at simulated driving and other tasks, and changes in the electrical impulses in the brain."

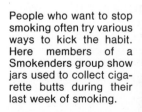
People who want to stop smoking often try various ways to kick the habit. Here members of a Smokenders group show jars used to collect cigarette butts during their last week of smoking.

As for tolerance, the Royal College report continues: "When inhaling cigarette smoke for the first time, most people have symptoms such as palpitations, dizziness, sweating, nausea, and vomiting. Subsequently, if they continue to smoke, they acquire tolerance to nicotine, and over a period of two or three years the smoking pattern usually changes so as to allow a high intake of nicotine. Tolerance to nicotine has been shown to develop rapidly in rats and to persist for 90 days after the last injection."

Smoking does not, it is true, lead to antisocial behavior—so long as cigarettes are cheaply and ubiquitously available. But, as evidence from war-time shortages and prisoner-of-war camps reveals, smokers will go to considerable lengths to get cigarettes, even bartering badly needed food for tobacco.

Cigarette prices are high in many areas, and the brisk traffic in bootleg cigarettes is a measure of the illegal activity many people are willing to condone for a cheaper smoke. It suggests that if cigarettes were outlawed like heroin or if cigarette prices were raised to the heroin level, cigarette junkies might soon engage in antisocial behavior closely resembling that of heroin junkies today.

INDIVIDUAL VARIATIONS

Almost all the nicotine research described above suffers from a plaguing short-coming: not all cigarette smokers are alike. In almost every study, smokers turn up who do not increase the number of cigarettes smoked, do not take more puffs, or do not smoke to a shorter butt when nicotine content is lowered. Indeed, Schachter points out, "There are a small number of long-time, light smokers who give no evidence of nicotine regulation and no indication of withdrawal when deprived of nicotine . . . By any of the standard criteria of addiction they appear to be genuinely nonaddicted smokers."

It has been this variability that has buttressed the unwillingness of public-health officials to recognize smoking as a form of nicotine addiction. These officials continue to aim anti-smoking campaigns on the older view that smoking is just a hard-to-break habit.

A NICOTINE RECEPTOR

Nicotine produces widespread effects on both the central nervous system and the cardiovascular and peripheral systems. It has long been assumed that it does this by means of a major neurotransmitter, acetylcholine. Dr. Leo G. Abood and associates at the University of Rochester's Center for Brain Research in Rochester, New York, have found evidence to the contrary.

In studies in which he injected nicotine into the brains of rats, Dr. Abood found that

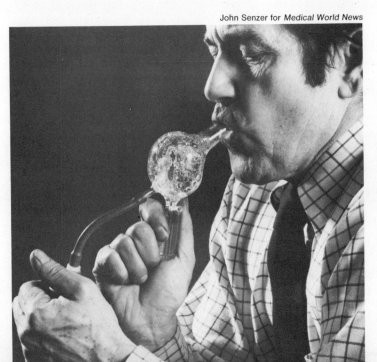

A safer way to get what the heavy smoker wants—the nicotine—without the added tar and carbon monoxide found in cigarettes: Researcher Alfred A. Smith has used a nebulizer to deliver a nicotine mist deep into the lungs of test subjects. Most subjects showed a drop in cigarette smoking, apparently getting their "nicotine fix" in this highly unusual way.

In an American Cancer Society-sponsored Great American Smokeout Day thousands of San Francisco, California, residents tossed their cigarettes into the "world's largest ashtray."

American Cancer Society

at least one effect of nicotine is "unrelated to any known neurotransmitter system." He is searching the central nervous system for a specific nicotine receptor and for a substance or substances naturally produced by the body that bind to it. The finding of such a receptor and natural substance might revolutionize nicotine research and lead to new anti-smoking strategies.

A SAFER CIGARETTE?

"If you can't stop smoking, switch to a cigarette with less tar and less nicotine." That advice has now been acted upon by vast numbers of smokers. The tar-and-nicotine yield of the average cigarette has been cut roughly in half since 1954. Can tar and nicotine be lowered very close to the zero level and the smoking problem solved while smokers continue to smoke?

Researchers have found it possible through a variety of manipulations to lower the amount of almost any component of smoke to almost any level. But, alas, the safer-cigarette project runs up against the stone wall of nicotine addiction. No "flavor" has as yet been found to take the place of nicotine.

In 1978 Dr. Gio B. Gori, head of the U.S. National Cancer Institute (NCI) smoking and health program, published a paper indicating that low-nicotine, low-tar cigarettes may be less hazardous than the conventional brands. That statement was promptly challenged, and the evidence is now being reviewed. A major issue is whether smokers who increase the number of cigarettes smoked and alter their puffing patterns to get more nicotine immediately after switching to a low-nicotine brand continue this behavior, or whether they return to their prior smoking patterns and thus benefit from the lower nicotine-and-tar yield.

An American Cancer Society 12-year-study of over 1,000,000 people indicates that smokers of low-nicotine, low-tar cigarettes have a somewhat lower death rate. They are less likely to suffer a cardiovascular death and run a lessened risk of death from lung cancer than do smokers of high-tar-and-nicotine cigarettes. They remain in far greater hazard, however, than non-smokers.

ON THE WRONG TRACK?

The carbon monoxide in cigarette smoke has been a source of serious concern and even alarm to public-health agencies since 1974, when two Danish investigators published findings showing that "carbon monoxide, and not nicotine, is the toxic compound of major importance for the increased risk of smokers to develop atherosclerosis and heart disease."

Public concern was exacerbated when other studies indicated that a cigarette's carbon-monoxide yield is not necessarily proportionate to its nicotine-and-tar yields. Some low-nicotine, low-tar cigarettes actually yield more carbon monoxide than some conventional cigarettes.

Permission Wall Street Journal & Bo Brown

Considering these data, Drs. Russell and Schachter and Consumers Union have called attention to a different approach to a safer cigarette—namely, one with a minimum of tar and carbon monoxide plus plenty of nicotine.

Carrying this line of thought one long step further, New York Medical College professor Alfred A. Smith used a nebulizer to deliver a nicotine mist deep into the lungs. The tar content of the mist was zero and the only carbon monoxide inhaled was that in the ambient air. A report, after two clinical trials with 60 subjects, indicated that the nicotine aerosol "can be used over a prolonged period of time without noticeable toxic or harmful effects."

Subjects in the trials were smokers who were trying to quit after having failed other quit-smoking programs. They were free to smoke cigarettes in addition to using the nicotine aerosols. Blood levels indicating nicotine and carbon monoxide intake were checked periodically. Some subjects maintained high nicotine levels throughout the trial but had decreased carbon monoxide exposure. This indicated that they were getting most of their nicotine from the aerosol rather than from cigarettes. Many other subjects

"showed a sharp drop in the use of nicotine compared with their customary cigarette consumption, indicating this approach to smoking reduction or cessation is likely to be feasible."

Much further down the road is the synthesis of nicotine analogues that will satisfy the central nervous system's craving for nicotine but lack nicotine's cardiovascular effects. Dr. Abood has tested a number of recently synthesized nicotine analogues and has found several that are active in the central nervous system. Whether any is inert in the cardiovascular system has not yet been reported. If such a molecule is found, smokers may at long last have available a safe substitute for conventional cigarettes—if, of course, they have not already died of cancer or cardiovascular disease while waiting for the laboratory miracle □

SELECTED READINGS

"Cold turkey: study of cigarette smokers" by Saul M. Schiffman and Murray E. Jarvik. *Human Behavior,* March 1979.

"Smoking—a manmade dragon" by N. Wellard. *World Health,* June 1979.

"Smoking—slow-motion suicide; Surgeon General's report." *Chemistry,* March 1979.

Nightmares inspired some of Spanish painter Francisco Goya's best work.

NIGHTMARES AND NIGHT TERRORS

by Sara Lazaroff

At half-past eight one evening Johnny's parents tucked their four-year-old son into his bed, kissed him goodnight, and turned off the light. Less than one hour later, they were wrenched from their easy chairs by a blood-curdling scream. Rushing into their son's room, they found him sitting upright, dripping with perspiration, and crying hysterically. After calming the child down, they asked what had happened—had he had a bad dream? Johnny just looked confused and said he didn't know. Within a few minutes the episode passed and he was sleeping soundly again. When his parents mentioned the incident to him the following morning, Johnny couldn't remember a thing.

WHAT Johnny experienced and couldn't recall was a night terror—an event that scientists have described as "perhaps the most helpless and terrifying experience known to man." Night terrors, and their cousins nightmares, are frightening features of human sleep that afflict people of all ages and cultures. Occasionally they have inspired painters and poets—the Scots writer Robert Louis Stevenson, the English author Henry James, and the Spanish painter Francisco Goya, to name a few. Now research into the physiology of sleep is providing clues to the causes of these night phenomena and suggesting ways of treating those who are plagued by them.

TERROR—WITHOUT WARNING

Night terrors occur without warning. The victim is brutally roused from his deepest, most restful sleep when his heart rate, for no apparent reason, suddenly skyrockets from, in an adult, about 65 beats per minute to upwards of 150 beats per minute. Dr. Edwin Kahn of Mt. Sinai Medical Center in New York City calls this event "the greatest heart-rate acceleration possible in man." At the same time the tormented sleeper starts panting, screaming, and often cursing.

Oddly, although displaying all the bodily signs of extreme terror and fear, the person can rarely explain the source of his horror. At best, the victim says vaguely, "I felt smothered" or "I thought I was choking." This lack of detailed dream content helps distinguish the night terror from the more common nightmare.

Had Johnny experienced a nightmare instead of a night terror he probably would have responded to his parents' inquiries with graphic descriptions of "fire-breathing vacuum cleaners trying to eat me" or "ferocious dinosaurs chasing me." His parents could have reassured him that he was only dreaming—perhaps even showing him that there were no vacuum cleaners or dinosaurs in his room—and he would have calmed down enough to fall back to sleep.

Nightmares and night terrors are superficially similar in that during either event a person's heart rate increases and he or she sweats, breathes rapidly, and often cries out loud. Nightmares are, however, much milder than night terrors—the nightmare victim suffers at most a 20 per cent increase in heart rate. Furthermore, the nightmare victim shows signs of fitful sleep with symptoms that build up gradually until they are intense enough to rouse him. It seems paradoxical that the night-terror victim who doesn't know what is causing his fear experiences greater physiological anxiety than the dreamer who can directly connect the horror of his or her nightmare to a particularly grisly image or thought.

DIFFERENT SLEEP STAGES

The fundamental research tool of sleep physiologists is the electroencephalograph, or EEG, which graphically records a person's brain-wave activity through electrodes placed at specific points on the head. During the 1950's Drs. William Dement and Nathaniel Kleitman showed that a person's brain-wave activity varies in a regular and repeatable way during sleep, and based on EEG recordings, they divided sleep into several distinct stages. A major breakthrough was the discovery by Drs. Eugene Aserinski and Kleitman that one of the stages was uniquely associated with dreaming and could be readily detected by the presence of rapid eye movement—REM, for short.

Night terrors and nightmares occur at completely different stages of sleep. Night terrors are not associated with dreaming but with the transition from deep sleep to wakefulness. For this reason, Dr. Roger Broughton of McGill University suggests that night terrors are really a "disorder of arousal," not of sleep. They might occur, he suggests, in those people—approximately one per cent of the population—who have difficulty in shifting gears smoothly from the quiescent state of deep sleep where brain activity is slow and steady to the tumultuous condition of wakefulness where brain activity is erratic. In deep sleep the ego's defense mechanisms are largely turned off and a person is in his or her most helpless state. If jolted at this vulnerable time, the body is apt to recoil in terror, especially if the mind had been dealing with sensitive issues that are normally repressed.

Nightmares, on the other hand, are associated with dreaming, or REM periods, of sleep. Simply put, nightmares are bad dreams unpleasant enough to wake the sleeper. And, according to at least one study, most dreams are unpleasant.

TOO MUCH CAKE?

What causes nightmares? Until the 18th century, they were considered the work of nocturnal demons. Years later Sigmund Freud argued that all dreams stemmed from one's repressed sexual impulses. And, of course, for generations mothers have insisted that they are the price we pay for eating rich foods too close to bedtime. While these theories have their merits, they say little about the biological causes of nightmares.

During REM sleep the brain's activity is greater than during any other sleep stage and closely resembles wakefulness. What role do rapid eye movements play in the dreaming process? Dr. Howard Roffwarg at the Albert Einstein College of Medicine, in New York, has proposed that eye movements represent one's eyes following the visual story line of the dream.

Dr. J. Allan Hobson of Harvard University, on the other hand, has offered the reverse interpretation. Perhaps, he says, the eye movements themselves determine dream imagery. What then determines the eye movements? To try to answer this question, Hobson is studying the complex firing patterns of individual nerve cells in the brain during REM sleep. His theory presents a novel explanation for the bizarre, often irrational thoughts we experience in dreams and nightmares. It might be that during REM sleep certain nerve cells are triggered that evoke memories that have little or no relationship to one another. The dreamer then attempts to arrange these random thoughts in a half-meaningful way. Nightmares, according to this model, result from an unlucky combination of random memories strung together in a frightening or horrifying manner.

MORE COMPLICATIONS

As in so much research, soon after the straightforward ground rules are formulated, exceptions start popping up. Thus, new evidence suggests that the sleep stages are probably more complex and less distinct than originally proposed. For instance, dreamlike thoughts need not be confined to REM sleep: they have been observed in subjects just falling asleep—a phenomenon termed "sleep-onset mentation." Substantial mental activity may even occur during deep sleep. And to complicate matters even more, Kahn at Mt. Sinai claims to have observed night-terror victims who vividly remember the thoughts that triggered the terror.

TREATMENTS

In the midst of these complications, researchers are trying to develop effective treatments for chronic nightmare and night-terror sufferers. Since night terrors occur almost exclusively in deep sleep, researchers have given victims drugs that specifically reduce or eliminate this sleep stage in an effort to reduce the frequency of attacks. Some drugs such as diazepam have worked especially well. Not only does diazepam reduce the frequency of night terrors but its effects often persist after drug treatment has been discontinued. With some other drugs deep sleep is eliminated—but the night terrors start occurring in other sleep stages.

Chronic nightmare sufferers have been treated with drugs that preferentially eliminate REM sleep. Nightmare sufferers who have been diagnosed as depressed find this treatment effective. However, when healthy, non-depressed subjects are deprived of REM sleep for several nights in a row, they experience numerous side effects: increased hunger, anxiety, tension, and aggression—even though they are sleeping the same number of hours as usual. When REM-deprived persons are then allowed to sleep without disturbance they immediately experience extra-long REM periods—as if their bodies were trying to make up for their previous lack of REM.

An extreme case of the body's daily requirement for REM sleep is seen when chronic users of REM-suppressing drugs, such as alcohol, heroin, or amphetamines, go "on the wagon." Suddenly the body tries to compensate for some of the REM sleep it has lost and the abrupt drug discontinuer usually experiences terrible nightmares and tormented sleep.

Additional research to develop new and more effective treatments for night terror and nightmare victims is under way. Much of the work is being done at 15 sleep-disorder clinics in North America. According to Dr. Arthur Arkin of the City College of New York, one advantage of studying sleep disorders at these special centers is that "dream reports elicited in the laboratory are 'as hot off the griddle' as we can get." If Johnny's night terror attacks continue, his wise parents may consult one of these centers—to help their son and others □

 SELECTED READINGS

Nightmares and Human Conflict by John E. Mack, M.D. Little Brown, 1970.
"Sleep disorders: disorders of arousal?" by Roger Broughton. *Science,* March 8, 1968.
Sleep, the Gentle Tyrant by Wilse B. Webb. Prentice-Hall, 1975.
The Mind in Sleep: Psychology and Psychophysiology, edited by A. M. Arkin, J. S. Antrobus, and S. J. Ellman. Lawrence Erlbaum Associates, 1978.

© Warner Bros., Inc. 1966

One of the world's best-known stutterers was cartoon character Porky Pig.

STUTTERING

by Sara Lazaroff

FOR approximately two million Americans, simple daily tasks such as answering the telephone, ordering a meal in a restaurant, or asking directions of a stranger can be traumatic and tortuous. These people are not suffering from some bizarre phobia or mental imbalance, but from a common speech disorder. They are stutterers.

Just the act of picking up a ringing telephone and saying "hello" to an unidentified listener can be an interminable struggle for a stutterer. Some report ordering meals they don't want in restaurants because they are unable to articulate the names of the foods they like to the waiter. Some can't pronounce their own names without stammering. One man tried to avoid this embarrassing problem by legally changing his name; to his dismay, he soon found himself stumbling on the new name. Writer and stutterer Edward Hoagland has described his affliction as the equivalent of "vocal handcuffs."

Although stuttering has been a part of the human condition for thousands of years—Moses was a stutterer—both its cause and cure remain largely unknown. As Dr. R. W. Rieber of The City University of New York has written, "stuttering is the great white whale of speech disorders," because after centuries of hard work trying to understand and cure the condition, it remains elusive and mysterious.

WHAT IS STUTTERING?

Stuttering can most simply be defined as improperly timed speech. For the stutterer, the smooth and steady flow of normal speech is rudely interrupted by long hesitations, word repetitions, and sound prolongations. Even more noticeable than these disruptions are the bodily movements that often accompany stuttering. The sufferer may contort his face, grimace painfully, or jerk parts of his body in an attempt to release himself from his momentary block. Sometimes the stutterer grows so dependent on these behaviors that he is unable to work his way out of the impediment without them. One little girl, for example, had to pull a hair from her head each time she stuttered to end the attack.

Some stutterers, particularly as they reach adulthood, assume more discreet and socially acceptable ways of snapping themselves out of a stuttering episode. One man developed the habit of putting his hand in his trousers pocket and secretly pinching his thigh whenever his speech faltered. Such behavior works, experts in this field believe, because it distracts the stutterer—sometimes painfully—from his immediate verbal plight.

Paradoxically, virtually all stutterers are fluent some of the time. The same individuals who blanch when the phone rings will talk out loud to themselves without the slightest slip. Most stutterers sing perfectly normally and whisper fluently. Some display no traces of their disorder when acting the part of someone else in a play, or when mimicking a foreign accent or a Southern drawl.

Any reasonable theory on the cause of stuttering, then, must explain why it occurs only in certain situations. Why do high-anxiety predicaments exacerbate the condition? Why might a stutterer regularly stumble over the "t" sound in "to," but have no difficulty saying the words "too" or "two?" Why did the man who changed his name suddenly start stammering over a word that had never troubled him before?

The theory must also address itself to other facts about stuttering. In all cultures, approximately four times as many men stutter as women. Why? It has been observed that close relatives of stutterers are far more likely to have the disorder than are relatives of non-stutterers. Does this mean stuttering "runs in families?"

NO SINGLE CAUSE OR CURE

Over the years scholars have suggested many possible causes of stuttering, including evil spirits, chills, muscle weakness, repressed sexual impulses, brain dysfunction, and poor learning habits. Sir Francis Bacon, Shakespeare's contemporary and founder of the scientific method, proposed "The Cause (of stuttering) may bee, the Refrigeration of the Tongue; whereby it is lesse apt to move ..." As a remedy, Bacon recommended drinking wine, as it tends to "heat the Body."

We still have no definitive understanding of what causes stuttering. Sometimes it is hard even to identify a stutterer.

The lack of success in curing or even understanding stuttering is probably due to the complex nature of the disorder. It is no single, pure phenomenon, and opinions vary widely with respect to the basic question—how much of a stutterer's problem is physical and how much is psychological?

At one extreme, researchers like Dr. Marcel Wingate at Washington State University argue that stuttering is a purely physiological event, like eye-blinking or swallowing. His work, therefore, looks for physical differences between stutterers and non-stutterers—both in the anatomy of their speech-producing organs and in the way they use these organs. Successful treatment for stutterers, by this view, would come through surgery or other means of abolishing or compensating for physical abnormalities.

At the other extreme are the psychiatrists who maintain that stuttering is caused by some deep-rooted emotional problem and that psychological counseling or analysis is what the stutterer needs to overcome his handicap. Thus far, however, psychiatric therapy has been of little help in alleviating the symptoms of this socially-unacceptable speech disorder.

Middle-of-the-road researchers try to encompass all views. At the University of Iowa Dr. Jerry Zimmermann along with John Hanley and Dr. Anne Smith suggest that proposing separate psychological, physiological, and genetic causes of stuttering is an artificial and unproductive way of viewing the data. A stutterer himself, Zimmermann compares these arbitrary classifications to looking at a football field and trying to decide how much of its area is due to its length and how much to its width. A more satisfying and realistic approach, he says, is to decide on an all-inclusive framework into which every aspect of stuttering can eventually be incorporated. Zimmermann suggests thinking of stuttering as a physiological event that can be influenced by a great number of variables—including environment, psychological make-up, and heredity.

NEW TOOLS AND TECHNIQUES

"Cinefluorography" is the technique that has allowed Zimmermann and his co-workers to compare with great precision the mouth movements of stutterers and non-stutterers. This high-speed motion-picture method involves placing metallic markers on the subject's lips, tongue, teeth, and jaws. An X-ray movie is made of the tagged speaker, and analyzed frame by frame with the help of a computer, tracing the exact locations of the metallic markers. Graphs representing the extremely detailed mouth movements of different subjects are then prepared and compared.

Using this method, Zimmermann has made a striking finding: stutterers, even when they are speaking fluently, move their mouths differently than non-stutterers. Furthermore, among stutterers, coordination of their speech-producing organs is slower and less precise than among non-stutterers. This finding suggests that although stutterers are capable of fluent moments, their underlying speech production is at all times different from that of normal speakers.

Other notable information on the physiology of stuttering has come from examining the role of the larynx, or voice box, in speech disorders. The tool that has enabled researchers to watch the voice box in action is the "fiberscope." Under local anesthetic a flexible, four-millimeter-wide tube containing a bundle of optic fibers is gently inserted through one of the subject's nostrils and gradually pushed toward the back of the throat until the tip of the tube rests with very little discomfort slightly above the subject's larynx. The optic fibers transport the light around dark corners and illuminate the speaker's throat.

PHYSIOLOGY, PSYCHOLOGY, AND GENETICS

Dr. Frances Freeman at Northwestern University has also tested stutterers and normal speakers with fiberscopes and she finds stuttering events to be associated with incorrect muscle use. Stutterers tend to contract simultaneously the two sets of muscles which open and close the larynx. Normal speakers contract these muscles at different times. Freeman suggests, therefore, that relaxation therapy might help the stutterer.

Future work on the physiology of speech is expected to extend to the much more basic level of the individual nerve cells that control muscle movement—motor neurons. Dr. Michael McClean at the University of Washington is developing a non-invasive way to record the electrical activity of single motor neurons in the lip muscles of human subjects. Work by Russian neurophysiologists has suggested that the nervous system gets ready for all movements before they occur in a measurable way. McClean, Zimmermann, and Smith hope to test whether stutterers differ from normal speakers in the way they prepare for speech.

Research is under way on the psychology of stuttering. A number of studies have shown that stutterers as a group are not psychologically different from everyone else. Yet a stutterer will manifest his impediment in a way corresponding to his personality.

Genetics too plays a part in stuttering. Among identical twins, there is a greater than 90 per cent chance that if one stutters the other will too. For non-identical twins, the percentage drops to less than seven. Recently, Dr. Kenneth Kidd of Yale University examined 555 stutterers and their 2,000 closest relatives to see if relatives of stutterers were more likely to stutter than those of normal speakers. Kidd found this to be the case and asserts that "the susceptibility to stuttering is genetically transmitted." He also feels this susceptibility is sex-related, since male stutterers outnumber females four to one.

RESEARCH LEADS TO THERAPY

Recently intensive therapy programs for stutterers have been instituted at speech-disorder centers around the country. One of these, the Precision Fluency Shaping Program for Stutterers at Hollins College in Virginia, has been of tremendous help to Mrs. Annie Glenn, wife of Senator and former astronaut John Glenn. A stutterer all her life, Mrs. Glenn can now speak smoothly, although at an unnaturally slow tempo and in a monotone voice. The Hollins College program, like several others, is devoted to teaching the stutterer to speak fluently by carefully controlling his breath and learning to coordinate his speech movements.

Universally successful treatments for adult stutterers have yet to be developed, however. Some methods work excellently for a while, but later the condition returns as severely as ever. For children there is more hope. About 80 per cent of all childhood stutterers outgrow the disorder by adolescence. Adults have more difficulty in overcoming their affliction, says Dr. David Prins of the University of Washington, because "stuttering is what the speaker does to help himself in perceived emergency." That is, stuttering is a way in which some people cope with stress and anxiety. If the person has been coping in this way for 20 or 30 years, it is almost impossible to learn to do something else, especially in an emergency.

Unfortunately, for the stutterer, "emergencies" mean the insistent ring of the telephone or the expectant look on some waiter's face □

With a simulated mating dance, Kerry Hoffman of the International Crane Foundation helps prepare a female whooping crane to accept artificial insemination.

BIOLOGY

BIOLOGY
REVIEW OF THE YEAR

MIT

Professor Alexander Rich with models of DNA in the background. Rich believes left-hand helices interspersed with predominant right-hand helices may explain some gene functions and other phenomena.

Micromanipulation of cells and embryos. New ability to manipulate cells and the genetic material—genes made of DNA—within them allowed scientists to perform subcellular remodeling for experimental purposes during 1979. W. French Anderson of the U.S. National Institutes of Health (NIH) reported success in injecting genes into mouse cells grown in the laboratory. The genes were prepared from viral or human DNA material. They were able to function in the mouse cells, and they were reproduced as the cells divided. Descendant cells 30 generations later still made the product of the transplanted gene. Such a transplanted gene could be used to correct a genetic deficiency in the mouse cells. This research opens the door to the possibility of medical therapy involving the direct replacement of defective genes.

Manipulation of egg cells created novel embryos in 1979. A mouse embryo with two mothers and no father was produced at Vanderbilt University by Pierre Soupart. He combined two unfertilized eggs by cell fusion techniques, thus creating a cell with the normal mouse chromosome number, the number normally produced by a sperm-fertilized egg. The double egg divided in the laboratory to become an apparently normal 64-cell embryo. This procedure produces only females since sperm-carried chromosomes are necessary for the production of males. The next step will be to transfer the embryos into foster mothers to see if development continues normally. If successful, the procedure would be of great value in animal husbandry, especially in the dairy industry.

The cloning of mammals became more feasible with a major advance in experimental embryology during the year. Karl Illmensee of the University of Geneva in Switzerland switched the genetic information of a fertilized egg. He transferred the nucleus, which contains a cell's genes, from one mouse embryo cell into the fertilized egg cell of another mouse and removed that egg's original genetic material. The egg, with its new nucleus, developed into an early embryo under laboratory conditions and was then transferred into a mouse foster mother. Three mice were born of this procedure, and each was shown to be the genetic offspring of the transplanted nucleus and not of the egg and sperm.

E. coli, the common intestinal bacterium, may become a useful factory—producing growth hormone, insulin, and other substances from transplanted genetic material.

David Scharf

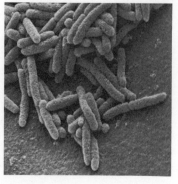

Analyzing genetic material. During 1979 scientists were able for the first time to resolve a segment of DNA into its individual atoms. They were surprised to find a zigzagging, left-hand helix instead of the smooth spiral right-hand conformation that had been indicated by earlier experiments. The surprise finding may bear on an understanding of gene function and the development of some cancers. Alexander Rich of the Massachusetts Institute of Technology suggests that in long molecules of natural DNA left-hand helices are interspersed with predominant right-hand forms. In a left-hand helix, certain major DNA components—nucleotide bases—are exposed at the edges of the molecule and are not sheltered in the center as in right-hand forms. Exposed bases could be more exposed to cancer-causing chemicals and to modifications by cellular proteins that switch genes on and off.

The deciphering of the genetic code was one of the most important advances in biology in the late 1960's and early 1970's. In 1979 scientists at the Medical Research Council in England and at Columbia University in New York City found the first exception to the code. Previously in all viruses, bacteria, plants, and animals examined, each three-nucleotide sequence in DNA coded for a particular amino acid in a protein product or for an "end-of-product" signal. Now analysis of mitochondria in both yeast and human cells has revealed an exception. Mitochondria are semiautonomous subcellular structures that act as the cell's powerplants. In the mitochondria analyzed, at least two three-nucleotide sequences were found to have a different meaning in the DNA within these structures than in the genetic material of the surrounding cells. Scientists are looking at the DNA for clues to why a different code evolved in the mitochondria.

Recombinant DNA research. Recombinant DNA research involves the splicing together of genetic material from more than one organism. For several years the possibility that this research could unleash a new disease-causing organism or otherwise cause harm has concerned some scientists and the NIH has periodically issued research guidelines. In December 1979 they presented a proposal to relax the safety requirements. This proposal reflected the absence of health problems attributed to the increasingly widespread research technique and the results of experiments specifically designed to assess the risk of the laboratory technique causing an epidemic.

The gene for the human form of growth hormone was introduced into bacteria in 1979 and the bacteria were made to produce the human hormone. Growth hormone is a medically important material that has been in short supply. Hormone prepared from animals is not active in people and the small amount isolated from cadavers has been used to treat children that have hereditary pituitary dwarfism. Two groups of scientists, using somewhat different techniques, succeeded in creating the hormone-producing bacteria. Each group teamed up with a major drug company to attempt the large-scale production required to provide sufficient hormone for clinical trials.

Chemical basis for dog sexual behavior. One active ingredient of the odor of a female dog was identified by Purdue University scientists. Michael R. Goodwin and Fred E. Regnier found that the chemical methyl *para*-hydroxybenzoate could trigger a male dog's full range of sexual behavior. The chemical, isolated from vaginal smears, was present only on the days of the estrous cycle when the female was most receptive to mounting. When the chemical was applied to unreceptive female dogs, males attempted to mount even though the females barked and snapped. The research demonstrated that a single compound can initiate the complex behavior normally triggered by a female dog in heat.

Notations on a whale song. The song of the humpback whale is an evolving art form. By analyzing more than 20 years of underwater recordings from whales wintering near Bermuda and Hawaii, investigators discovered that the song changes progressively from year to year. When Roger and Katy Payne of the New York Zoological Society and Sylvia Earle of the California Academy of Sciences recorded a full season of songs, they found that the whales return to their winter grounds singing the song of the previous year and then introduce new phrases and phase out old parts as the winter progresses. Evolution of the song, therefore, is not simply a consequence of the whales forgetting parts of their tune over the summer. The scientists have found that the songs, produced by air shuttling within a whale's head, have a defined structure and about 14 simple rules can describe the modifications. Circumstantial evidence suggests that the songs play a courtship role.

Julie Ann Miller

Des & Jen Bartlett/Bruce Coleman
Roger Payne and his associates recorded a full season of the humpback whale's song. They found that the songs have a defined structure and change from year to year.

Pierre Soupart is one researcher involved in the production of novel embryos through manipulation of egg cells. Such work reveals important data about early development.

Lennart Nilsson

Derek Fell

THE AMERICAN CHESTNUT

by Richard Jaynes

WHY is the American chestnut tree spoken of with such reverence and nostalgia? Surely the rotten stumps, sprouts, and small trees seen today in forests of the eastern United States tell little of its past. But the older folks among us remember a noble tree that was many things to many people.

The American chestnut, *Castanea dentata,* grew from Maine to Alabama, most abundantly on upland, well drained, acid soils. It was ordinarily found growing in mixed stands with hickory, oak, and maple but occasionally grew in pure stands. It is a member of the beech family. It may be confused with the horsechestnut *Aesculus hippocastanus,* a member of the horsechestnut family.

The Indians from New York State called the tree "O-heh-yah-tah," meaning prickly bur, and anyone who has tangled with the spiny bur that surrounds the three nuts has a vivid memory of how well the chestnut seeds are protected from early predation. When the nuts were ripe, the bur opened and the nut fell to the ground. Most were eaten by wildlife, but enough were left in the forest litter, or hidden by rodents, to perpetuate the species.

The leaves of the American chestnut resemble those of the beech, but are longer and more sharply toothed on the margin. As the pollen is shed the entire crown of the tree becomes golden yellow in color, resembling a giant plume.

COLONIAL FENCES

The colonists found in the American chestnut a beautiful timber tree, often with a straight clear trunk, some 20 to 30 meters tall, and up to 120 centimeters in diameter. Its closest relative in Europe is the European, or Italian chestnut, which thrives in the Mediterranean countries. The European chestnut produces a larger nut, but on trees that are limby and of spreading habit.

The American chestnut reached its greatest development in the Great Smoky Mountains of Tennessee and North Carolina, where specimens nearly four meters in diameter and 36 meters high were found. Indeed, one giant American chestnut reportedly reached a diameter of five meters.

The settlers certainly had a surplus of wood as they cleared land for tilling and pasture, but the special attributes of decay resistance and easy splitting with ax or wedge meant chestnut was the prime fencing material. Long stretches of split-rail fence meandered through the countryside, confining the farm animals and delineating property boundaries. Few such fences are left, although traces of them abound. Because their presence is associated with the pastoral beauty of the country, new fences of similar design are still being constructed, but with substitute materials.

POLES, TIES, AND FUEL

The greatest use and appreciation of chestnut came in the 1800's during the period of rapid industrialization. The durable wood was the choice for mine shafts and underground supports. Although not a dense or particularly valuable firewood, its great abundance made it a competitive, major source of fuel in brick yards and in charcoal production. The charcoal fired the furnaces of the iron and brass industry.

The developing railroads as well as the trolleys laid their tracks on chestnut ties. The telegraph wires were strung on chestnut poles; expansion of telephone and electric service to rural areas followed on more poles. And then the development of gasoline powered cars brought about chestnut guard-rail fences.

ATTRACTIVE TRIM

The stiff but relatively soft wood worked well and had an attractive grain. Thus, interior trim and furniture of chestnut was once common. The wood wore too fast for use as flooring. However, it did serve well for framing as well as finishing buildings and was preferred in construction of barns and stables for its decay resistance.

Our forebears also found that chestnut made good shingles. They covered their cabins with them before western red cedar was discovered. Even the bark made a good siding as attested by at least a few buildings remaining in the Appalachian area.

NUTS—AS CASH AND FOOD

Many a youngster filled his or her pockets with the freshly fallen nuts in the fall to eat out of hand or to take home for roasting. In those more frugal times, chestnuts were a rare source of cash for the rural folks,

The durable yet easily worked chestnut was used extensively both inside and outside 19th-century American homes, like this one in North Carolina.

American chestnut leaves resemble the beech; its pollen turns the tree golden yellow.

who sold them to agents from town. The nuts found their way into soups, stews, vegetable dishes, and desserts. And they were particularly valued in stuffing.

Hogs fed on chestnuts produced the sweetest meat, and Appalachian farmers depended on the annual bounty of chestnuts to fatten their animals prior to slaughter in the fall.

The appreciation of good street and shade trees increased with the growth of cities and suburbs. American chestnut, along with elm, became one of the favorite big landscape trees.

SUPERIOR FRUIT

Another famous American nut tree species, the pecan, was selected and propagated for its outstanding nut characteristics. There was, however, little such selection and propagation of the American chestnut. Chestnut was first grafted in this country in Pennsylvania about 1888. And during the 1890's a few chestnut orchards were established. But most of these were grafts of European cultivars onto American rootstock. Unfortunately, the larger European nuts were not so sweet or so easy to peel as those of the American chestnut tree.

Meanwhile, variation among fruits of the native trees did not go unnoticed. A report in *American Garden Magazine* in 1890 stated that, "Samples of American chestnuts superior to those of foreign growth both in size and in flavor, have recently been received at the Department of Agriculture, affording a striking illustration of the results of culture and selection." However, these selections never became widely established in commercial orchards.

BREAD-AND-BUTTER TREE

In addition to the versatile assets of the wood, bark, and nuts, chestnut demanded little from the site. It grew on thin and impoverished soils and performed remarkably well on fertile, well-drained sites. Trees growing in the open could grow at the rate of two-and-one-half centimeters in diameter per year. They could keep up that growth rate as witnessed by a tree that was 150 centimeters in diameter at 70 years. However, a diameter of 20 centimeters at 20 years and 30 centimeters at 30 years was close to the normal rate for forest-grown trees.

Coppice, or sprout growth, could be expected to be large enough for posts in 15 to 20 years and cross ties and telegraph poles in 25 to 35 years. Furthermore, when cut, the tree stumps responded by producing fast growing sprouts, negating the need for reseeding and replanting.

Chestnut was the bread-and-butter tree of the eastern hardwood forest. A bulletin published in 1906 to serve as a guide for the better management of woodlots states, "Since chestnut is such an important factor ... the treatment of the lot must in most cases conform more or less closely to the demands of this species." For any single use (posts, shingles, beams, tannin, nuts) there was probably another tree species that was better, but for all-around versatility and abundance, the chestnut was unmatched.

FUNGUS ATTACK

The agent for the demise of this stalwart of the forest came unseen and unheralded. Sometime in the late 1800's the disease agent was imported inadvertently on Chinese or Japanese chestnut seedlings shipped from the Far East into the port of New York. The fungus-produced disease went unnoticed for several years but found a host with no resistance in the American chestnut. Signs of the coming epidemic were first noted in 1904 on trees at the New York Zoo. In due course, an organism, *Endothia parasitica,* the chestnut-blight fungus, was named.

The canker-causing fungus attacks through openings in the bark. From there it rapidly spreads in an ever enlarging circle, girdling the tree in one to three years. In 1910 it was difficult to find a blighted tree in central Connecticut. By 1915 it became a question of salvaging the dead and dying trees throughout the state.

The demise of the last American chestnut trees was not recorded, but it must have occurred in the South in the 1940's or early 1950's. The rapid spread of the chestnut blight and its total destruction of a native tree species was something never witnessed before or since that time. (The destruction of the American elm runs a close second.)

Sprouts still persist, marking the sites of former trees. These shoots may reach diameters of up to 30 centimeters but usually succumb to infection. As the older sprouts are killed, new ones are formed. Thus the species is perpetuated, for the present at least.

VIRUS CURE

Attempts to save, replace, or revive the American chestnut are legion but, unfortunately, fruitless. Still, there is now renewed hope and interest in controlling the chestnut-blight fungus.

Natural control of the chestnut blight is occurring in parts of Europe, where the disease rampaged for several years after its introduction into Italy in 1938. Control of the blight has apparently resulted from the presence and spread of virus-carrying strains of the blight fungus. These virus-carrying strains do not kill the tree but can and do convert the killing strains of the blight into non-killing strains.

Such beneficial strains have been imported into the United States. Research with them is being pursued by scientists at the Connecticut Agricultural Experiment Station in New Haven, as well as at several other locations in the eastern United States. It is hoped that this research will lead to a practical, biological method for controlling the chestnut blight.

This promise of biological control of chestnut blight in America stimulated the U.S. Forest Service and the University of West Virginia to sponsor an American Chestnut Symposium at Morgantown, West Virginia, in January, 1978. It was the largest gathering of people convened to discuss research on the American chestnut since 1912. In addition to researchers from throughout the eastern United States, Drs. Tullio Tur-

New sprouts of American chestnut appear in spite of blight that has destroyed most of the species.

Richard A. Jaynes

Two mature American chestnuts survive alongside a typical fence in Madison, Virginia.

Richard A. Jaynes

Courtesy of the Longfellow House

Under a spreading horsechestnut tree

Longfellow's legendary spreading chestnut tree has caused considerable controversy through the years, first when it was felled amidst protests in 1876, and again 100 years later when a question arose over its true identity.

The poem itself had by then become such an old chestnut that the tree was taken for granted: under what but an American chestnut tree would a village smithy stand?

The staff of the Longfellow National Historic Site (the poet's home in Cambridge, Massachusetts) had their doubts. One clue was the poet's sketch of the tree and blacksmith shop (above) made in 1840. If the smithy's shop was the usual 12 to 15 feet high, the tree would appear to be some 50 to 60 feet high—a normal height for European horsechestnuts, but short for the native tree. Moreover, an armchair made of wood from the tree, given to the poet by the children of Cambridge on his 72nd birthday, bore a large leaf carved on its back: it was a horsechestnut leaf. Finally, a sliver of wood from the chair was examined under a microscope and confirmed that it was horsechestnut.

The scholars were thus satisfied. Longfellow, however, knew it all the time. His notebooks include clippings from some Cambridge newspapers of the day, which describe the tree as a horsechestnut. When he wrote the poem, he simply cast botany to the winds to save a telltale syllable.

chetti and Lorenzo Mittempergher from Italy and Jean Grente from France described the situation in their countries. Natural control has occurred in Italy, and control of blight in France is being brought about through careful selection and inoculation of cankers with disease-curing strains.

SPREADING THE CURE

Significant differences between the European and American situation are apparent. The chestnut species are different, although both are attacked by the normal or killing strains of blight. In Europe chestnut trees are usually grown in pure stands managed for nut production, whereas the American chestnut grew in mixed hardwood stands and was unmanaged. Now, of course, it exists as an understory shrub.

Individual cankers on American chestnut have been controlled in tests with the disease-curing strains, but the means of spreading the curative factor to other cankers is not yet known. Insects could play a role in moving the viruslike particle from canker to canker. Means of spreading the curing strains, variations among the many blight strains, and how the strains interact are under study. We can hope that Robert Frost was truly prophetic when he wrote the following poem in 1930:

EVIL TENDENCIES CANCEL

Will the blight end the chestnut?
The farmers rather guess not.
It keeps smoldering at the roots
And sending up new shoots
Till another parasite
Shall come to end the blight.

 SELECTED READINGS

"Army offers proving ground for endangered species: American chestnut tree." *National Parks and Conservation,* September 1977.

"Born-Again Chestnuts" by Janet Hopson. *Outside,* October 1977.

"On the trail of the chestnut tree" by E. W. Littlefield. *American Forest,* March 1976.

"A fungus beats the chestnut blight at its own game" by Rudolph Chelminski. *Smithsonian,* June 1979.

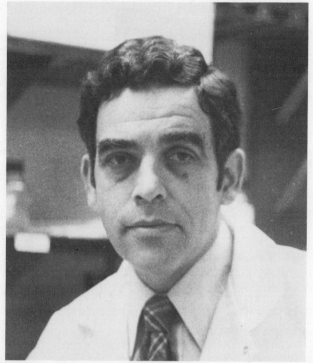

Dr. Philip Leder thinks that split genes may have an evolutionary value but exactly what, he holds, we may never know. Intervening sequences, he suggests, may prevent or encourage genetic recombination.

NIH

SPLIT GENES

by Jenny Tesar

TO the average person no two organisms seem more dissimilar than a bacterium and an elephant. Molecular geneticists, however, are only secondarily interested in such things as an organism's outward appearance. Their main concern: the genetic material that occurs in every living cell and that contains all the information needed to construct a particular organism. How is this material organized? How does it function?

As a result of experimental work done by numerous geneticists around the world, clear answers to these questions gradually emerged. Most of the work was done with the bacterium *Escherichia coli,* a common inhabitant of the human intestine. *E. coli* is readily available and easy to culture. Its genetic information is less complex than that of higher organisms. Also, it has long been possible to reproduce bacterial genes in a test tube,

whereas techniques for doing this with animal genes were not developed until recently. Nonetheless, geneticists had no reason to doubt that their *E. coli* findings were equally true for higher organisms such as humans and elephants.

The genetic information, or blueprint, of an oganism is contained in large molecules of DNA (deoxyribonucleic acid). The parts, or links, of a DNA molecule are called nucleotides. The same nucleotides are found in all organisms. They are linked together to form long chains called chromosomes. The chromosomes are divided into units called genes. Each gene consists of a continuous sequence of DNA and is responsible for one piece of information—the information needed, say, to make a certain protein or to carry out a particular function.

This information is transcribed, or copied, in a linear fashion to messenger RNA. (Messenger RNA is a sort of "negative print" of a "positive" DNA molecule.) The messenger RNA then moves to another site in the cell where it is responsible for the production of proteins.

Simple. Clear. Straightforward. But, though correct for bacteria and blue-green algae, this picture turns out to be incorrect for all other organisms. As a result, something akin to a revolution is occurring in the field of molecular biology.

EXONS AND INTRONS

The first indications that the traditional picture did not apply to higher organisms and viruses were announced in 1977. Since then it has been shown that, with rare exceptions, each gene in higher organisms and in viruses is split into segments. Two different types of units make up the DNA strands. Harvard's Walter Gilbert named these units "exons" and "introns."

Exons, or expressed units, are units that end up being transcribed to messenger RNA. Introns, or intervening units, are not transcribed. The number of intervening units varies. Most genes studied so far have two to four intervening units. The gene that codes for chicken egg white has seven. An egg white protein called conalbumin has 16 intervening units.

Francis Crick, who together with James Watson received a Nobel Prize for determining the structure of DNA, calls this arrangement "almost as surprising as if you were reading, say, a novel by Jane Austen and in the middle of a paragraph you found a rather garbled version of an advertisement for a deodorant."

Not a short advertisement, either. Some of the introns observed by scientists contain up to 10,000 nucleotides. Gilbert writes: "I expect the amount of DNA in introns will turn out to be five to ten times the amount in exons."

In order to end up with messenger RNA that has all its nucleotides strung together in proper, continuous alignment, the introns must be removed and the exons must be joined together. This is accomplished by one of two mechanisms:

1. At the DNA level: Something happens to the chromosomes that cuts out the introns and moves together the exons.

2. At the RNA level: All the information in the chromosome is copied, forming a very large messenger RNA. Then the introns are removed, creating a mature form of messenger RNA that has all the exons spliced together in the correct order.

Although both mechanisms are used, they are used in different situations. The first is known to be used in the immune system but has not been observed elsewhere. The second, called *gene splicing,* is widespread.

Enzymes are responsible for cutting out the introns and for splicing together the exons. But researchers do not yet know how may different enzymes are involved. Perhaps only one enzyme does all the cutting, another all the splicing. Perhaps hundreds of enzymes are involved, each responsible for a specific exon.

Crick indicates some other questions to be answered: "How does the enzyme (or enzymes) recognize where to splice? Is an intron always removed in one go, or does the splicing enzyme sometimes need to take several bites at it? What happens to the intron when it is excised?"

QUESTIONS OF PURPOSE

What is the function of the excess DNA and RNA? And why are the genes in pieces? Here, too, definitive answers remain to be discovered. But some data has been gathered and some theories have been proposed.

In at least some cases, one gene's introns may be another gene's exons. That is, what must be cut out to join the exons of gene A and eventually form protein A may be part of gene B, needed to form protein B.

Gilbert believes the fragmentation has an evolutionary value for most genes. He argues that recombination, or the shuffling of pieces of DNA to form new combinations, is faster and easier than if a gene is continuous. And, he says, the greater the distance between two pieces of DNA the greater the chance that they will recombine. New combinations produce a diversity that increases the rate of evolution.

Such a system is not needed by bacteria. Their rapid rate of reproduction—they divide about every 15 minutes—guarantees a rapid rate of evolution. Nor is such an evolutionary system an advantage to the genes responsible for the production of basic proteins called histones. Histone genes are among the few genes in higher organisms that are not split. At certain times, cells must rapidly produce large quantities of histones. This process would be slowed by the need to make RNA copies of all the DNA in the introns.

Philip Leder of the National Institutes of Health agrees that split genes have an evolutionary value. But he suggests that the arrangement of exons and introns may just as likely prevent recombination as encourage it. He argues that the introns serve as stabilizers, keeping genes in place and decreasing the chance that they will be lost due to recombination of DNA.

The issue may never be resolved. "Evolutionary arguments can't be proven conclusively one way or the other," says Leder. "Intervening sequences may have arisen for reasons that will forever remain obscure."

MEDICAL IMPLICATIONS

The discovery of split genes has made it necessary for molecular biologists and medical specialists to reevaluate their beliefs about disease. "It has opened us up to an entirely new way of thinking about genetic disease," says Leder. It is now apparent that such diseases may result from the recombination of DNA, from the loss of exon material at some step along the way, or from mutations at the boundary between exons and introns. The result: insufficient production of proteins essential to good health.

At the same time that some researchers are delving into the mysteries of split genes, other researchers are learning to imitate a cell's genetic apparatus. These scientists are cutting, splicing, and otherwise manipulating genetic material, then transplanting this material to bacteria. The bacteria are induced to make the product specified by the transplanted DNA. That is, they function as miniature factories. And since the bacteria reproduce so rapidly, their output can be significant.

UPI

Dr. Francis Crick, co-discoverer of DNA structure, was surprised by the discovery of intervening sequences in DNA.

This technique promises to be the basis of a major industry, for it is expected to allow large-scale production of scarce substances at relatively low cost. Pharmaceutical firms are beginning to use the technique to produce several important human substances, including human growth hormone, insulin, and interferon (a chemical compound used by cells to fight viral diseases and cancer). People whose bodies do not produce these substances in sufficient amounts—perhaps because of diseases caused by disruptions of certain exons and introns—can look forward to plentiful supplies of the substances □

SELECTED READINGS

"Genes in Pieces" by Gina Bari Kolata. *Science,* January 25, 1980.

"Split Genes and RNA Splicing" by Francis Crick. *Science,* April 20, 1979.

"Advances in Gene Splicing Hint Scientific-Industrial Revolution" by Harold M. Schmeck Jr. *The New York Times,* January 27, 1980.

The grape leaf is an example of palmate venation (see page 83).

Grant Heilman

THE LEAF'S PLUMBING

by Richard M. Klein

WHEN a pipe breaks in a home or an apartment, we suddenly realize just how dependent modern society is upon its plumbing systems. Plants, too, depend upon an intricate piping system to move liquids.

Early land plants, such as some of the algae and the ancestors of mosses and liverworts, were pressed to the moisture of the soil. This meant that water and dissolved minerals didn't have to move long distances from the soil into the photosynthetic tissues. The sugars formed in photosynthesis had to be transported only a few centimeters to supply food to the non-green cells.

As plants began to exploit the various land habitats, they gradually became upright with long stems. Eventually, as in giants like redwoods, stems rose well over 100 meters into the air. The distance between the point of water supply and the place where the water was used became very long. Therefore, the simple movement of water from cell to cell would have been just too slow.

NEW STRUCTURES DEVELOP

A whole series of new plant structures had to develop to exploit the land habitat. Roots probed the soil for water and minerals. They became anchors and supports for vertical stems. As seen in fossils, the roots of early land plants developed relatively primitive plumbing systems. These branched into the stem and its flattened, photosynthetic branch tips. Eventually, the plumbing system—veins—extended into the leaves, which were modified branches.

Ferns and the allied horsetails and ground pines were fully plumbed. The engineering efficiency of these liquid-transmitting systems permitted the evolution of giant tree ferns, cycads, and gymnosperms. Later the system led to the development of the flowering plants.

The leaf is a most elegant structural and functional solution to several difficult problems of getting along in this world. If a plant is to capture sunlight efficiently, the chlorophyll-containing tissues should have maximum surface area—a characteristic of the flattened leaf. By having almost uncountable numbers of leaves precisely arranged about a stem or branch, each leaf will be exposed to sunlight.

There was a problem that had to be worked out by evolutionary interactions between organism and environment: how to connect the plumbing system of the root and stem with that of the leaf. This had to be done not only to get water and minerals into the leaf, but also to move sugars formed in the leaf the long distances to the root system.

DEVELOPMENT OF A PLUMBING SYSTEM

To some extent, we can visualize what happened in the evolutionary process by following the growth of the leaf. The leaf starts as a small bulge of cells on the side of the stem tip. As this bulge increases in size and in cell numbers, some of the cells in the mass

Most monocotyledons like corn have their major veins running parallel.

Grant Heilman

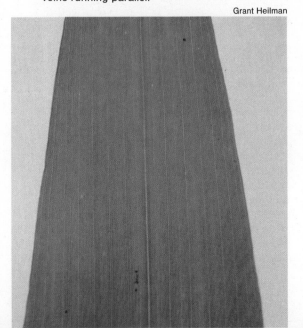

begin to elongate more than their neighbors. Some develop spiral thickenings of cellulose around their walls. Furthermore, cell contents disappear, and their end-walls dissolve, thus forming a continuous open tube. This connects with similar tubes in the young stem. These tissues—*xylem tissues*—then form a complete plumbing system to move water upward through the plant.

At the same time, other cells in the young leaf, closely associated with the developing xylem, are changed into different cell types, called *phloem* cells. These are cells that make up another system of tubes. Through these tubes dissolved food (sugars) moves from the leaves to the stem and roots. Finally, cells in contact with both xylem and phloem may form very heavy wall thickenings. They serve to strengthen the vascular, or plumbing, system of the leaf. All these cell types make up the veins of the leaf.

The precise physics of water and sugar movement into and out of leaves is still not completely understood. During the 19th century some believed that there was some kind of a pump in plants comparable to the heart. This idea was not laid in the dustbin of scientific speculation until the early decades of the 20th century.

Modern research has shown that water moves up from the root-soil interface into the stem. Then it moves into the leaves and eventually evaporates through the many pores, or *stomates,* of the leaf into the atmosphere. It is, in fact, the suction action of this evaporation that pulls the water up the plant. Measurements of this suction force show that it is more than enough to pull water in the microscopic xylem pipes to vertical distances much higher than the tallest trees. We are much less confident in our understanding of the physical forces that move dissolved sugars in the phloem system down from the leaves.

THE PATTERNS IN THE PLUMBING

Just by looking at leaves, we can get a good idea of how beautifully designed the vein system is. The vascular connections to the plant stem are most easily seen on twigs in winter after the leaf has fallen. The place where the leaf stalk joined the stem is seen as

Most dicotyledons have a net venation pattern—usually either pinnate as in the oak (left) where one main vein divides the leaf into two halves, or palmate, as in the maple (right) where several main veins emerge fanlike from the leaf stalk.

a scar. At one or more places on the scar can be seen small dots. Each dot is the plugged end of a vascular bundle of xylem, phloem, and supporting tissues, which had entered the leaf stalk. The fact that these vascular bundles (plumbing pipes) traverse the leaf stalk can be easily observed. For example, in the greatly elongated leaf stalks of celery, the bundles are the small dots forming an arc on the concave side of the stalk.

At the junction of the leaf stalk and the flattened leaf blade, the vascular bundles become apparent as the leaf veins. The two general leaf vein patterns, also called venation patterns, correlate with the two major groups of flowering plants. One group is the monocots, in which the embryo of the seed has one cotyledon, or seed leaf. The other group of flowering plants is the dicots, in which the embryo has two cotyledons. It has long been a botanical rule of thumb that most (but not all) of the monocots have their major veins running parallel to each other. The parallel-venation pattern probably replaced that of the dicots, which usually have a repeatedly branching network of veins.

The grasses, palms, orchids, and lilies are monocots and are parallel-veined. If you trace the veins, you will see that there are usually one or several veins of equal diameter extending the length of the leaf. They have smaller veins branching off in regular order. The smaller veins also usually run parallel to one other, with very little secondary branching to the sides of the leaf. It's worth noting that not all monocots have parallel veins, but the rule of thumb is still useful.

Net venation patterns typical of dicots include two major sub-pattern types, the most common being the *pinnate* arrangement. In pinnate patterns, such as in elm and beech leaves, there is one main vein that divides the leaf into two halves. Secondary veins diverge from this midrib. Then tertiary veinlets divide, subdivide, and rejoin to give the leaf's netted appearance.

In dicots such as household ivy and maples the vein system is called *palmate*. There are several main veins, all originating from the leaf stalk-leaf blade junction to give a fan-like array. Each of the major veins shows the net branching and sub-branching design. In a third variation, much less common than the others, called *dichotomous branching,* the main vein divides into two veins, each of these again divides into two and so on.

LEAFY ORIGIN OF THE FLOWER

Venation is not restricted to leaves. It is also seen in plant parts that are derived from leaves, such as the flower. Flower parts retain the vein patterns of the plant parts from which they develop. Each of the petals of a rose shows its leafy origin. So do the green sepals and, not surprisingly, the male and female reproductive structures. Indeed, the filaments of the anthers are almost entirely vein tissues. They contain xylem, phloem, and the strengthening cell types found in foliage leaves. In most fruits the vein system is less apparent. It is present, however, and active during the period in which the fruit is developing.

To understand the roles of the veins, we would have to study the microscopic structure of leaves. However, we can get a pretty good idea of how intimate is the association between veins and the tissues they serve just by examining a leaf skeleton.

If you pick up a leaf that has over-wintered in a pond, you will see that the softer tissues have disappeared. They have been broken down by bacteria and fungi, leaving intact just the tougher vein tissues. The net or parallel venation patterns are beautifully apparent. You can also see that the very fine veins are ordered in space so that each of the photosynthetic cells of the active leaf would have been only a fraction of a centimeter from a veinlet.

The veins are arranged so that water coming into the leaf can be rapidly diffused to the cells that need it. Water also goes to the stomates, where the evaporation takes place. Sugar and starch, formed in photosynthesis, has an equally short path. The food material moves from the food-producing chloroplast factory to the pipes that move it to the consuming cells as far away as the bottommost root tip.

STRUCTURE AND ENVIRONMENT

Has one form of venation permitted a particular plant to be better adapted either to its present habitat or to conditions that might

Flower parts show the vein patterns of their leafy origins. Below: closeup of part of funnel-shaped gladiolus flower; opposite page: colorful petals of anemone.

Manuel Rodriguez

Manuel Rodriguez

have existed during the evolution of that plant? No correlations have been proposed with which all botanists can agree.

Small, net-veined leaves with toothed margins are common leaf types in the harsh environments of the cool-to-cold forests of northern North America. The alder shrubs are an example. More open parallel or palmate patterns predominate in some tropical areas. In very rainy areas, such as the tropical rain forests of the Philippines or the Hawaiian Islands, many plants have leaves with thin ends—drip-tips from which water can flow. Particular leaf patterns are not always found in association with a particular habitat. Plants with one type appear to grow as well or as poorly as those with another. Therefore, the significance of the patterning is obscure.

Gardeners, only slightly more than other mortals, are enchanted with the intrinsic beauty of the patterning of veins. They select and breed plants that have vein patterns they find pleasing.

In the prayer plant, *Maranta,* the epicias, and caladiums, certain cells associated with the veins synthesize pigments that contrast with the green color of the rest of the leaf. Botanists have bred caladiums with only the vein-associated tissues green and aphalandras with the veins white. We can purchase nasturtiums with yellow petals streaked with red along the veins. Gardeners have created bearded iris with bold white veins contrasting with rich blue petals.

The variation in vein appearance in peperomias is due to puckering around the veins or the swelling of interveinal tissues. These plants are selected, but far from isolated, examples of some of the most beautiful plumbing in the world □

 SELECTED READINGS

Basic Concepts in Botany by Watson M. Laetsch. Little, Brown and Co., Boston, 1979.

Plants and Life by Alan W. Haney. Macmillan, New York, 1978.

THE 1979 NOBEL PRIZE IN PHYSIOLOGY OR MEDICINE

by Barbara Tchabovsky

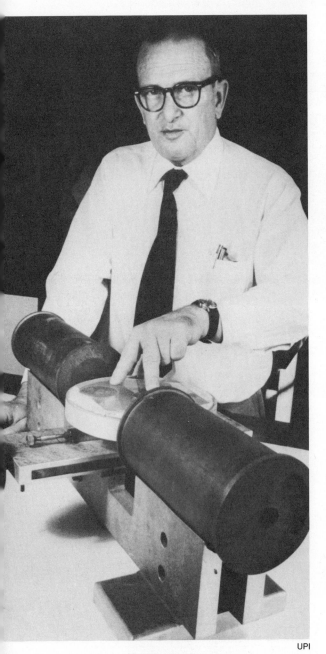

UPI

Allan M. Cormack

THE 1979 Nobel Prize in Physiology or Medicine was awarded to a U.S. physicist and a British electronics engineer for their development of a new X-ray technique that provides a remarkably clear look inside the human body. The technique is called computerized axial tomography, or CAT, for short. The winners were Allan McLeod Cormack, a Tufts University physicist, and Godfrey Newbold Hounsfield, an engineer at the British company EMI, a British-controlled international complex of companies involved in electronics and related work. The two men pursued their research independently and, in fact, at the time of the Nobel announcement, had never met.

In computerized axial tomography an X-ray tube is rotated around a specific area of the body, such as the head. This allows the physician to take pictures that reveal specific "slices" of the anatomy in greater detail than any other nonsurgical technique. Since its introduction in 1973, CAT scanning has been used on millions of patients and revolutionized the practice of medicine, particularly neurology. The "slices" are especially helpful in diagnosing disorders of the brain, spinal cord, kidney, and associated lymph glands, and in revealing certain facial and pelvic cancers.

In announcing the award, the Nobel Committee said, "It is no exaggeration to state that no other method within X-ray diagnostics within such a short period of time has led to such remarkable advances in research and in a multitude of applications."

HOW MUCH FOR EACH TISSUE

Cormack became interested in medical physics while serving a brief stint as a medical physicist at Groote Schuur Hospital in Cape Town, South Africa. He was troubled about deficiencies in the diagnosis and treatment of cancers through radiation techniques and wondered "how can you give a dose of radiation if you don't know the material [tissue] through which it has to pass?"

He then began to calculate how tissues respond to radiation, developing mathematical formulas to compute the absorption of X-ray radiation by various tissues of the body. This work was used to determine how much radiation to use in obtaining X-ray slices of various body parts and how to analyze the "slices."

COMPUTER SCANNING

Research at EMI on the design of computers that could recognize printed characters led Hounsfield to his award-winning work. Hounsfield headed a team that developed the first large solid-state computer built in Britain. Work on a large-scale memory and on techniques whereby the computer could "read" printed characters provided the raw material for CAT development. Then it was just a step to using the scanning system for medical diagnosis.

CONTROVERSIAL AWARD

The 1979 award recognized a discovery with immediate practical applications. As such it was opposed by some who believe that Nobel awards should recognize basic science and not its applications. The CAT scanner reflects advances in mathematical physics, but its development has its greatest application in medicine. Thus it was awarded the medical prize.

As controversy met the award announcement, so too has controversy surrounded the increasing use of the CAT scanner itself. A CAT scanner can cost $500,000 or more. More than 2,000 have been sold in more than 50 countries, and some hospitals have begun using them almost routinely. The high cost of these machines must, of course, be absorbed—in higher medical bills for patients. Herein lies much of the problem.

Some health officials question the cost-effectiveness of the CAT scanner. They ask: Is the technique being overused? Is it being used—at high cost—when older, techniques could provide the same diagnostic information—in strokes, for example? Are too many hospitals rushing to get the newest medical gadget when, in fact, fewer machines well

UPI

Godfrey N. Hounsfield

distributed in terms of population density and geography would suffice?

Allan MacLeod Cormack was born in Johannesburg, South Africa, on February 23, 1924. He studied physics at the University of Cape Town, intending to pursue a career in astronomy. He received his bachelors degree in 1944, his masters in 1945. He did postgraduate work in theoretical physics at Cambridge University in England, apparently giving up thoughts of becoming an astronomer.

In 1956 Cormack moved to the United States as a research fellow at Harvard University. One year later he joined the staff of Tufts University, where he has held various posts, including chairman of the physics department. There he has pursued his main interest—theoretical research on the interactions of subatomic particles—leaving medical physics to pursue as a hobby.

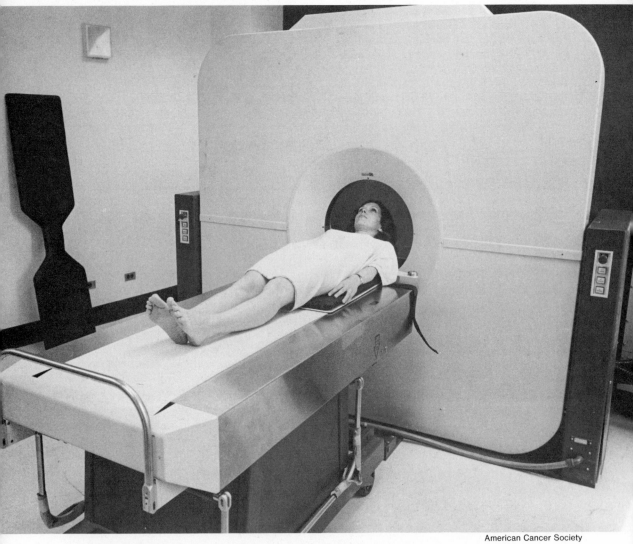

Use of the computerized axial tomography (CAT) scanner provides medical diagnoses through computer technology.

Cormack became a U.S. citizen in 1966. He is married and has three children.

Godfrey Newbold Hounsfield was born in Nottinghamshire, England, in 1919. He became interested in electronics at an early age, perhaps influenced by his father, an engineer turned farmer.

During World War II Hounsfield served as a radar lecturer at the Royal Air Force College radar school. After that he attended Faraday House Electrical Engineering College in London. Upon his graduation in 1951, he joined EMI, where he did his award-winning work.

Hounsfield is the recipient of more than 25 awards. In 1975 he was named a Fellow of the Royal Society, Britain's highest scientific honor. A bachelor, he enjoys "rambling"—as he describes his long-distance walking—through the countryside of Britain and the Continent □

Sidney Harris cartoon

"I think you should be more explicit here in step two."

COMPUTERS & MATHEMATICS

COMPUTERS & MATHEMATICS
REVIEW OF THE YEAR

Bill Auth/Georgetown University

A scientist seated at a console controls procedures administered to patient at left and reads the test data on the video monitor during a CENOG procedure.

During 1979 trends toward smaller, less expensive computers continued; there was increased computer use in many diverse fields; and some technical advances were seen in a new series of computers. The year also saw important advances in mathematics.

Home and small-business use of computers. Although not yet mass-market items, computers inexpensive enough for home use have been on the market since about 1976. Ranging in price from about $500 to $3,000, they are ready to take over such household tasks as balancing the checkbook, making the grocery list, and even keeping the children occupied with video games. Now a new service, named NewsShare, links home computers with newsroom computers, making news articles directly available to the home. The user simply punches out a code on the home computer keyboard.

The time for minicomputers and microcomputers for small businesses has really arrived. The software for these small machines is especially easy to use, and the machines can be programmed to handle payroll, invoices, inventories, mailing lists, and other duties. This ease and versatility of use is coupled with decreasing costs—computing costs have been dropping 20 to 25 per cent each year.

Efforts were made during the year to enable potential users to become familiar with computers. Digital Equipment Corporation, a leading manufacturer of minicomputers, opened a "Computer Store" near Boston's financial district. It is one of a growing number of small computer outlets hoping to get the attention of small business firms. ■ Micronet, another leading manufacturer, opened a "Paperless Office" demonstration in Washington, D.C. This fully automated office uses an impressive array of modern information systems.

Modern offices may become practically paperless—with an array of word processors, automated retrieval and voice-input systems, and optical character-recognition systems.

Micronet

Expanding consumer use. Consumers were also coming into more and more contact with computers—directly and indirectly. Airlines are increasingly using JetPlan. A computer analyzes weather conditions, jet type, payload, and engine size and decides on the best route—to save time and/or fuel. ■ Meanwhile American Telephone & Telegraph (AT&T) is testing a "phone-number fetcher." A small computer terminal rests by a dialless phone. Pressing a few computer buttons brings any number in the directory to a small screen and automatically dials the number.

Computers are also answering questions for lawyers and students. Harvard professor of law and expert in land-use planning, Charles M. Haar, programmed a computer with over 1,200 zoning-amendment appeal cases. When questioned, the computer turned out the same answer as did the judges in 99 per cent of the cases. And in schools, Discover, a new IBM computer, gives students current information concerning careers and training programs.

Expanding use in science. Charles Kohlhase and Jim Blinn at the Jet Propulsion Laboratory in Pasadena, California, used computer graphics to create the animated films of Voyager's Jupiter-encounter seen on television news programs during 1979. And for the 1980–81 Saturn encounter Kohlhase will use computer simulation to determine the best positions for Voyager cameras.

A new computer at Georgetown Hospital in Washington, D.C. is being used to diagnose serious nervous-system disorders, including Huntington's chorea, myasthenia gravis, Parkinson's disease, and some eye diseases. CENOG—Computerized ElectroNeuro Ophthalmograph—exposes the eye to light in various forms. If there is any eye or brain disease, electrodes placed on the skin around the eyes detect an abnormal reflex motion. ■ Similarly researchers hope to learn more about paranoia through use of a new computer programmed by researchers at Stanford University to respond in a paranoid fashion.

New computers and technical advances. During 1979 International Business Machines (IBM) came out with a new series of small and medium-sized computers—series 4300. Analysts report that the new series will have at least twice the price-performance ratio of earlier IBM model 370's. In producing these new computers IBM made several technical advances. A single chip type is produced and then modified for special functions by use of an electron beam, significantly reducing cost per circuit. ■ In another technical advance, bulky cables normally used to hook individual terminals to central control units have been eliminated by using infrared waves for wireless transmission of data.

New Math Discoveries. On May 23, 1979 Harry Nelson and David Slowinski, computer specialists at the Lawrence Livermore Laboratory in California, discovered a new prime number. A prime number is a number divisible only by itself and the number one. As numbers get larger, primes become harder to identify and increasingly rare. When written out the new prime has 13,395 digits. Six students spent three hours just printing it on a blackboard. Clearly the new prime won't prove useful for measuring anything real. However, computer experts and cryptographers hope that it will provide keys to the complex codes needed to insure the secrecy of data banks.

Late in 1979 there was considerable excitement in the mathematical world: The famous "traveling-salesman problem," it was believed, had been solved. The problem: Find the shortest possible route a salesperson can take to visit x number of cities without backtracking. Such problems face industries each day. Ordinarily they are handled in a hit-or-miss fashion. Computers using the simplex method, invented by George B. Dantzig of Stanford University, devise a flat-sided polyhedron and then hop from vertex to vertex testing possibilities one by one. This system sometimes requires so many steps that it drags on for years.

In 1979, it was reported that 27-year-old Soviet mathematician Leonid G. Khachiyan had provided a new answer to a similar problem. He proposed that computers design a multi-dimensional curved ellipsoid surrounding the area of possible solutions. The smallest ellipsoid the computer can devise in the space allotted represents the best solution. This shortcut drastically reduces the steps needed to find a solution.

Because this problem is similar to the "traveling-salesman problem," it was believed that the latter problem had been solved. It had not been solved, however; nor did Khachiyan ever claim that he had solved the problem. See "Problems Too Hard for Computers" on page 98.

Jeanne O'Neill

IBM

The new IBM series 4300 computers, the result of several technical advances, are expected to have twice the price-performance ratio of earlier IBM 370 computers.

The newly discovered prime number goes on, and on— for 13,395 digits.

Tom Tracey

© David Sharpe

Mapmaking made easier—a cartographer reads map coordinates directly into a computer.

TALKING TO COMPUTERS

by Arthur L. Robinson

FORECASTS of the impending computerization of society tend to focus on the ever-decreasing cost of computer power. Just as important in deepening the computer's penetration into our daily lives, however, is the prospect of communicating with a computer through human speech.

All computer users agree it would be highly advantageous to be able to talk to a computer in a conversational way. A hotly debated question is: How natural does voice communication with a computer have to be to be useful? Surprisingly, the answer is not very.

Researchers and engineers in numerous companies are producing speech-recognition machines with limited capabilities. These machines can be bought off the shelf today for many applications, mainly industrial and military. All projections are that computer-speech processing is on the verge of becoming a booming business, even if the personable computer epitomized by Hal in *2001* remains a dream that is decades or more away.

NICER—AND MORE EFFICIENT

One reason that development of a voice-communication capability may be imperative for expanding the uses of the computer is in part psychological. Many people will prefer—and thus be willing to purchase—a machine that they can talk to (and that can talk back) to one that must be communicated with by way of an inflexible, artificial computer language and a typewriter-like keyboard.

Another reason is efficiency. Experiments have shown that when two persons work together to solve problems, they find solutions roughly twice as fast when they communicate with speech as compared to the time taken when they communicate by other means, such as visual signaling, typing, or handwriting.

A second source of efficiency is that the ability to convey information by talking frees a person to do other tasks simultaneously—as in sorting or inspecting operations. In these cases, a worker has to determine, say, the destination of a sack of mail by inspection and then has to turn to enter the information on a keyboard. He or she could perform both operations without moving by reading into the microphone of a speech-recognition machine.

RECOGNIZING AND COMPARING SOUND PATTERNS

The source of the difficulty in speech recognition lies in the complex acoustic wave patterns of the sounds of the human voice. The pattern for any given sound consists of many waves with different frequencies and amplitudes superimposed on one another. Moreover, the pattern is stable only over periods of about 10 milliseconds. Therefore, the frequencies and amplitudes making up the pattern vary constantly. An additional complication is that the sequence of patterns of a sound depends on such variables as where in a word it appears and what the sounds in the following or previous words are.

Finally, the physical differences between people cause differences in their speech. Also a given person will speak differently when suffering from a cold, when in a highly emotional state, when very tired, and so on. The basic speech-recognition act consists of a comparison between the acoustic wave patterns made by a speaker and reference patterns stored in the machine's memory to find the best match. To say that this task is formidable is an understatement.

SOUNDS INTO SENTENCES

On top of the sound-recognition task is the job of converting a string of sounds into words and the words into meaningful sentences. More than mere pattern matching is required to translate sounds into sentences. The machine must "understand" what every human more or less knows—the basic rules of grammar, syntax, and semantics. Incorporating such knowledge into computers is part of the domain of artificial intelligence. This draws upon the talents of linguists and psychologists, as well as computer scientists.

An alternative course is followed by researchers and engineers more attuned to the electrical-engineering discipline of signal processing. They attempt to match the acous-

Left: a reading machine being used in a library. Right: children in classroom using Texas Instrument's Speak and Spell learning instrument.

tic-wave patterns of entire words spoken with well-defined pauses between them. Placing periods of silence between the words means that the machine can more accurately tell when a word begins and ends.

Words spoken in isolation also do not exhibit the changes in the sounds that take place when words are spoken continuously, as in "Did" "You" versus "Dija." A disadvantage is that there are many more words (tens of thousands) than basic sounds (40 to 60 depending on the means of classifying them). Existing computer-memory devices are too expensive and computer processing is too slow to permit matching patterns for such large vocabularies. Isolated-word speech is, moreover, somewhat unnatural and requires concentration on the part of the speaker.

However, machines that recognize isolated words can be built with today's technology. Isolated-word-recognition machines are priced from $10,000 to $80,000. The price

The "Cray I" is the most powerful computer now in use; its hexagonal design has proved exceptionally efficient for interwire hook-ups.

could drop to about $5,000 or less by the end of 1980, a price some market researchers feel is a critical level below which sales could grow significantly.

Adding to the excitement is the fact that there is an advanced device based on an extension of currently available techniques. It is capable of a limited amount of continuous word recognition. It is produced by one of Japan's largest electronics companies, the Nippon Electric Company (NEC).

TECHNIQUES OF MATCHING

Numerous techniques exist for accomplishing the acoustic-wave-pattern matching needed for recognizing words. Nowadays, however, all word-recognition machines make comparisons between sets of variables derived from reference and sample-speech patterns.

Linear-predictive coding (LPC) is the most widespread scheme of this type. It has been developed since the early 1970's by several researchers. Linear-predictive coding is based on a model of the human voice that takes into account such variables as frequency and intensity. A speech sample is electronically divided into segments 10 milliseconds long. Each segment is analyzed by one of numerous possible techniques. The analysis yields the set of LPC variables.

Over the years numerous isolated word-recognition systems have been put together. The best of these can correctly identify words with an accuracy of 98 to 99 per cent in a controlled laboratory setting for vocabularies up to 100 words. Operation in the field, however, is an altogether different matter. Correct identifications can slip to 50 per cent or less.

A good portion of infield error consists of instances in which the machine could not make an identification. It therefore asked for a repeat-speech sample, rather than misidentifying the word, which is a much more serious mistake. Major progress in the field operation of isolated-word-recognition systems is being made, however.

SOURCES OF ERROR

Numerous sources of error exist. In addition to the obvious problem of interference from background noise, machines are exceptionally sensitive to microphone placement. Another problem is the need for "training" the word recognizer. In training, the user must repeat each word in the vocabulary from five to ten times to the machine so that it can generate the reference patterns. If the user changes the way he talks or fails to observe the requirement for a pause between words, the word recognizer can botch an identification.

Another source of difficulty is psychological. People who do not think the word recognizer will work fail invariably to have their speech correctly identified. One story concerns employees whose job was inspecting glass tubes with stringent quality standards. For one or another reason, they were unsympathetic toward or distrusted a word-recognition machine. The machine was to replace a system in which inspection data were manually written down and later entered into a computer by way of punched cards. At first, workers complained they could not make the word recognizer understand them. In desperation, their supervisor spent an evening testing the machine and found little difficulty in being understood. The next day, the supervisor showed the workers how to make the machine understand spoken words and told them if they could not do as well, another job could be found for them. From then on the machine worked without error.

NEW USES

In many of the uses of isolated-word-recognition machines, the word recognizer simply replaces a keyboard terminal or some other input device to a computer. The direction of current activity is finding all-new applications and tailoring the properties of the word recognizers to these new uses.

One company taking this tack is Logicon Incorporated of San Diego, which builds automated training systems of various types. Logicon has put together a prototype air-traffic-controller training system. The unit is to be tested at an air-traffic-controller school in Memphis, Tennessee.

During training, the student sits before a simulated radar screen and is expected to give vocal instructions appropriate to the indicated air-traffic pattern. A computer gen-

© David Sharpe

Workers at Continental Can Company can inspect and sort cans while at the same time reading information into the microphone of a speech-recognition machine.

erates the simulated radar display. The same computer interprets the student's vocal instruction as analyzed by the word recognizer. Then it provides feedback to the student by way of a voice synthesizer. The machine is capable of replacing a human instructor and other support personnel for a considerable portion of the training procedure.

Air-traffic-control terminology is rigidly defined, and a trainee must control his or her speech anyway. Therefore, the limited speech-understanding capability of the isolated-wood-recognition machine is not necessarily a hindrance.

SPEAKER-INDEPENDENT MACHINES

Another direction of current research is to extend the capability of isolated-word-recognition machines. Training the machine requires considerable time and is not at all practical in easily envisioned applications involving the public. One goal is, therefore, to reduce the need for training. What would be desirable is to find universal characteristics of all speech, so that once trained with one or a few speakers, the word recognizer could understand everyone.

Recently, Lawrence Rabiner, Aaron Rosenberg, and Stephen Levinson of Bell Laboratories reported progress toward developing a so-called "speaker-independent" isolated-word recognizer. It is to be used in an automated telephone directory-assistance system.

According to Rabiner, the researchers found that when the speech patterns of a group of 50 men and 50 women were ana-lyzed, most of the patterns divided nicely into from 6 to 12 groups. Within each group there is little difference between the patterns of different individuals. There are large differences between the groups.

The result is that, having reference patterns for each group, the word recognizer can identify speech from a speaker who has not previously provided speech samples to the reference collection. The penalty, which entails much extra computation, is that speech samples must be compared with reference patterns from all 12 groups. At present, the machine can understand digits, letters of the alphabet, and certain control words. It can retrieve the correct phone number about 97 per cent of the time when the questioner spells out the name of the person sought.

CONTINUOUS SPEECH RECOGNITION

A major issue among speech-recognition researchers is how close one can come to recognizing continuous speech without extensive use of techniques involving artificial intelligence. How well can machines recognize continuous speech from only the information contained in the acoustic wave pattern itself? One answer is that given by the NEC machine, which has been praised by many as the new standard in the field.

The machine has a vocabulary of up to 120 words, which are selected by the user during the training of the machine. After being trained, the system is said to be able to identify, with about 98 per cent accuracy in the laboratory, any combination of five words that together do not take more than 2.5 sec-

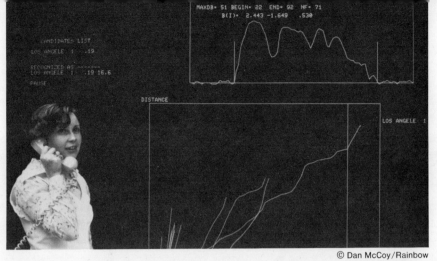

Bell Labs is working on a "speaker-independent" isolated-word recognizer that it hopes to use in an automated telephone directory-assistance system.

onds to say. Response time is a fraction of a second.

A major disappointment to many is the price of the machine, which ranges from $67,000 to $78,000, depending on the number of speech input channels. If the system becomes a big seller, however, the price could plummet. The U.S. Postal Service, for example, has just begun a test of the NEC system in one of its bulk-mail distribution centers. If the test is a success, a major market could open very quickly.

One of the secrets of the NEC speech recognizer is a well-known technique called dynamic programming. In continuous speech, it is difficult to determine from the acoustic wave pattern when one word ends and another begins. This is true in part because there may not be any pause between the words. It is also true because people speak words one way when talking naturally and another when saying words in isolation.

Dynamic programming provides a way of finding word boundaries that do not depend on there being a pause or a break in the acoustic wave pattern. The technique is not a final answer, however, because considerable computation is required, and this limits the size of the vocabulary. According to some estimates, however, 99 per cent of the current types of tasks envisioned for the machine do not require more than a 200-word vocabulary.

MATCHING NUMBER AND VOICE PATTERN

With an obviously bright future ahead for speech recognition, observers argue about what new uses will come forth and how fast. The conservatives talk mainly in terms of expansion of the existing industrial and military uses.

Texas Instruments is working on an advanced version, for the U.S. Air Force, of a speaker-verification system to control access to restricted areas such as its central computer facility. In this system, a speaker orally gives his or her identification number, which the machine checks. If the number is valid, it then compares the speaker's voice pattern with a reference to determine if the speaker is the individual who should have the number given. A similar system, some predict, could be used for automatic financial transactions over the telephone.

Ultimately, the largest markets are in the home. Futurists forecast that eventually such fancies as voice-actuated appliances will be commonplace. One can just imagine: "Television, please turn to Channel 7. 'Wonder Woman' is on tonight and they have this fantastic computer you can talk to" □

SELECTED READINGS

"Communicating with computers by voice" by A. Robinson. *Science,* May 14, 1979.

"Look ma, I'm talking; computerized voice synthesizers." *Time,* May 14, 1979.

"Speech recognition enters the real world; speech is another microelectronics conquest" by A. Robinson. *Science,* February 16, 1979.

"Synthesized speech researcher" by C. Dodge and K. Terry. *Down Beat,* January 12, 1978.

"Synthetic speech from a $50 teaching aid" by W. Hawkins. *Science,* March 1979.

Illustrations by John Huehnergarth

Hard problem: How many of these disparate guests can you invite to the same party?

PROBLEMS TOO HARD
FOR COMPUTERS

by Gina Bari Kolata

A FEW years ago, officials at the Bureau of Fisheries called on Shen Lin at Bell Laboratories. Lin is a computer scientist who works on finding ways to solve a certain kind of problem with which the Bureau was confronted. The Bureau monitors fish populations in the Gulf of Mexico. Each day it chooses some 300 points in the Gulf and then it sends people out in a boat to sample the fish and the currents at each point. The problem was, what is the shortest route the boat can take and still pass each point?

Before coming to Bell Laboratories for advice, the Bureau of Fisheries officials just took a map and drew what they felt was the best route for the boat. This method, they realized, was extremely inefficient. Surely there was a computer program to find the shortest route? Surprisingly, there was no such program. Lin could help the officials to shorten their route by seven to eight per cent. But neither he nor anyone else could be sure of finding the shortest route without spending billions of centuries of computer time.

That inconceivable length of time is even more remarkable in view of the speed at which computers calculate. A medium-fast computer can add one million times faster than a person, and a fast computer can add 1,000 times faster still.

Computers have dramatically expanded mathematicians' horizons, allowing them to make calculations never before dreamed of. But, at the same time, they have made mathematicians recognize the limits of their ability to solve certain types of problems. Within the past decade, mathematicians and computer scientists grouped together hundreds of related problems. These, in principle, can be solved primarily by adding and multiplying. However, even the best methods of solving these problems can require billions upon billions of calculations—enough to keep the computers busy for years, even centuries. The scientists are now learning to live with this impediment. And perhaps they can even exploit it to create a new kind of seemingly unbreakable secret code.

RELATED UNSOLVABLE PROBLEMS

These simple, but possibly unsolvable, problems are not new. Many have been around for decades. And they crop up in many practical situations. But until 1971 mathematicians and computer scientists did not realize the problems were related. Then, Stephen Cook of the University of Toronto made a discovery. He found that several of these problems were equivalent. This means that if anyone could find a shortcut to solving one of them, the shortcut could be adapted to solve the others.

Previously, mathematicians had been looking at each problem separately, hoping somehow to find a way to solve it in a feasible length of computer time. But Cook's discovery systematized the study of these problems. Shortly afterwards, Richard Karp of the University of California at Berkeley greatly extended the list of equivalent problems. Then a scramble began in the scientific community to find which problems were equivalent to these hard ones. So far, hundreds have been added and more are under consideration.

A HARD PROBLEM BY ANY OTHER NAME

The name given to such problems is "NP-complete" (NP stands for nondeterministic polynomial). This is a technical term in obscure language having meaning chiefly for mathematicians and computer scientists. But a layperson might find it convenient to

think of them simply as "hard" problems.

What sorts of problems are classified as "hard?" One example is the traveling-salesman problem: a salesman wants to plan a tour of a number of cities so that he visits each city only once and wants to find the shortest possible route. This problem turns up in numerous guises in practical situations—such as the Bureau of Fisheries problem. The telephone company must solve a traveling-salesman problem when it plans collections from payphone booths. As Lin explains, the telephone company divides each city into zones. Each zone contains several hundred coin boxes. The company supervisors must decide the best order to collect coins from the phones in each zone.

Another hard problem is the bin-packing problem: Suppose there are a given number of identical bins and a group of odd-shaped packages. What is the minimum number of bins necessary so that each package is in a bin, and none of the bins overflows? It is a bin-packing problem to decide how to schedule television commercials to fit in one-minute time slots. It is also a bin-packing problem to find out how to cut up the minimum number of standard-length boards to produce pieces of particular lengths.

A hard problem of another kind is what mathematicians call a "maximum-independent-set" problem—but which can be more

No one has proved the polynomial-time method doesn't exist, so scientists go on pursuing it.

easily understood as a "party problem." One homely example: pick from a group of potential guests, some of whom are incompatible, the largest number of guests you can expect to get along with one another at a party.

TRIAL AND ERROR

The only general method of solving these hard problems is to try out all possible solutions until you find the best one. For small problems, this isn't too hard. If a salesman had to visit only four cities, he could plan his tour himself with just a pencil and paper by considering all 24 possibilities.

But if the salesman had to visit ten cities, it would be considerably harder to try out all routes, because there would be more than 3,500,000 of them. The task is, however, well within the capabilities of a computer. But if a salesman had to visit 18 cities, and he had a computer that could test one million routes per second, it would take the computer about 4,000 years to try all possible routes. If the salesman had to visit 60 cities, it would take a computer billions of centuries to try out all the routes.

Why does it take so long to try out all possible solutions to a hard problem? The reason is that the number of possible solutions increases explosively (or, as mathematicians say, "exponentially") as the size of the problem grows. In a bin-packing problem, for example, this rate of increase is found by multiplying a certain fixed number by itself each time you add another object to be packed. The fixed number equals the number of bins. The number of multiplication steps required varies with the number of objects. Thus, if you have two bins and two objects, the number of possible solutions is four (2×2); with three objects, there are eight possible solutions ($2 \times 2 \times 2$). Each object you add multiplies the number of possible solutions.

In a bin-packing problem of this kind, computer scientists have calculated that with ten objects, the possible solutions could be tried in 1/1000 of a second. With 20 objects, trying all the solutions would take about one second, with 30 objects, about 18 minutes would be needed; and with 100 objects to pack, trying all the possible solutions would take more than 400,000 billion centuries. (By contrast, the entire universe is only about ten billion years old.)

Obviously, exponential-time methods are out of the question for large problems. What mathematicians really want to find is a "polynomial time" method. This would require dramatically less computer time. (A supermarket's computer checkout system, tabulating the day's sales, use polynomial time.) Suppose, for example, a polynomial-time method could be found for a typical bin-packing problem with two bins. Then the number of possible solutions would be equal to the number of objects multiplied by itself—*but just once.* With ten objects, a polynomial-time method would entail only 100 (10×10) possibilities, rather than the 1,024 ($2 \times 2 \times 2 \ldots$ 10 times) of an exponential method.

Computer scientists calculate that a problem that would take billions of centuries to solve by an exponential method might be solved in a matter of seconds if a polynomial method were found. Although no one has

Mathematicians may have inadvertently hit on a new source of unbreakable secret codes.

The bin-packing problem: how to fit odd-shaped packages into the fewest bins.

ever found a polynomial-time method of solving a hard problem, some scientists have not yet given up hope that someday they may discover one. They retain this glimmer of hope because no one has yet been able to prove that there is no such method.

HOPELESS PROBLEMS

Some problems, in contrast, are provably hopeless. Certain kinds of theorem-proving procedures and some kinds of games provably require exponential time. The reason for this is because the computer must go through incalculably long trial-and-error procedures to try to find the best answer.

Mathematicians also suspect that computers will probably never play perfect chess because these computer programs, too, may require exponential time. Of course com-

puters don't have to play perfect chess to be impressive—they just have to play better than most humans. Scientists have devised programs that enable computers to play very well, and they're getting better all the time.

In short, it remains a frustration and a mystery to mathematicians that they cannot prove that hard problems are hard. Some mathematical logicians speculate that the internal logic of mathematics prevents people from proving anything about these methods. But the logicians have been unable to decide whether their speculation is correct.

It may seem as if the mathematicians have come to an impasse. However, they are learning to live with their inability to find shortcuts to solving the hard problems. Furthermore, they are learning to work around or even to exploit this impediment.

Because the hard problems are of such practical importance, many mathematicians and computer scientists are developing methods that work well, on the average. But there is no guarantee that they will work for every possible problem. Nor is it certain that the solution arrived at is always the best possible one.

An example of the kinds of methods being developed for approximate solution of these problems is one devised by Ronald Graham, Michael Garey, and David Johnson of Bell Laboratories, Murray Hill, New Jersey. They studied ways to solve the bin-packing problem. From this they showed that a method, which they call "first-fit-decreasing," always gives an answer within 22 per cent of the best solution. The "first-fit-decreasing" method involves ordering the packages according to size, largest first, and then putting each package, in succession, into the first bin in which it fits.

SECRET CODES A SPIN-OFF

Perhaps the most exciting spin-off from the discovery of hard problems is the idea of using them as the basis of a new kind of secret code. Such a code was first suggested a few years ago by Whitfield Diffie, Martin Hellman, and Ralph Merkle of Stanford University. The reason the code may be unbreakable is that an eavesdropper trying to decipher a message would have to solve a hard problem to do so.

Computer crime has burgeoned, costing American business $300 million a year. There is an example of how easy it can be to commit a computer crime. A man called the Federal Reserve Bank in Minneapolis and identified himself as Michael Charles, Midwestern banker. Having illegally obtained the day's code word, he arranged a computer transfer of $16,255 from a South Dakota bank to one in Atlanta. It was six months before Charles was discovered.

A computer might have to work longer than the universe has existed to solve some hard problems using the exponential-time method.

International and industrial spies can easily steal a computer's secrets if they are not carefully encoded.

The new codes, then, have come at a perfect time. Suddenly a computer-security industry has cropped up. Traditionally, secure codes have been the province of the military and intelligence agencies, but academic scientists are beginning to take an interest in developing sophisticated codes for private and commercial use.

Diffie and Hellman's idea for designing codes is to base the codes on well-studied mathematical procedures that are easy to compute. Then once the computations are done, the procedures are impossible to reverse without some secret information. To encode a message, a person would use the easily computed procedure. But any electronic eavesdropper trying to reverse the procedure to decode would have to know the secret information. Or the eavesdropper would have to carry out computations that could take centuries.

The hard problems seem to offer a wealth of procedures on which to base these codes. For example, Merkle and Hellman have designed a coding system based on the bin-packing problem. This involved deciding which of a large collection of numbers adds up to a particular sum. It is easy, of course, to add up any group of numbers from the collection. But it is a hard problem to reverse that procedure unless you know how the numbers were chosen to add up.

Although it is too soon to say whether the new codes based on hard problems will turn out to be practical, they are extremely promising. Of course, if someone were suddenly to discover a polynomial-time method for solving a hard problem, any codes based on these problems might be easily broken. But most experts think that such a discovery will be a long time coming, if it comes at all ☐

 SELECTED READINGS

"Mathematicians Amazed by Russian's Discovery" by Gina Bari Kolata. *Science,* November 2, 1979.

A home-computer store. You can write BASIC programs for these computers.

BASIC

by Edwin R. Sage

TO many people, computers are the most powerful instruments of the 20th century. Once the province of scientists, engineers, and systems analysts, they are now being used in homes by high-school students as well as their parents.

A computer, though, is completely useless without a program—a set of instructions that tell it what to do. This applies to any computer, from a sophisticated IBM to a small, personal home computer (micro-computer).

Because computer programs are like languages, they are often called "programming languages." There are several programming languages in use today, but for those who own, or plan to own, a home computer, there is one programming language that surpasses them all. It is called BASIC.

See Acknowledgments, page iii.

(For *B*eginner's *A*ll-Purpose *S*ymbolic *I*nstruction *C*ode.)

BASIC is the most widely used programming language among home computers. It's not hard to see why. It was designed primarily as an educational tool, and it is very easy to master.

In this article we are going to learn the first steps in BASIC. There's a lot more to BASIC, of course, but you should be able to master the language easily once you learn the fundamental steps.

A GOOD START

A good beginning toward getting acquainted with your computer is to get it to add, subtract, multiply, and divide numbers for you.

To start, we shall write a series of instructions that will cause the computer to find the value of:

$$3+2, \quad 3-2, \quad 3 \cdot 2, \quad 3 \div 2$$
$$4+3, \quad 4-3, \quad 4 \cdot 3, \quad 4 \div 3$$
$$8+3, \quad 8-3, \quad 8 \cdot 3, \quad 8 \div 3$$

These twelve problems are, of course, entirely too trivial to do on a computer. In fact, they're very easy to do by hand. The numbers are small and the operations are simple. We begin with small numbers, however, to concentrate your attention on the operations. First, do the twelve simple computations "by hand" and write your answers on a sheet of paper. Later on we'll compare your results with the computer's. Let's return now to the job of writing a set of instructions for the computer.

You are probably aware that computers are built to add, subtract, multiply, and divide. Your first task is to learn how to communicate with the computer so that it performs these operations when you want it to. To do this we will use the following symbols: + for addition, − for subtraction, ∗ for multiplication (∗ will be referred to as a star), and / (slash) for division. The computer has been programmed to accept only these symbols for the respective operations. Hence, you must be precise and learn the symbol to use for the operation you want the computer to perform.

ADDING NUMBERS

Now that we know how to designate to the computer the operation to be performed, the next task is to invent some method whereby we cause the computer to perform the operation. For example, if you want the computer to add 3 and 2, you indicate operation by +. You write 3+2. But the computer will not perform this task until you give it an order to execute the operation. One of the following English words will tell the computer to find the sum of 3 and 2. (Note that all the command words are printed in upper case letters. This is because on the video screen, all letters of the alphabet are shown in upper case.)

1. DO
2. COMPUTE
3. LET
4. FIND

Actually any of the above words could be used, as long as the computer was given the meaning of the word. In the BASIC language, the computer language you are learning, the word LET is used.

This does not mean, however, that we would write:

LET 3+2

This is not a sentence. BASIC is a language for you to use in expressing your thoughts to the computer, and LET 3+2 does not express a complete thought. The next step is to learn how to complete a simple sentence beginning with the word LET.

A suitable simple sentence would be LET S=3+2, where we understand that S is a variable which holds a place for the answer to 3+2. Why use S? S reminds us that we are finding the sum. It is easier to remember what the variable is if we select a letter that is suggestive of what the variable represents.

Most home computers include a cassette recorder for data storage.

Courtesy of Heath Co.

Now if we follow LET with symbols that make a simple sentence we have:

$$LET\ S = 3+2$$

This is called a command. How does the computer react to this command? It does the following:

1. First, the computer finds the value of 3+2, which is 5.
2. Next, S is assigned the value of 5.
3. Finally, the computer stores the value of S in its memory.

Memory? Let's talk about a computer's memory. It will help if you imagine that a computer's memory looks like a set of post office boxes at the local post office. So when we say that the computer stores 5 for the value of S, we can visualize that the computer selects one of these mail boxes, assigns S as the label of the box, and then puts the value of 5 in the box. There the value of 5 remains until the computer is instructed to do something with the value of S. Therefore, our imagination tells us that the space allocated for data storage in a computer's memory looks like:

labels	S			
values	5			
labels				
values				
labels				
values				

All the other boxes remain nameless and obviously have no values stored in them.

Our next task is to cause the computer to take the value of S stored in memory and to print it on the video screen. Which of the following would cause the computer to tell us the answer?

1. WRITE
2. TELL
3. PRINT
4. TYPE

PRINTING THE ANSWER

While any of the above words might have been used, in BASIC we only use PRINT. Thus, PRINT S instructs the computer to go to memory, find the memory cell labeled S, make a carbon copy of the value stored in S, and then print this value on the paper.

Notice that the actual value of S is not removed from the memory location labeled S. Only a carbon copy of the value is made and transmitted by the computer to the terminal. The box in memory labeled S still contains the number 5 in case we might want to use it again. We say that the computer has non-destructive read-out. Values of variables can be read out of memory without destroying or changing them. Now back to writing a series of instructions to get the sum of 3 plus 2.

Which of the following set of instructions would get the job done?

SET 1:   PRINT   S
             LET   S = 3 + 2

SET 2:   LET   S = 3 + 2
             PRINT   S

Either will work if the computer understands that it is to execute the LET statement first. Let's examine the statements:

PRINT   S
LET   S = 3+2

Imagine walking into a room and having a person in the room ask you to tell him the value of S. You couldn't answer his question. It is meaningless since you do not know what S is. The computer acts in the same manner. At the time we turn on the computer, the computer's memory contains no labels or values.

If we instruct the computer to PRINT S, what happens? There is as yet no box labeled S, no value for S. Hence the command PRINT S cannot be executed. However, if we first say LET S = 3+2 and then say PRINT S the job can be done. Remember, LET S = 3+2 instructs the computer to find the value of 3+2 and store this in the box labeled S. After that has been done, then the command to PRINT S can be executed.

So that the computer knows the exact sequence in which to execute a set of steps, we number each statement. In a set of two statements, the statement to be done first is given the lower of the two numbers. Statement numbers in BASIC may be any integer between 1 and 99,999. Thus, we might write:

10 LET S = 3 + 2		1 LET S = 3 + 2
	or	
20 PRINT S		2 PRINT S

uate twelve expressions. This program handles only one. More commands are needed. The other three problems which go with this one are 3−2, 3∗2, and 3÷2. We will use the variable D to hold a place for the difference, P for the product, and Q for the quotient.

DIFFERENT PROGRAMS

Several decisions have to be made before we can complete the program. Do we want *all* the computations performed, the values stored, and then all the answers printed? Or do we want *each* answer to be printed after it is computed and stored? With this set of problems, it makes no difference which route we choose, but we must make a selection. Let's do it both ways.

By the end of the 1980's, most homes in the United States, it is believed, will have personal computers.

The first method of numbering is more desirable and provides for more flexibility than the second. For if you desire, you may enter additional steps between 10 and 20 simply by using any integer between 10 and 20. With the second method there is no possibility of inserting steps between 1 and 2 without changing these numbers.

Is our program

10 LET S = 3 + 2
20 PRINT   S

containing just two statements complete? Recall that the original problem was to eval-

PROGRAM 1	PROGRAM 2
10 LET S = 3 + 2	10 LET S = 3 + 2
11 LET D = 3 − 2	20 PRINT S
12 LET P = 3 ∗ 2	30 LET D = 3 − 2
13 LET Q = 3 / 2	40 PRINT D
20 PRINT S	50 LET P = 3 ∗ 2
21 PRINT D	60 PRINT P
22 PRINT P	70 LET Q = 3 / 2
23 PRINT Q	80 PRINT Q

If we wanted to do only one computation at a time and then print the result we would write Program 2.

The end result is the same for both sets of instructions. Both are correct programs. A

Courtesy Apple

BASIC programs for special purposes, such as home finance, are now available.

good axiom to remember is that if a program does the job, it's right.

Let's return to program 1 for a minute to see if a better, shorter, or more elegant way exists to get the same job done. Look at the four PRINT statements:

```
20 PRINT S
21 PRINT D
22 PRINT P
23 PRINT Q
```

With this program, the value of S is printed on one line, the value of D on the next, and so on. The use of four separate lines is not as bothersome as the fact that in entering the program we have to type four different PRINT statements. Is there a better way? Yes, we can write one compound statement:

```
20 PRINT S, D, P, Q
```

This one command takes the place of steps 20–23 in program 1. What does the computer do with this command? Whenever the computer sees the command PRINT followed by a string of variables *separated by*

commas, the computer always envisions the video screen as being divided into five imaginary columns. Thus, in the first column the value of S is printed; in the second column the value of D is printed; in the third column the value of P is printed; in the fourth column the value of Q is printed; and in the fifth column no value is printed since a fifth variable is not specified in PRINT S, D, P, Q. Hence, the output would look like this:

5   1   6   1.5

With this new information program 1 can be shortened from eight instructions to just five:

```
10 LET S = 3 + 2
11 LET D = 3 − 2
12 LET P = 3 * 2
13 LET Q = 3 / 2
20 PRINT S, D, P, Q
```

Unfortunately we cannot shorten program 2 since we wanted each value to be printed immediately after it was computed and stored. These two examples make it clear that one route, or one way to look at a problem, may in fact be better than another.

Courtesy Radio Shack

Many junior and senior high schools now have computer courses.

Can the program be refined more? Yes. Suppose we write:

10 PRINT 3+2

How does the computer interpret this command? The computer operates as follows:

1. First it finds the value of 3+2;
2. Secondly, it prints this value.

Notice that no mention is made of storing a value at S. In fact there is no mention of S. The value of 3+2 is printed immediately after it is computed and *not stored*. This seems reasonable; for how can the computer store a value without a label? The computer can only store values if each value is associated with a variable. We can now rewrite program 1 as:

10 PRINT 3 + 2
11 PRINT 3 − 2
12 PRINT 3 * 2
13 PRINT 3 / 2

Program 1 is thereby shortened from five commands to four.

THE SHORTEST PROGRAM

What can we do now? Here is the shortest possible form of program 1:

10 PRINT 3 + 2, 3 − 2, 3 * 2, 3/2

Once again the PRINT command instructs the computer to compute each value and print that value in the appropriate column. Look back to the problem on page 105. Does program 1 handle the entire problem? No. To solve the remaining problems, we add steps 20 and 30 to obtain:

10 PRINT 3 + 2, 3 − 2, 3 * 2, 3/2
20 PRINT 4 + 3, 4 − 3, 4 * 3, 4/3
30 PRINT 8 + 3, 8 − 3, 8 * 3, 8/3

Only one step remains. We know the problem is complete after step 30, but does the computer know it? No, it has to be told by using one of the following words:

1. STOP
2. END
3. DONE
4. FINI

In the BASIC language we use the word END to indicate that there are no more steps to be executed. Thus, in program 1 the last step is written:

40 END

Here is our complete program now:

10 PRINT 3 + 2, 3 − 2, 3 * 2, 3/2
20 PRINT 4 + 3, 4 − 3, 4 * 3, 4/3
30 PRINT 8 + 3, 8 − 3, 8 * 3, 8/3
40 END

This program is now ready to be entered into a computer.

EXECUTING THE PROGRAM

Let's enter the program into the computer via the keyboard and have the computer execute the program. Below is a copy of the program and the output from the computer.

PROGRAM

10 PRINT 3 + 2, 3 − 2, 3 * 2, 3/2
20 PRINT 4 + 3, 4 − 3, 4 * 3, 4/3
30 PRINT 8 + 3, 8 − 3, 8 * 3, 8/3
40 END

OUTPUT

5	1	6	1.5
7	1	12	1.33333
11	5	24	2.66667

Notice that the computer gives the answers to 3 ÷ 2, 4 ÷ 3, and 8 ÷ 3 as decimal values. The number of significant figures in the answer and whether it is rounded off or cut off depends upon the computer you're using. Let's demonstrate with $2/3 = .666666....$ If we round off 2/3 correctly to six significant figures we have .666667 as the answer. However, if after the first six 6's we just chop off the rest we have .666666. The latter way of obtaining the answer is known as truncation. Look at the printout above. Does this particular computer round off its answers or truncate them? It rounds them off to six significant figures.

In the process of arriving at our final program we gained a better feeling and understanding of how a computer works. In addition we learned how to use three BASIC words:

1. LET instructs the computer to perform a calculation and then store the result in memory with a label attached to the box.

Example: LET S = 3 + 2 causes the computer to calculate 3 + 2 and store the result, 5, in the box labeled S.

2. PRINT can be used to do one of two things:

A. First, PRINT will print the value of a variable specified after the word PRINT.

Example: PRINT S causes the computer to go to memory, find the cell labeled S, copy the value in that cell, and print it.

B. Secondly, PRINT will evaluate an expression and immediately print its value without storing anything.

Example: PRINT 3 + 2 causes the computer to add 3 and 2 and print the result.

3. END is used as the last statement in a program to indicate that there are no more steps in the program.

ANOTHER PROBLEM

Now let's write a program that will find the sum, difference, product, and quotient of any two numbers. This problem is similar to the first problem. In that problem, however, we knew exactly what numbers were to be used before we wrote our program. Now the task is to write a sequence of instructions that will allow us to specify the numbers we want to use at the time the computer executes the program. To do this we will use variable names to hold places for our numbers. A will represent the first number and B the second. Here are the data for this problem. (They are the same numbers we used in the first problem.)

A	B
3	2
4	3
8	3

Courtesy IMSAI

Keyboard and video terminals are the input and output of a home computer.

If you do the actual computations, your results will look like the ones in the following table:

A	B	SUM	DIFFERENCE	PRODUCT	QUOTIENT
3	2	5	1	6	1.5
4	3	7	1	12	1.333333
8	3	11	5	24	2.66667

"INPUT" AND "GO TO"

Now our task is to write an instruction in a language acceptable to the computer. BASIC uses the word INPUT to get the values for A and B. We therefore write:

10 INPUT A, B

What exactly does the computer do when it executes this command? First, upon seeing the word INPUT, the computer prints a question mark (?) on the screen and stops. What action do you take in response to the ? . You know that two values are to be supplied, the first one being for A and the second for B. So your reply to the ? is to type in 3, then a comma, then 2, and then press the return key. The commas are used to separate the values; the pressing of the return key indicates that you have no more values to supply.

What has been going on in the computer's memory? When the computer sees

INPUT A, B

it realizes that two values will be given it from the person operating the keyboard.

Therefore the computer sets aside two mail boxes and labels them A and B. Graphically, the memory might be represented like this:

Label	A	B
Value		

When (in response to the question mark) we supply 3 as the first value and 2 as the second value, the computer stores 3 in the box labeled "A" and 2 in "B." Now the memory looks like this.

Label	A	B
Value	3	2

Since the computer now has values for A and B, it can perform the operations. From the first problem, we know that the computer understands four operations, addition, subtraction, multiplication, and division, if we use the appropriate symbols. Our next step in the program would be:

20 LET S = A + B

How does the computer interpret this? Here is what happens:

1. The computer goes into memory and finds the boxes labeled A and B.

2. A carbon copy of the values in A and B is made.

3. These two values are added.

4. The result is stored in the box labeled S.

After step 20 is completed, memory looks like this:

LABEL	A	B	S
VALUE	3	2	5

Now let's translate the next three flow chart instructions into computer language. We write:

$$30 \text{ LET } D = A - B$$
$$40 \text{ LET } P = A * B$$
$$50 \text{ LET } Q = A / B$$

You can talk directly, and give orders, to these late-model home computers.

After step 50 is completed, memory looks like this:

LABEL	A	B	S	D	P	Q
VALUE	3	2	5	1	6	1.5

The next step is to print the answers. We write:

$$60 \text{ PRINT } S, D, P, Q$$

After the print statement we want the computer to shift its attention immediately to step 10. That is, we want the computer to go back and start over with step 10. We enter:

$$70 \text{ GO TO } 10$$

STARTING OVER

Now we are back at the beginning of the program. The computer confronts us with another question mark. We reply by entering 4, 3. Since the first number typed is a value of A, the computer places the value 4 in the box labeled A. (The value 3, which was occupying the box, is destroyed.) Likewise, the computer enters the value 3 in box B. (The value 2 is removed.) Thus, when the com-

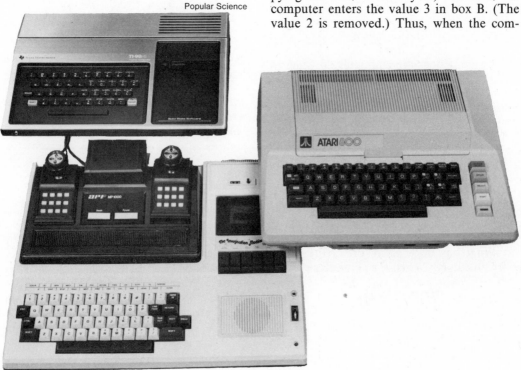

puter enters a new value in memory, it first looks to see if a box exists which has the same label as the new value. If such a box does exist, the new value goes into that box and destroys the old value. If a box with the label doesn't exist, the computer finds a spare box and puts the new value there. Now, after the second execution of step 10, memory looks like this:

A	B	S	D	P	Q
4	3	5	1	6	1.5

Compare this picture of memory with the picture taken following step 50. Have the values of S, D, P, and Q changed? No, in step 10 only the values of A and B were changed. When steps 20–50 are executed, new values will be placed in the boxes labeled S, D, P, and Q.

The complete program is:

PROGRAM

```
10 INPUT A,B
20 LET S=A+B
30 LET D=A−B
40 LET P=A*B
50 LET Q=A/B
60 PRINT S,D,P,Q
70 GO TO 10
80 END
```

Here is the output of the program, as printed on the screen:

OUTPUT

```
?3,2
  5        1      6       1.5
?4,3
  7        1     12       1.33333
?8,3
 11        5     24       2.66667
?STOP
```

In this particular example we want to compute results for only three sets of A and B values. What do we do when the question mark appears for the fourth time? There must be some way of telling the computer

Dartmouth Press Office

BASIC was developed under the direction of John J. Kemeny, Dartmouth College former president.

A BASIC program, recorded on a cassette, is inserted into the computer.

Popular Science

that we do not wish to input any more values, and to stop the execution of the program. The procedure depends on the type of computer used. With this computer we type the word STOP, and press the return key.

As in the first problem, another program can be written which involves fewer steps. Remember that we can use the PRINT statement to perform a computation and print the result. Here is the shorter program:

PROGRAM

```
10 INPUT A,B
20 PRINT A+B,A−B,A*B,A/B
30 GO TO 10
40 END
```

OUTPUT

```
?3,2
  5          1      6      1.5
?4,3
  7          1      12     1.33333
?8,3
  11         5      24     2.66667
?STOP
```

Both programs produce the same output, but the second one involves less typing and does not require the computer to go through the process of storing values and then retrieving them later. The second program is the better of the two.

Let's add one more frill to our second program. Look at the output. Unless you know the program, it might not be clear which number is the sum, which the difference, and so on. The print statement may be used to have labels printed. If you want labels or messages printed, use the command PRINT followed by the labels enclosed in quotation marks. The quotation marks signal the computer to print all the characters exactly as they appear between the pair of quotation marks. Notice that the print statement is inserted between steps 10 and 20. Thus, as soon as you finish entering a set of values in response to the question mark, column headings will be printed as shown below.

PROGRAM

```
10 INPUT A,B
15 PRINT "SUM","DIFFERENCE","PRODUCT","QUOTIENT"
20 PRINT A+B,A−B,A*B,A/B
30 GO TO 10
40 END
```

OUTPUT

```
?3,2
SUM          DIFFERENCE      PRODUCT      QUOTIENT
  5          1               6            1.5
?4,3
SUM          DIFFERENCE      PRODUCT      QUOTIENT
  7          1               12           1.33333
?8,3
SUM          DIFFERENCE      PRODUCT      QUOTIENT
  11         5               24           2.66667
?STOP
```

If you want column headings printed only once, insert the print statement as step 5 instead of as step 15.

```
PROGRAM

 5 PRINT "SUM","DIFFERENCE","PRODUCT","QUOTIENT"
10 INPUT A,B
20 PRINT A+B,A−B,A∗B,A/B
30 GO TO 10
40 END
```

OUTPUT

SUM	DIFFERENCE	PRODUCT	QUOTIENT
?3,2			
5	1	6	1.5
?4,3			
7	1	12	1.33333
?8,3			
11	5	24	2.66667
?STOP			

A modem, shown here, allows your computer to communicate with other computers over telephone lines.

Courtesy of Heath Co.

MORE BASIC COMMANDS

So far we have learned the meaning of five different BASIC words: INPUT, LET, PRINT, GO TO, END. Let's learn how to use two more. Suppose that we have the following 10 sets of values for A and B:

A	9	6	7	9	10	4	7	13	5	8
B	8	4	8	3	8	6	9	13	7	2

There is an easier way to tell the computer the values of A and B than sitting at the keyboard and typing in a set of numbers each time we see a question mark. The answer to our problem is the READ statement.

READ indicates to the computer that the values for A and B are to be found in the program. When it encounters a READ statement, the computer automatically looks for a line beginning with the word DATA. The

word DATA is followed by the values, each value separated from the next by a comma. To gain this advantage we change step 10 from

10 INPUT A, B to 10 READ A, B

and we add a new step:

35 DATA 9, 8, 6, 4, 7, 8, 9, 3, 10,
    8, 4, 6, 7, 9, 13, 13, 5, 7, 8, 2

Notice what happens when the program runs. (Remember that steps 10 and 35 are working as a team. If we have a READ statement in a program, we must have a DATA line.) The first time through A = 9, B = 8; the next time A = 6, B = 4. The computer is smart enough to keep track of where it is in the DATA line at any given moment (all together ten pairs of numbers).

On the eleventh pass through the program the computer will realize that all the numbers have been used and it will type "OUT OF DATA IN 10" and stop. A final remark about the use of the DATA command: since the DATA line holds only information to be read by the READ statement, the DATA line may be placed *anywhere* in a program prior to the END statement. Let's enter this program and look at the output.

```
PROGRAM

  5 PRINT "SUM","DIFFERENCE","PRODUCT","QUOTIENT"
 10 READ A,B
 20 PRINT A+B,A−B,A∗B,A/B
 30 GO TO 10
 35 DATA 9,8,6,4,7,8,9,3,10,8,4,6,7,9,13,13,5,7,8,2
 40 END

OUTPUT
```

SUM	DIFFERENCE	PRODUCT	QUOTIENT
17	1	72	1.125
10	2	24	1.5
15	−1	56	.875
12	6	27	3
18	2	80	1.25
10	−2	24	.666667
16	−2	63	.777778
26	0	169	1
12	−2	35	.714286
10	6	16	4

OUT OF DATA IN 10

The execution of a program is faster if a READ statement is used to input data, so READ should be used whenever possible instead of INPUT.

That's it. With these seven commands, you have a good introduction to BASIC. There are several more BASIC words you can learn, of course, but with almost any good book on the subject you can master the most popular computer language in the world □

 SELECTED READINGS

Problem-Solving with the Computer by Edwin R. Sage. Entelek Incorporated, Ward-Whidden House, Portsmouth, N.H., 1969.
Illustrating BASIC by Donald Alcock. Cambridge University Press, 1977.
The Little Book of BASIC Style by John Nevison. Addison-Wesley, 1978.

Lorenz for Datamation

"I don't know what you guys see in these computers…"

Woods Hole Oceanographic Institution's submersible ALVIN is one of several sophisticated research ships now exploring, sampling, and photographing the ocean floor.

EARTH SCIENCE

EARTH SCIENCES
REVIEW OF THE YEAR

Wide World

After being dormant for more than a century, Mount St. Helens in Washington erupted in early 1980—in March spewing smoke and ash, as shown here, and on May 18 exploding violently.

Earth Structure and Climate. Traditional theory holds that the earth has a solid core, a mantle, and an outer crust. New evidence now suggests that the mantle may be composed of two layers. The new theory is based on analyses of continental and ocean-bottom lavas. It holds that an unaltered, primordial, and unmelted lower mantle layer, at depths of 600 to 1,000 meters, is the source of continental lavas and that an upper layer of nearly molten material is the source of mid-ocean lavas. If confirmed, the theory may shed light on crust formation and movement.

Ice Ages—what causes these periodic episodes in earth history? Recent evidence seems to confirm a theory proposed in the 1930s by the Serbian geophysicist M. Milankobitch that ice ages are the result of regular, subtle changes in earth orbit. The orbit changes, which occur in 23,000, 41,000, 93,000, and 413,000 year cycles, have been correlated with sediment evidence of climatic changes occurring at the same time.

Earthquakes and Seismology. Six major earthquakes occurred during 1979. A major earthquake is rated as having a magnitude of 7 or higher on the Richter scale. The largest of the year—8.1 on the Richter scale—occurred near the sparsely populated island of Yapen in Cendrawash Gulf on the northern coast of Irian Jayan in western New Guinea. Fifteen people were killed and many injured. Additional damage was done by a resulting tsunami, or seismic sea wave, that struck the islands of Biak and Yapen. ■ A 7.75-magnitude earthquake hit central Mexico on March 14, leaving three dead, many injured, and more than 1,000 villagers homeless. Flooding and structural damage caused millions of dollars of damage in Mexico City.

Chinese scientists finally released details of the Tangshan earthquake of July 28, 1976—a quake many seismologists believe was the greatest earthquake disaster in recorded human history. Measuring 7.8 on the Richter, it devastated 52 square kilometers and killed 750,000 people.

Research on earthquake prediction continued throughout the year. Increasing attention was given to the pre-quake behavior of animals as precursors of quake activity. The relationship of earth tides—deformations of the earth caused by the pull of the sun and moon—to quakes and volcanic eruptions was also investigated. ■ Efforts were also made to identify earthquake-prone areas. A fault, or crack in the earth's crust, was discovered in Arkansas. It may explain the quakes that hit the New Madrid, Missouri, area in 1811–1812 and marks the junction area of Missouri, Kentucky, Tennessee, and Arkansas as possibly prone to seismic activity. Meanwhile the Palmdale Bulge received more attention. This southern California area astride the San Andreas fault was thought to have bulged vertically in recent years as a result of stress buildup in underlying rocks. New evidence questions the vertical bulge but reveals that the area has stretched horizontally—and at a rate that surprises many geologists.

A 7.75-magnitude quake hit central Mexico in March 1979, causing widespread damage, including these crushed autos in a downtown Mexico City parking lot.

Wide World

Volcanology. In early 1980 Mount St. Helens in southern Washington exploded—after more than a century of dormancy. In March the snow-covered mountain slopes began to shake with localized earthquakes that geologists said indicated the volcano's reservoir was filling with molten material. On March 27 the volcano began spewing forth ash and steam. On May 18 the volcano erupted, releasing a pillar of ash, pumice, and steam. Resultant mudslides and floods caused several deaths. The volcanic cloud spread eastward. reducing visibility and threatening water supplies, agricultural products, and health. (For more on Mount St. Helens, see the article beginning on page 136.)

The eruption of Soufrière Volcano on the West Indian island of St. Vincent—starting on April 13 and continuing for six months—was one of the best documented eruptions in history. An orbiting weather satellite studied the eruption cloud and air-borne instruments analyzed other aspects of the eruption. Other major volcanic eruptions during 1979 included the February eruption of Java's Djieng volcano complex, killing 149; the September eruption of Aso Volcano in Japan, killing three; and the August and September eruptions of Italy's Mt. Etna, which killed nine.

In recent years two geological theories have become widely accepted. One, the theory of plate tectonics, holds that the earth's crust is composed of large plates that move about and collide, carrying the landmasses with them. The other, the hot-spot theory, holds that there are fixed warm areas on the earth's crust where magma, or hot molten rock, may well up from beneath the crust, causing crustal movements. The relationship of these two theories to volcanism was investigated during 1979—in Iceland where plate movement is thought to be occurring, and beneath the Rio Grande Rift in New Mexico where geophysicists are trying to locate chambers of magma. (For more on plate tectonics, see the article "Plate Tectonics," which begins on page 145.)

Paleontology. Paleontologists have long tried to explain why a mass extinction of hundreds of species, including dinosaurs, occurred some 65,-000,000 years ago. Now two more theories have been proposed. Walter Alvarez, a University of California at Berkeley researcher, has found a sudden jump in the amount of iridium in 65,000,000-year-old rocks. Iridium is much more abundant in extraterrestrial material than in the earth's crust. Alvarez suggests that an extraterrestrial source—perhaps a solar flare, a meteorite, or supernova—may have caused the increase and that animals could not adapt to the change. Meanwhile Stefan Gartner of Texas A&M University proposes that a spillover of the once-isolated freshwater Arctic Ocean into the world's salt-water oceans reduced their salinity, killing susceptible marine species, and altering the earth's climate enough to kill some land-dwelling animals.

Dinosaur studies also continued. Teeth discovered in Alberta, Canada, confirm long-standing ideas that dinosaurs were cold-blooded. The teeth have annual growth rings. Growth rings are common in cold-blooded animals that become sluggish in the cold season. The fossils are from 65,-000,000 to 75,000,000 years old and represent both herbivorous and carnivorous species. ■ The only whole dinosaur eggs known in North America were found in north-central Montana. Bones found with the eggs suggest that the dinosaurs may have been carnivores. If so, these would be the first eggs of meat-eating dinosaurs yet discovered.

Older fossils were also discovered. In July 1979 Chinese geologists reported the discovery, in Hubei province in east central China, of more than 100 species of marine fossils estimated to be about 1,900,000,000 years old. ■ And scientists at the University of Maryland believe that they have found "molecular fossils" made of hydrocarbons in western Greenland. The specimens were found in granitelike rocks believed to be about 3,800,000,000 years old.

William H. Matthews III

Texas A & M

Stefan Gartner thinks that a spillover of the once-isolated freshwater Arctic Ocean led to the mass extinction of many species some 65,000,000 years ago.

Whole dinosaur eggs were found in north-central Montana during 1979. Bones with the eggs indicate that the dinosaurs may have been carnivorous.

Bert Lindler

Douglas Faulkner

Isolated equatorial Pacific atolls provide an ideal place to study the oceanic and atmospheric conditions that lead to El Niño.

EL NIÑO

by William J. Cromie

A SUDDEN freeze in Florida destroys the orange crop. Hail in Kansas damages the wheat. Prolonged drought in California burns the lettuce.

Food supplies have always been subject to the uncertain whims of the weather. Nowhere is the connection more curious, or more predictable, than in the phenomenon known as El Niño, which links weather patterns in the South Pacific Ocean to soybean futures and the price of chickens in Peoria.

The phenomenon centers on a small patch of ocean off the coast of Peru that is the world's most productive fishery. There, cold bottom water rises to the surface carrying a rich load of nutrients on which feed microscopic plants.

The plants in turn feed uncountable numbers of anchovies, which are hauled from the sea in huge nets. At the fishery's

peak in 1970, Peruvian "bolichera" (dragnet) boats harvested over 13 million tons of the tiny, finger-length fish—one-fifth of the fish haul from all the world's oceans.

About every seven years the upwelling pattern is disrupted by a current of warm water that flows eastward across the equatorial Pacific and southward along the Peruvian coast. The current is known as El Niño ("the little one"), a reference to the Christ child because it comes near the Christmas season. But the warm water brings no holiday joy. It devastates the fishery, idling the fishermen, and starving millions of coastal birds. Loss of the anchovies and the protein-rich fish meal made from them hits hard at both the Peruvian economy and the world market for animal feed. During the last severe El Niño in 1972–73, prices for soybeans, the main substitute for fish meal, nearly tripled. Poultry prices in the United States and elsewhere went up 40 per cent.

Now, after a decade of intensive oceanographic and climatological studies, the origins of this destructive current have been discovered. El Niño is the only major natural disaster that has been predicted as much as a year in advance—a significant step toward the elusive goal of long-range weather prediction. Short-term warnings are often available for tsunamis (so-called tidal waves), severe storms, and other weather-related phenomena, but until recently the prospect of seasonal and longer forecasts has been doubtful. In this still uncertain field, however, predictions of El Niño's impending appearance have attained unusually high credibility among scientists and commodity traders.

Understanding the subtle links between ocean and atmosphere that give rise to El Niño has focused scientists' attention on similar interactions that may influence weather patterns over the United States. In mid-1979, however, seven years since the last major El Niño, the attention of scientists and many others was focused on the mid-Pacific. Peruvian economic ministers, soybean traders, farmers, fishermen, all were waiting for word from the field: Is El Niño coming?

THE HEAT ENGINE

The equatorial Pacific is a good place to take the pulse of the air-sea system because it is free from the influence of mountains and other land, and it receives the major input of solar energy. "This region forms the core of the heat engine that drives the world's weather and climate," says oceanographer William Patzert of Scripps Institution of Oceanography, La Jolla, California. Ocean and air movements carry this heat northward, making the temperate regions temperate and enabling life to survive even in the high latitudes of the polar regions.

Meteorologists once believed that winds moved the bulk of the heat, but oceanographers have shown that the oceans move more than half this energy. The oceans also provide a "flywheel" for the heat engine, because changes occur more slowly in the waters than in the air. The oceans create a memory for the air, feeding back conditions from a previous season, changing the circulation patterns of the atmosphere and, with them, the weather.

Of course, the interaction goes both ways; the atmosphere continually changes the ocean. "The old idea of warm air moving poleward at the surface, rising and returning to the equatorial regions has been replaced by a complex feedback between ocean and atmosphere," explains Jerome Namias, a Scripps meteorologist.

Scientists taking part in the International Decade of Ocean Exploration concluded that the Line Islands—small atolls, isolated in the center of the equatorial Pa-

The demand for—and price of—soybeans grown in the midwestern United States depend to a large extent on Peruvian fisheries—and El Niño.

George Gerster/Photo Researchers
Anchovies and fish meal made from them form a large part of the world market for animal feed.

cific—are an ideal place to study how ocean and air embrace each other. "Small and low, these atolls are like ships anchored in mid-Pacific," comments Martin Vitousek, a University of Hawaii geophysicist who has maintained a network of instruments on the Line Islands since 1972.

Without the static of seasonal fluctuations and frontal systems common to the United States, researchers can listen to the basic rhythms of ocean-air interaction. Palmyra, at the north end of the chain, lies in the area where northeast and southeast trade winds converge. Strong weather patterns in the area sometimes act in concert with patterns to the north to produce dramatic effects, such as simultaneous flash floods in Hong Kong and Honolulu.

The Line Islands stretch across great oceanic currents that move warm water east and west across almost half the circumference of the world. "The huge amounts of heat involved must influence weather and climate in Asia and the Americas," says Vitousek.

THE LOCAL NIÑO

In the early 1970's, oceanographers believed El Niño was the offspring of local winds near South America. According to this theory, strong winds blowing offshore normally pushed coastal water seaward, and cool water upwelled to fill the gap, bringing with it nutrients such as nitrogen and phosphorus from the sea floor. The nutrients feed vast numbers of single-cell plants called diatoms that make the water off Chimbote and Callao, Peru, 500 to 1,200 kilometers south of the equator, the most fertile patch of ocean in the world.

When the offshore winds stopped or weakened, according to the theory, warm water flowed south from the equatorial region and capped the upwelling nutrient-rich water. With no diatoms, the anchovies starved, the fish-meal processing plants shut down, and consumers of chicken and soy everywhere faced higher prices. To add insult to the injury El Niño does to Peru's economy, the warm water also brings flooding rains to the normally dry coastal areas.

Recognition that El Niño was more than a local phenomenon came from the work of two scientists. Meteorologist William Quinn of Oregon State University analyzed rainfall records in Peru dating back to 1793 and concluded that a strong El Niño strikes every seven to eight years, on average. He became interested in the causes of the phenomenon and decided to look further. Meanwhile, Klaus Wrytki of the University of Hawaii examined meteorological records and found no evidence that diminished off-shore winds brought on El Niño. In some cases, local winds blew stronger during niños. Wrytki decided to look beyond Peru for an answer.

He discovered that strong southeast trade winds blew over the entire South Pacific for a year or more before the birth of each niño. Tide gauges on the Line Islands also showed increases in sea level and temperature prior to the arrival of a niño. Wrytki concluded that upwelling is produced by local winds, but that El Niño is an event of oceanic proportions and much longer gestation.

William Quinn came to the same conclusion after studying atmospheric-pressure differences between the high-pressure area, common over Easter Island in the Southeast Pacific, and the persistent equatorial low over Indonesia. When the pressure difference is large, the southeast trade winds blow strong, and vice versa. Quinn found that the pressure difference increased 12 to 18 months before the arrival of a strong niño, then dipped below average just prior to it.

CAUSES

Just what causes El Niño? The two scientists proposed, on the basis of their findings, that the warm current off Peru has its origins in the interaction of the southeast trade winds and the entire equatorial Pacific Ocean (see map).

The trades blow westward across the full reach of the Pacific and are normally mild. When they blow strong for a year or more, however, they pile up water against the coast of Southeast Asia. The winds raise the average sea level off Southeast Asia as much as a half meter above the ocean level near South America—an effect analogous to tilting the surface of a cup of coffee by blowing on it.

As shifting global weather patterns gradually weaken the low-pressure center over Indonesia and the high-pressure area near Easter Island, the trades slacken and the piled-up water sloshes back toward South America. The water makes its return journey near the equator in warm eastward-flowing currents and can be detected by an increase in water temperature and sea level in the Line Islands. When this warm current reaches the South American coast, it moves southward as El Niño.

A MYSTERY IS SOLVED

The proposed theory was bold and far-reaching. If correct, the scientists believed they could predict not only the timing but also the intensity of a niño, three months to a year ahead of time, by monitoring atmospheric-pressure patterns. They soon had a chance to test the theory. In October of 1974, Quinn saw signals of an impending El Niño, albeit a small one. An expedition was hastily planned. In February 1975, the University of Hawaii research ship *Moana Wave* arrived off Ecuador. Oceanographers aboard found and traced a large mass of warm water flowing eastward and then southward along the coast of Ecuador and Peru. No doubt about it; it was El Niño. An old and costly mystery of the sea had been solved.

Despite the niño's 1975 visit, bolichera crews hauled in nets teeming with anchovies, and birds filled the air in many places. "This was the first time we realized that El Niño is not an all or nothing phenomenon," says Deane Holt of the National Science Foundation. "The simplified picture of a warm current shutting off upwelling like you shut off a faucet is incorrect. The upwelling apparently never stops. In years of strong niño activity, nutrient-poor water comes up, instead of nutrient-rich water, and wreaks havoc on the fishery. During weak events, such as the one in 1975, pockets of high productivity still exist. This means that many of the earlier weaker niños may have gone undetected."

The warm current can appear at any season of the year, but has little impact on the fishery unless it comes during the southern hemisphere's summer, when water temperatures are already high. According to Quinn, the weather pattern that gives rise to El Niño has occurred in winter as well as in summer, and is apparently not closely tied to the calendar. The ocean-air system, he says, "oscillates between an El Niño condition and the opposite, more normal pattern over a period of years."

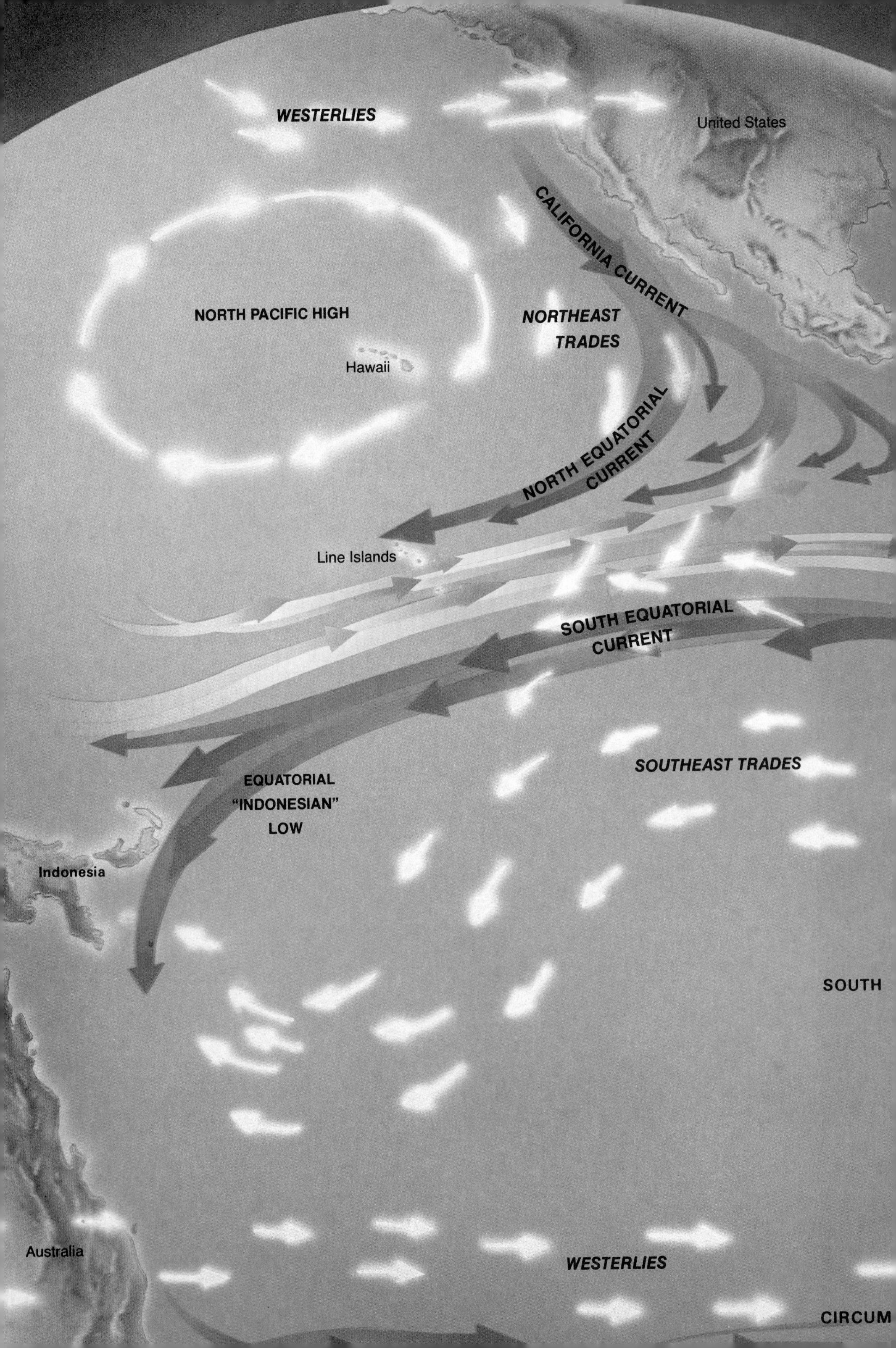
WESTERLIES
United States
CALIFORNIA CURRENT
NORTH PACIFIC HIGH
NORTHEAST
TRADES
Hawaii
NORTH EQUATORIAL
CURRENT
Line Islands
SOUTH EQUATORIAL
CURRENT
SOUTHEAST TRADES
EQUATORIAL
"INDONESIAN"
LOW
Indonesia
SOUTH
Australia
WESTERLIES
CIRCUM

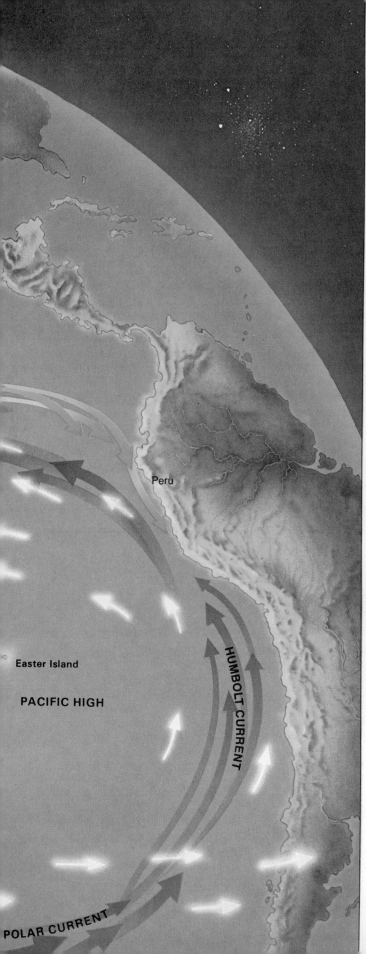

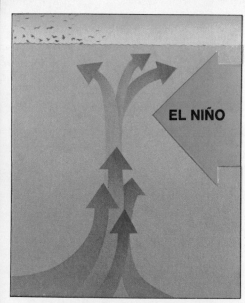

EL NIÑO

Air-sea interaction over the Pacific Ocean is still imperfectly understood, but the principal elements that contribute to El Niño are shown here schematically. When climatic conditions establish a strong atmospheric high-pressure region near Easter Island and a strong low-pressure center near Indonesia, the Southeast trade winds blow stronger. This in turn enhances the wind-driven South Equatorial Current and piles up water in the western Pacific. The atmosphere over the Pacific interacts with weather around the world, however, and eventually the high and low pressure centers weaken and the winds die down. When this occurs, the excess water returns eastward—due to forces associated with the rotation of the earth—as a greatly strengthened equatorial counter-current and flows southward along the South American coastline as the warm El Niño current. Air-sea interaction in the South Pacific oscillates slowly between the pattern associated with El Niño and the more normal pattern of weaker winds and currents, with El Niño conditions occurring every three to four years and lasting from a few months to a year or more. Whether a similar phenomenon occurs in the North Pacific, as some scientists expect, is still under investigation, as is the effect of these climatic shifts on weather at higher latitudes, such as over the United States. Above, upwelling of cool, nutrient-rich bottom water off Peru, driven by local offshore winds, is disrupted by the warm El Niño current. Upwelling continues, but the warm equatorial water brought to the surface lacks the nutrients to sustain the enormously productive anchovy food chain.

Peru

Easter Island

PACIFIC HIGH

HUMBOLT CURRENT

POLAR CURRENT

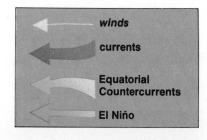

winds

currents

Equatorial
Countercurrents

El Niño

Illustration by John Youssi

Will El Niño strike this year? How much fish meal will be available? Commodity traders ponder these questions in determining soybean prices.

BEYOND THE PACIFIC

Now that they have a key piece of the ocean-air puzzle, researchers are looking beyond the equatorial Pacific. "Oscillations of pressure and warm-water flows that produce niños change the distribution of heat and moisture over one-quarter to one-half the earth's circumference," asserts Tim P. Barnett of Scripps Institution of Oceanography. "This must affect the temperate regions and possibly the weather over the entire globe."

Just how equatorial phenomena connect to winds and currents in the North Pacific and hence to weather over the United States remains uncertain. In the North Pacific, El Niño may be associated with changes that produce huge pools of water—up to 150 kilometers across—that are up to three degrees Celsius warmer or colder than the surrounding ocean.

These anomalous pools in turn change the course of the winds that bring weather to the North American continent. Scripps' Namias blames recent severe winters in the United States on the position of these anomalous pools, but he does not believe they originate from events connected with El Niño.

Meteorologist John E. Kutzback of the University of Wisconsin believes that the presence of large amounts of unusually warm water in the equatorial regions intensifies the northward movement of heat. "This produces changes in the jet stream, which in turn can cause changes in weather from California to Maine."

On the basis of studies with a computer model, he asserts that "a plausible mechanism exists by which anomalous sea surface temperatures can influence weather." To study the connection, oceanographers joined meteorologists from 70 nations in a year-long Global Weather Experiment that ended November 30, 1979. The scientists hope the information gained will contain enough pieces of the global puzzle to allow forecasting of U.S. weather six months in advance, the way El Niño can now be predicted.

In Peru, meanwhile, El Niño predictions have provided a note of hope in an otherwise grim picture. Despite the weak 1975 niño, anchovy stocks were recovering nicely from the 1972 disaster, aided by tighter controls on overfishing and the nationalization of the industry.

El Niño stayed away in 1977, 1978, and 1979. The diatoms returned, but not the anchovies in anything like their former numbers. Instead, sardines increased their numbers and grazed the diatoms. Peru, which had borrowed heavily against future fish harvests, put its idle fishermen to work again. The sardines are not as efficient in the food chain as anchovies, however, and the catches are far smaller—one million tons in 1977. Peruvians and scientists alike are still uncertain whether the anchovies will return. In addition, with the country's economic future hanging in the balance, Peru's fishery officials, along with bankers, scientists, and poultry raisers all over the world, began to worry anew about another strong El Niño, now statistically overdue.

In the summer of 1980, tide gauges and barometers in the Line Islands and all over the Pacific again monitored wind and ocean levels. Oceanographers and meteorologists are carefully examining the data not only for signs of El Niño 1980–81, but also for clues to air-sea interactions that might affect weather in North America, Asia, and perhaps the rest of the world □

Wolf von dem Bussche/Time Inc

A sophisticated oil pump signals the advance of modern technology in a rural area where children ride horseback through the countryside.

MEXICAN OIL

by William D. Metz

INTENSIVE exploration in Mexico is turning up oil fields so immense that they could overturn the conventional wisdom about world oil supplies and significantly alter the geopolitics of energy.

Since the mid-1970's we have believed that most of the world's major oil fields have already been discovered. This would mean that the United States would have to rely more and more heavily on the Middle East for future supplies of oil. It was also believed that the giant oil fields around the Persian Gulf are the result of a unique geological occurrence that is unlikely to be matched anywhere else.

Not only does this information appear to be wrong, it appears to be spectacularly wrong. Oil fields apparently equivalent to those in Saudi Arabia have been found only about 1,000 kilometers from the United States border. Recent discoveries indicate that an area along the southeast coast of Mexico surrounding the Yucatan peninsula and extending offshore more than 200 kilometers may be one of the world's richest oil fields.

The apparent magnitude of the Mexican oil deposit is a "tremendous shock" that "boggles the mind," according to oil experts who are familiar with the discoveries. The potential impact of these finds is all the more substantial because the national oil company, Petroleos Mexicanos (Pemex), has explored only a fraction of Mexico's prospective oil regions.

Every year since 1974 Pemex has revised its estimates of the country's potential oil reserves upward. By 1977, Mexico had equaled the Alaska North Slope. By early 1978, it was clear that Mexico was at least the equal of another Kuwait, and in September, 1978, Mexican President José Lopéz Portillo announced reserves that would match Saudi Arabia's. Oil experts expect the figures to continue to rise.

All structures drilled in the Chiapas-Tabasco area have been oil producing. This fact, plus what is known about the geology of the Yucatan area, leads observers to predict that Mexico's total oil and gas reserves will soon surpass those of any of the countries that now qualify as oil superpowers.

Workers are changing the drill bit and extending the piping at an oil installation.

EARLY CONCESSIONS AND OVERPRODUCTION

At the turn of the century, the head of the Mexican railway persuaded a California oilman to start exploration on the east coast of Mexico near Tampico. A string of very productive fields was found in the geological formation known as the Golden Lane. The major oil companies moved to obtain concessions in this area. By 1921 Mexico was the world's second largest oil producer after the United States. But the companies drew oil at an exorbitant rate. By 1930 Mexico's output had dropped to one fifth of the 1921 level, the fields virtually ruined by overproduction.

This experience, coupled with labor strikes in the mid-1930's, led Mexico to reclaim its concessions, expel the foreign companies, and establish Pemex to replace them. (Nationalization of resources by a developing country is now a familiar action. But when Mexico did it in 1938, it was an audacious act. Until then, only the Soviet Union had nationalized its oil resources.)

Most of the oil fields known at the time of nationalization were on the east-central coast, in the state of Veracruz. It was not until 1949 that the first oil and gas field was found along the southeast coast, in the state of Tabasco. More fields were found in the southern area in the 1960's. These, like Mexico's original fields near Tampico, were shallow and relatively modest.

During the first 30 years of Pemex management, Mexico's projected oil reserves did not change much, fluctuating about the figure of 2,500,000,000 barrels. Before 1972, Mexico was projected to be a net importer of oil during the 1980's.

THE OIL FIELD AT REFORMA

Such projections began to change quickly when Pemex drilled deeper and discovered two huge fields in the south not far from the town of Reforma. After that it seemed that almost every potential petroleum structure (previously found by seismic mapping) turned out to be a prodigious producer. For example, Pemex found that five or six nearby structures not only were first-rate reservoirs of oil and gas, but were in fact connected to each other to form one giant field over 200 square kilometers in area.

Pemex is still trying to find the limits of this field as it continues to come up with wells that produce 9,000 barrels per day. And these drillings are thought to be at the extreme flanks of the field. From top to bottom, the thickness of the oil pool has been found to be as great as 2,000 meters in places. This is more than at any other site in the world, according to one petroleum geologist. This field alone—the Bermudez—is thought to have about 5,000,000,000 barrels of recoverable oil and 560,000,000,000 cubic meters of gas (about one-sixth the amount of United States reserves). The bulk of Mexico's current production—2,200,000 barrels per day—comes from Bermudez plus the first two deep fields that were found in the Reforma area in 1972.

MORE OIL FIELDS

Pemex carefully mapped the Chiapas-Tabasco area by various seismic techniques and found 125 to 150 potential oil structures. So far only 40 or 50 of these have been investigated by exploratory drilling and about 25 are proving to be rich oil producers.

Offshore, in the Gulf of Campeche, Pemex has found even more potential oil structures. Pemex director Diaz Serrano told the *Oil and Gas Journal* in an interview in June 1978 that in the Gulf of Campeche "we have mapped over 200 seismic structures, all of them with surprisingly gentle slopes and thus quite larger than those of Reforma." "Should they be oil-bearing," he said, "they would dwarf the potential of Chiapas-Tabasco."

Most of Pemex's offshore drilling has been 60 to 100 kilometers from shore, north of the island of Ciudad del Carmen. Pemex first struck oil there in 1975. Geologically, the offshore structures are similar to the onshore ones. Out of ten drilled so far, seven have turned out to be prolific oil fields. One of the largest is the Chac field.

The oil-trade journals call the discoveries in the Chiapas-Tabasco area and the offshore fields in the Gulf of Campeche the largest oil province ever discovered in the Western Hemisphere.

Based on Pemex exploration in these two relatively compact regions, President Lopéz Portillo said in his state of the union address in September 1978 that Mexico now has potential hydrocarbon reserves equiva-

Oil from spill burning on Campeche Bay, site of a very large oil field.

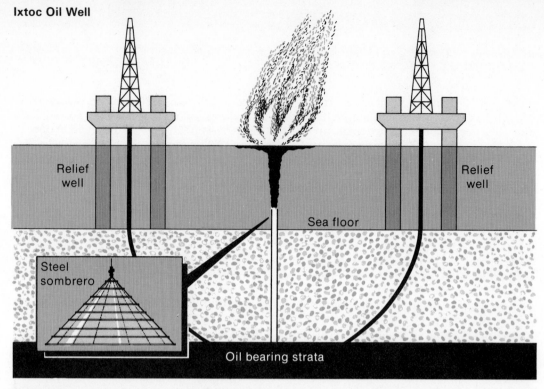

Relief wells were used to try to capture some of the oil lost when an offshore Mexican well blew out, spewing countless barrels of oil into the water.

lent to 200,000,000,000 barrels of oil. (Saudi Arabia's proved oil reserves are estimated to be 150,000,000,000 barrels, and those of the whole Persian Gulf region about 400,000,-000,000 barrels.) Yet a large portion of Mexico has not yet been subjected to even the first stage of exploration. The geological explanation of the origin of Mexico's flush harvest of oil and gas offers some clues to what may remain to be discovered.

OIL FORMATION IN SOUTHERN MEXICO

During Jurassic-Cretaceous time, some 130,000,000 years ago, the southern region of Mexico was surrounded by a wide barrier reef. The reef created a giant atoll-like island with a huge brackish lagoon in the center. Over the centuries, the barrier reef collected rich layers of marine life. This was the organic residue that would later become oil. Evaporation of the lagoon laid down thick deposits of salt.

The reef was not very similar in shape to the present land mass. Instead, it resembled the shallow shelf called the Yucatan platform, which extends out into the Gulf of Mexico 100 or more kilometers from the present coastline. Sediments from later periods

buried the reef, and with time the semiplastic salt began to flow toward the reef.

Later geological movements, both horizontal and vertical, folded together the reef sediments with a deeper layer of salt. Such folding produced sealed structures in which temperature and pressure transformed the marine sediments into oil. These are the potential petroleum salt domes Pemex has been mapping with seismic methods.

As pictured by geologists, the reef extends from the Papaloapan Basin (see map), where several promising new fields have been found, 300 kilometers east through the Chiapas-Tabasco region. From there it reaches out into the Gulf where it circles the Yucatan peninsula. It comes back onshore through Belize and Guatemala.

The Cretaceous edge of the reef has been traced all the way around the loop. The connection between the Papaloapan and Chiapas-Tabasco areas has been established. Both are part of the same formation found offshore, and all these are correlated with oil discoveries in Guatemala. The reef concept seems to be on firm ground. If it is, the oil basin is immense. The biggest accumulations of oil, Pemex geologists believe, will be near

Tatiner/Liaison

Oil spurts from the ground at one of the numerous fields shown on the map.

the ancient reef rather than in the center of the old lagoon. They believe that salt deposits at the center would be too thick and other rock conditions unfavorable.

POTENTIAL OIL RESERVES

The giant formations found in Chiapas-Tabasco and offshore in the Gulf of Campeche make up only a small portion of the reef's perimeter. "We are talking about 200 billion barrels in these two clusters onshore and offshore," says Bernardo Grossling, a scientist with the U.S. Geological Survey, who is regarded as one of the leading U.S. authorities on the Mexican situation. But there is a 100-kilometer gap between the two clusters that has not been drilled yet.

Farther into the Gulf there is another gap of 200 kilometers to the northwest corner of the atoll. At this corner Pemex has sunk one well, named Ixchel 1, as an "outpost" to see what might be encountered when exploratory activity reaches that region. It was a gusher. Beyond Ixchel, across the northern edge of the Yucatan platform, are hundreds of kilometers more of unexplored reef.

The general impression of geologists who have looked at the situation is that further

exploration, first by seismic mapping and then by exploratory drilling, can only find more oil. Pemex has two seismic-mapping ships working full time and 20 offshore drilling rigs (up from six in 1977) at work. But the potential offshore fields cover a huge region (Ixchel is 500 kilometers from the southernmost well in the Chiapas-Tabasco area).

"I estimate that it will take five years for Pemex to come to the boundaries of this resource," says Grossling, who is advising various government agencies on the matter. "The breathtaking news will come every 6 months," he says, and "what I think is the limit for Mexico I will not even say."

Such enormous stores of oil in a world thought to be hungrily draining its last reservoir present a potential revolution of energy expectations. Whether Mexico offers the world another 10, 20, 30, 40, or more years of oil cannot yet be determined. The stakes are high □

 SELECTED READINGS

"Blowout in the Gulf." *Newsweek*, June 25, 1979.

"Mexico: an oil giant emerges" by A. Starchild. *Current*, September 1979.

The great size of *Camarasaurus* may be imagined from its shoulder bone.

DINOSAUR HEAD HUNT

by Susan West

BRONTOSAURUS, lo these many years the epitome of the towering dinosaur, ogled by schoolchildren and advertised by an oil company, has a new head.

But that very public and somehow disturbing change is only the epilog of a century-long story. The great, familiar dinosaur, it seems, is the victim of hasty research. And the hasty research was made worse by repeated clashes of ego and reputation that occurred as the science of vertebrate paleontology (the study of ancient life through fossils) bloomed and matured. Bluntly put, *Brontosaurus* fell through the cracks.

To begin at the end, in October 1979 the curators of the Carnegie Museum of Natural History in Pittsburgh replaced the massive, snub-nosed skull that had topped their *Brontosaurus* skeleton for more than 40 years with a more slender, elongated version. The new

headgear is the direct result of a re-examination of the Jurassic-period (136 million to 190 million years ago) creature by John S. McIntosh of Wesleyan University in Middletown, Connecticut, and David S. Berman, associate curator of the museum. McIntosh and Berman first published their suspicions of *Brontosaurus*'s wrong-headedness in 1975.

Not that *Brontosaurus*'s predicament was unknown among vertebrate paleontologists. As Nicholas Hotton of the Smithsonian Museum of Natural History explains, "It's been hanging over people's heads ever since [*Brontosaurus* was first described in 1883]." Says John Horner of Princeton University, "People who study dinosaurs aren't surprised. We've known for a long time." Even McIntosh says he's been "positive . . . for at least 15 years."

Yet popular books on dinosaurs, encyclopedia articles on *Brontosaurus,* even vertebrate paleontology textbooks—not to mention museums—fail to note what seems to be common knowledge. Prior to McIntosh and Berman's work, only one largely unnoticed attempt had been published in the scientific literature to pin down what Hotton calls "lore."

A WATER CREATURE

By itself, the skull switch is not of great scientific significance. The 24- to 27-meter animal does not suddenly become a ravenous meat-eater, or change from a small-brained, lumbering giant to a crafty, fleet-footed hunter. On the contrary, the pencil-like teeth of the new head indicate that it probably nibbled grasses or aquatic plants. The broad, spoon-shaped teeth of the former skull attest to a coarser vegetarian diet.

The new head may, however, settle a few squabbles, such as the long-running debate about *Brontosaurus*'s predeliction for aquatic or terrestrial life. The more delicate teeth and slightly higher nares (breathing passages), say Berman and McIntosh, may mean it spent more time in water searching for softer grasses.

The new skull also throws *Brontosaurus* into a different classification. *Brontosaurus* is a member of the suborder *Sauropoda,* the largest four-legged creatures ever to shake the earth. The skull it sported this last century placed it in the same family as the less spectacular and quite different sauropod *Camarasaurus.* Its new head puts it in the same family as its nearly identical cousin, *Diplodocus.* While such taxonomic matters may be important for the record, they are really only of academic interest.

The plight of the *Brontosaurus* may indeed be small stuff compared to the entire field. But even small stuff is usually settled in the scientific literature, especially when it's so widely accepted. As Berman and McIntosh point out, the real story of the *Brontosaurus,* and the reason its head hasn't been put straight in the literature, lies with the roots of American vertebrate paleontology.

HISTORY OF THE MIX-UP

In the United States, vertebrate paleontology marks its birth in the mid-1800's when fur traders sent back scraps of bone from the upper Missouri River country. By the late 1870's, the great bone-hunts were on in Utah, Wyoming, and Colorado. The front runners at that time were two of the most vivid personalities of vertebrate paleontology. Othniel Charles Marsh of the Yale Peabody Museum of Natural History and Edward Drinker Cope of Philadelphia. They quickly became world leaders in the science. Between them they described more than half of the 3,200 species of vertebrate fossils known in the United States in 1900. Just as rapidly, they became fierce competitors. Their feud—called the "Dinosaur Wars"—ended up destroying both of them.

When the huge bones of the sauropods were found, the Dinosaur Wars reached their height. In the attempt to be the first to identify these giants, Marsh and Cope were naming new species as quickly as they could dig them up. Such haste inevitably resulted in mistakes. *Brontosaurus,* apparently, became one of their casualties.

Marsh first described *Brontosaurus* from a specimen found in 1879. Actually, he first found *Brontosaurus* in 1877. But he called it *Apatosaurus,* and in his haste did not realize they were the same. (Because it is the first name given the animal, *Apatosaurus* is the correct scientific name. *Brontosaurus,* because of its familiarity, is used here.)

Not mentioned in his paper, however, is the fact that the two skulls Marsh used in his restorations were found 6.5 kilometers and 650 kilometers away from the rest of the skeleton. Moreover, the skulls were found with skeletons of *Camarasaurus,* not *Brontosaurus,* and probably belong to that genus. It

Rivalry between O. C. Marsh (left) and E. D. Cope (right) in the 19th century "Dinosaur Wars" led to haste and mistakes in identifying some species.

Peabody Museum of Nat. History   Univ. of Pennsylvania

Carnegie Museum officials fit a new *Diplodocus* head onto old *Brontosaurus* bones.

is these *Camarasaurus*-like skulls that adorn every museum restoration of *Brontosaurus*.

Says McIntosh, "Marsh needed a head, so he guessed. Most of his guesses were remarkably good, but this was not." "We couldn't get away with that now," says Berman. "Their rush to publication was definitely the beginning of the problem—not doing careful work."

DIPLODOCUS-LIKE SKULL

Brontosaurus's first shot at vindication came in 1915. Earl Douglass, digging for the Carnegie Museum in what is now the Dinosaur National Monument in Utah, found a very complete *Brontosaurus* skeleton. Beneath its ribs was a very un-*Camarasaurus*-like skull. In fact, the skull looked much like that of the genus *Diplodocus*. However, its close association with the skeleton convinced Douglass it belonged to the *Brontosaurus*. In addition, none of the skulls recovered at the site, which contained only *Diplodocus* and *Brontosaurus*, resembled Marsh's *Camarasaurus*-like skull.

William J. Holland, the museum's director at that time, said, "Had nothing in the past been written in reference to the structure of the skull of *Brontosaurus*, the conclusion would have been reached that [the *Diplodocus*-like] skull belongs to the skeleton. . . ." Remarking on the distance between the head and body of Marsh's *Brontosaurus*, he said, " . . . perhaps an error has

been made and *Brontosaurus* . . . may have had a skull like that of *Diplodocus*."

According to McIntosh and Berman, the close association of the skull and skeleton should have been sufficient evidence to change *Brontosaurus*. But Marsh's word still carried weight, and Holland ran into resistance from another famous paleontological ego, Henry Fairfield Osborn. As director of the influential American Museum of Natural History in New York, Osborn "had authority with a capital 'A'," says Hotton, "He tended to throw his weight around in a field that was small and concentrated." Osborn had also studied *Brontosaurus*. And according to Berman, he had virtually called it and *Camarasaurus* the same creature. Osborn had good reason for wanting to retain a *Camarasaurus*-like skull.

"My good friend, Dr. Osborn," Holland said in the 1915 paper, "has in a bantering mood 'dared' me to mount the [*Diplodocus*-like] head. . . .At moments I am inclined to take his dare. . . ."

Holland never took the dare. Neither did he give in: The Carnegie's *Brontosaurus* stood headless until Holland's death in 1932. At that time, director J. LeRoy Kay, influenced by tradition, crowned it with a *Camarasaurus*-like skull. *Brontosaurus*'s hope, it appeared, had died.

Enter McIntosh. A physicist by profession, McIntosh is called by other paleontologists, such as Yale's John H. Ostrom, "The world's authority on sauropods." His fascination with sauropods, says McIntosh, goes back "years and years and years. Most of my life." After studying the tons of bones at the Carnegie and the field notes and correspondence between Holland and Douglass, McIntosh became convinced that Holland was right. He won the interest of Berman, usually a student of Triassic mammals, and the two nailed down their hypothesis.

ANATOMICAL SIMILARITIES

According to McIntosh, "it's obvious" from the rest of the skeleton that *Brontosaurus* shares many of the features of *Diplodocus* and nearly none of *Camarasaurus*. Those features include short front limbs two-thirds as long as the thigh, a very long, whip-

The original "wrong-headed" *Brontosaurus* (right) was a familiar sight in U.S. museums.

like tail, and more vertebrae in the neck than the trunk. It follows, says McIntosh, that the skull should also be similar. There was absolutely no evidence that it was like *Camarasaurus.* Now the whole skeleton makes sense."

The researchers discovered several previously undescribed pieces of skull that were found with Marsh's original, 1877 *Brontosaurus*—the one he called *Apatosaurus.* Berman and McIntosh demonstrated that these pieces, which are indisputably part of that skeleton, are of *Diplodocus* type, not *Camarasaurus* type. Together with the Holland-Douglass skull, they seem to cinch the hypothesis. "Had Marsh noticed and taken the time to describe these pieces," says Berman, "he would undoubtedly have given it a *Diplodocus*-like skull."

Their work satisfies their colleagues. "Berman and McIntosh have come up with quite a bit of new evidence," says Princeton's Horner. "No one can argue with it." Berman and McIntosh, however, still give the credit to Holland. "The whole data were not available to Holland," says McIntosh, "but he did recognize some *Diplodocus*-like post-cranial characteristics such as the tail. It was just a standoff between him and Osborn . . . a matter of inconclusive evidence."

HEAD CASTS NEEDED

What about other museums? The curators at the Museum of Geological History at the University of Wyoming in Laramie weren't even aware that their *Brontosaurus*—originally one of the Carnegie's—had any problems. "I doubt if we'll get massively excited and tear out the head," said Jeff Eaton, when told of the research. The American Museum of Natural History in New York, on the other hand, has had the new head for a few years since making a cast of it for the Carnegie. "In the interest of maintaining accuracy, I'm sure we'll mount it at some point," said curator Gaffney, who noted the museum is observing their dinosaur's 100th birthday.

Yale's Ostrom says the Peabody Museum will probably note the *Brontosaurus's* tale by a change in the label on their specimen, but both Ostrom and Bolt of the Field Museum in Chicago say they must wait until more casts are made of the Carnegie's head.

So it may take a while for museums and textbooks to catch up with Berman and McIntosh. In the meantime, it looks as if the last head has rolled in the Dinosaur Wars □

 SELECTED READINGS

A Closer Look at Prehistoric Reptiles. Watts. New York, 1978.

The Day of the Dinosaur by John Man. Bison Books Limited, London, 1978.

Know Your Dinosaurs by David Meadows. Rand McNally, Chicago, 1977.

MOUNT ST. HELENS ERUPTS

By Benedict A. Leerburger

Werth © Longview 1980/Woodfin Camp

A VOLCANIC eruption is a rare occurrence in the continental United States. At 8:39 on the morning of May 18, 1980, however, a volcano erupted with calamitous results. Mount St. Helens, located in Washington's Gifford Pinchot National Forest in the Cascade range about 45 miles northeast of Portland, Oregon, erupted with a violence seldom recorded by volcanologists. The north side of the 9,677-foot mountain exploded, sending superheated gases, pumice-like rocks, and ash into the atmosphere.

Major mudslides the consistency of wet cement cascaded down the sides of the mountain at up to 50 miles an hour. Walls of water and mud swept up cars and houses along a 15-mile path in the Toutle River Valley. Concrete and steel bridges were destroyed. More than 20 people were killed by the massive mud flows, flooded rivers, or fallen timber. At least 100 people were reported missing from campsites and homes located near the volcano.

Millions of tons of ash and fragments of volcanic rock were propelled as high as 63,000 feet. Scientists estimated that more than 1.3 billion cubic yards of material was blown into the atmosphere—more than a ton of debris for every person on earth. This massive accumulation of pyroclastic material drifted eastward, creating major problems throughout the entire northwestern United States.

The fine volcanic ash clogged roads and stranded motorists. In the town of Ritzville, Washington, more than 2,500 motorists were trapped by the falling ash as drifts reached three to four feet in height. In other parts of the state automobiles stalled as volcanic ash clogged carburetors. Cities and towns as far as 500 miles east of Mount St. Helens received the falling ash. The choking volcanic cloud spewed ash across Yakima, Spokane, and many smaller cities throughout the area. Streets were blocked, sewers clogged, and traffic came to a standstill. In Idaho's northern panhandle, up to half an inch of ash was reported.

PROBLEMS MULTIPLY

As the first volcanic cloud created problems of ash fallout, another problem loomed. In the area north of Mount St. Helens thousands of logs that had been cut and stacked for lumber, together with countless thousands of downed trees still bearing roots and crowns, drifted down the swollen Toutle River into the Columbia River below Longview, Washington. Here they mixed with other volcanic debris to clog the river. Mud filled the river channel that serves the Portland docks, one of the West Coast's most active harbors.

A more serious problem threatened thousands of residents living in cities and towns in the Toutle and Cowlitz River Valleys. When Mount St. Helens exploded, dirt,

Werth © Longview 1980/Woodfin Camp

The eruption of Mount St. Helens sent huge mudslides cascading down the mountain, snapping trees, and sweeping up houses and cars.

rock, ash, glacial ice, and debris jammed the outlet of Spirit Lake located at the source of the Toutle River. With the lake's outlet blocked, water began to build up behind the natural dam, and the lake began to rise. The dam was described by pilots as standing 200 feet high and a mile wide. Torrents of water poured down the mountain from melting glaciers heated by the volcano's hot core. Rising river water temperatures threatened the fish population.

Two of Mount St. Helens' largest ice masses, Loomis and Leschi glaciers, completely melted. Spirit Lake and neighboring Lake Mount St. Helens soon became one—New Spirit Lake. More than 50,000 people were threatened by a sudden surge of flood water should the new dam break.

LONG-RANGE FORECAST: ASH

As governors in Washington and neighboring states declared states of emergency and attempted to deal with the mounting problems, the massive cloud of volcanic ash drifted eastward. Scientists evaluated the potential problems the eruption might cause in other parts of the country. At the altitude the volcanic cloud reached—between 25,000 and 40,000 feet—the rapid movement of air brought it to the east coast in 72 hours.

Scientists at the National Oceanic and Atmospheric Administration (NDAA) estimated that by mid-summer 1980 the cloud would be homogenous, with a thickness of about two miles. They expected the cloud would drift in the Northern Hemisphere stratosphere at an altitude of more than 55,000 feet for about two years.

Another potential problem studied by NOAA's Geophysical Monitoring for Climate Change group was the possible effect the stratospheric cloud would have on the earth's climate. Some scientists speculated that the volcanic cloud could affect the

© Bill Thompson 1980/Woodfin Camp

Snow-capped Mount St. Helens before the eruption sleeps near sister peak Mount Hood (rear).

world's weather pattern and cause a slight reduction in the earth's temperature. Dr. Machta, who has studied the effects of most volcanic eruptions, stated that he did not believe Mount St. Helens' eruption would create any significant climatic changes. He said that a slight cooling effect, no more than a small fraction of a degree, could be produced as the tiny ash particles in the cloud reflected visible light back into space.

On the other hand, according to Dr. Machta, there could be some compensation for this minor loss of heat. The same ash particles that reflect light back into space would also reflect onto the earth the invisible infrared rays that are normally radiated into space.

Although the sudden eruption of the volcano came as a surprise to many, volcanologists have been monitoring Mount St. Helens as well as other West Coast "dormant" volcanoes for years. In 1976, for example, Dwight R. Crandell of the U.S. Geological Survey co-authored a report predicting an eruption of Mount St. Helens "perhaps before the end of the century." What did surprise volcanologists was not the eruption but the sudden cataclysmic force with which Mount St. Helens exploded.

Because of the volcano's unexpected behavior, geologists are becoming more concerned about Mount St. Helens' sister volcanoes in the Cascades, such as Mounts Hood, Rainier, and Lassen, which have the same explosive potential. Mt. Lassen, for example, last erupted in 1915 but on a far smaller scale than Mount St. Helens.

A LITTLE HISTORY

Mount St. Helens' history has been well documented by geologists. In recent geologic time the mountain has sprung to life every 150 to 500 years. In terms of volume of debris, several previous eruptions were far more massive. In 1900 B.C., for example, the volcano spewed forth three times as much debris as the latest eruption. Unlike the recent explosion, the earlier eruption oozed material out of vents in the volcano's crust, harmlessly building up the mountain's squat base. In 1500 the volcano erupted in a fashion similar to the 1900 B.C. eruption, although the amount of debris was about the same as the 1980 eruption. The mountain had been inactive since 1857.

In early 1980 localized earthquakes were detected beneath Mount St. Helens. Geologists believed the inactive volcano's reservoir was filling with molten material. For weeks before the eruption small earthquakes measuring from 2.5 to 4.0 on the Richter scale were recorded. On March 27th a small explosion sent steam and ash over eastern Washington.

Then on the morning of May 18th two earthquakes registering about 5.0 were recorded. Minutes later Dr. David A. Johnson of the U.S. Geological Survey, who was operating a solo observation post five miles from the peak of the mountain, transmitted his last message, "Vancouver! Vancouver! This is it!" His words were silenced as the mountain exploded.

TWO KINDS OF VOLCANOES

All volcanoes, whether on the sea floor or on the earth's surface, are created by the rising of extremely hot material, called *magma,* from as deep as 25 to 50 miles beneath the earth's surface. Geologists classify volcanoes into two groups, effusive and explosive.

It is generally the chemical composition of the magma that determines the nature and behavior of a volcano. Volcanoes in the Hawaiian Islands are composed of black or greenish-black basalt. This igneous rock is rich in calcium and its magma tends to fill readily with gas, becoming thin and soupy. It forces its way to the surface easily through cracks and fissures in the sides of a volcano. Thus, pressure is easily released without an explosion. Effusive volcanoes, such as Japan's Mt. Fuji, are typified by their symmetrical cones.

Volcanoes of the explosive type are often composed of rocks known as andesitic and dacitic. The Cascades are generally composed of these materials. When in magma form these rocks become thick and viscous. Pressure cannot easily escape. Thus, when pressure builds up beneath the surface, a mountain top acts like a giant cork in a bottle of boiling water. Gases and debris don't ooze out, they blow out.

One explosive volcano, Krakatoa in Indonesia, exploded in 1883 sending ten times the debris of Mount St. Helens into the atmosphere. Krakatoa's ash circled the globe for years. In terms of loss of life, the eruption

© Bill Thompson 1980/Woodfin Camp

Drifting volcanic ash fell like snow on nearby towns, clogging streets and sewers, and bringing business to a standstill until it could be swept up.

of Italy's Mt. Vesuvius is remembered for its destruction of Pompeii in 79 A.D. In 1470 B.C., however, an eruption at Thera in the Aegean Sea caused a tidal wave estimated to have been at least 800 feet high. It is believed that the wave hit the island of Crete, destroying the Minoan Civilization.

Geologists have yet either to predict accurately or to explain the exact cause of a volcanic eruption. It is believed that the hot magmas are a residual from the formerly molten state of the earth, which in spite of its age is still intensely hot at moderate depth. One theory to explain the rise of magma and imprisoned gases—mostly superheated steam—is analogous to cracked ice on a pond with water flowing out on the ice. According to this concept, the gross weight of the overlying cover of solid rocks forces the magma upward. Whatever the cause of Mount St. Helens' sudden eruption, geologists are unable to predict when or how seriously the volcano will explode again □

Gary Ladd

Lightning stages some of its most spectacular displays over Kitt Peak, Arizona.

JOVE'S THUNDERBOLTS

by Dava Sobel

LIGHTNING strikes with the speed of ... lightning. It's as brilliant as a ... a flash of lightning, and lights up the sky like ... well, like lightning. It's a superlative phenomenon—powerful, beautiful, deadly dangerous, the source of fire, and possibly the initiator of life itself.

Lightning in the atmosphere over the primitive earth may have fused the atoms and molecules that eventually became living things. And lightning helps to sustain life: right now, some 2,000 electrical storms breaking worldwide are changing a fraction of the nitrogen in the air to the form usable by animals and plants, and washing it down with the rain.

Only some of the lightning in the atmosphere ever hits the ground, but such strikes are thought to occur about 100 times per second. In an average year, lightning kills at least 125 people in the United States, injures another 500 (many of them golfers), and causes property losses figured in the hundreds of millions of dollars.

Lightning occurs most commonly during thunderstorms, but it can accompany snowstorms, sandstorms, tornadoes, erupting volcanoes, or nuclear explosions—or even come out of the proverbial clear blue sky. It is the result of an electrical disturbance in the atmosphere. An excess of charge builds up, say, from the turbulence inside a growing thunderhead, and lightning is the discharge that returns the balance between earth and sky.

The sight of lightning cracking open the sky, spreading over the surface of the sea like molten lead, or touching off forest fires, has spawned myths and legends in every culture. Yet, despite firsthand experience by generations of observers, lightning is still poorly understood. It became the focus of serious scientific investigation only a couple of centuries ago, and the precise causal relationship between lightning and thunder has only been known since about 1960.

ELECTRICITY

Benjamin Franklin designed the first experiments to prove the electrical nature of lightning. Miraculously, he lived to document the results of his 1752 kite flight. Others who tried to repeat the study were not so lucky.

The goal of the kite experiment was to demonstrate that thunderclouds were electrically charged, and that lightning, therefore, was an electrical phenomenon. Franklin tied a key at the bottom of a long kite wire, and held the assembly on a silk insulating string. The kite did draw charge from the clouds, and sparks jumped from the key to Franklin's knuckles. Had lightning actually struck the kite, however, Franklin would no doubt have been electrocuted.

Almost as dangerous as flying a kite in a sky full of lightning was Franklin's earlier plan (1750) to stand on a special ungrounded perch inside a sentry box on a high tower or steeple during a thunderstorm, holding onto the bottom of a six-to-nine meter iron rod. "If the electrical stand be kept clean and dry," Franklin wrote, "a man standing on it when such clouds are passing low might be electrified and afford sparks, the rod drawing fire to him from the cloud." The observation of sparks shooting from the rod during storms would prove that thunderclouds contained electric charge.

Franklin never tried this experiment himself, but several others gave successful demonstrations of it in France, England, and Belgium.

LIGHTNING RODS

It is uncanny to think that Franklin didn't recognize the danger in this experiment, since he was the first to suggest, also in 1750, that tall rods might protect houses and ships from lightning damage. He announced the idea in the 1753 *Poor Richard's Almanac,* saying, "It has pleased God in His goodness to mankind, at length to discover to them the means of securing their habitations and other buildings from mischief by thunder and lightning."

Franklin chose never to patent or profit from his invention of the lightning rod, which became popular immediately and hasn't changed much in two hundred years. It works by providing a safe path to ground for the lightning current, thereby protecting the attached house, barn, or ship.

Throughout the 19th century, traveling salesmen hawked lightning rods door-to-door during the late-summer thunderstorm season. Often unscrupulous, they sold unsatisfactory equipment to the unsuspecting, and their poorly installed rods caused considerable damage. Today there is scant "do-it-yourself"

in the lightning-rod business. Companies that sell them install them, and many states require special licenses for such work. Costs vary according to the size of the house, of course, but usually range from two hundred to four hundred dollars.

In addition to lightning rods, modern lightning protection for a large structure includes wires that connect the rods and run down the sides of the building into the ground, plus a grounding arrangement. Without these components, the rod is just playing with fire.

STEPPED LEADERS

Lightning strikes so quickly that it has to be timed in microseconds. One microsecond equals 1/1,000,000 of a second. The flash is too brief and brilliant for human eyes to notice that the light travels up, not down.

The bustle of motion inside a growing storm cloud knocks electrons off atoms of water or ice, and regions of dense negative and positive charge build up. The cloud's bottom is usually negatively charged, and drawn to the positive charge on the ground below.

In most instances, the free electrons in the cloud, pushed by the strong electric field, begin to flow toward ground, but they can't make a straight dash across large distances of intervening air. They proceed in short bursts, traveling maybe 50 meters at a time, carrying the cloud's negative charge toward earth in a jagged path called a "stepped leader."

For some the 19th-century lightning-rod bandwagon included lightning rods on hats and umbrellas.

both, Bettmann Archive

Lightning sets many trees on fire—and not always with bad effects.

stepped leader and the upward-surging positive charge build a conductive channel through the sky. When a positive spark meets the tip of the leader, it completes the channel at a "strike point" some ten to a hundred meters above ground. Then electrons flow violently to the earth, setting up large currents that illuminate the channel.

This "return stroke"—the one we see—travels thousands of times faster than the leader, and the flash seems to occur simultaneously all along the zigzag path the leader traced. The tremendous current excites the oxygen and nitrogen in the air to the point at which they radiate visible light, and the color of their combined emissions is white.

By various observational techniques, physicists have measured the temperature of the lightning channel to be roughly 27,000° to 28,000° Celsius, or more than four times hotter than the surface of the sun. The heated gases in the channel explode into the surrounding air as a shock wave. This wave travels only a short distance before it decays into the acoustic wave we know as thunder. For all its sound and fury, the lightning channel is only a few centimeters in diameter.

With the channel well established, subsequent strokes called "dart leaders" may carry more negative charge from the cloud. Although they travel the same route as the stepped leaders, the darts aren't pulsed. They flow continuously, moving faster, carrying a somewhat diminished charge. This results in smaller currents and less spectacular return strokes, until the cloud's charge is temporarily depleted.

CASUALTIES

In the United States alone, lightning starts about 10,000 forest fires a year, and one violent half-hour thunderstorm may ignite as many as 200 in a single area. Ecologists consider some portion of these "burns" beneficial, and note that many animals and plants are "fire adapted." The cones of the lodgepole pine, for example, are usually sealed shut with resin and don't fall off the trees. Fire makes the cones drop, open, and release their seeds. So, although the individual tree may be destroyed, new ones flourish in the fire's wake.

The stepped leader's whole halting, forked progression from cloud to ground—a distance of several kilometers—may take as long as twenty milliseconds (one millisecond is equal to 1/1,000 of a second). It is almost totally invisible.

Meanwhile, as the leader nears the ground, positive charge in the earth travels upward to meet it, shooting to the highest points of the landscape, of buildings, poles, trees, lightning rods, people, animals—any of which may begin emitting sparks.

Like two construction teams laying railroad track from opposite ends of the line, the

Alan R. Taylor of the U.S. Forest Service reports that most trees struck by lightning are not killed, yet the injury weakens them, making them easy marks for insects or disease. In a study of a thousand Douglas firs damaged by lightning in western Montana, Taylor found that most lightning scars ran spirals around the trees—peeling off long strips of bark the way a paring knife would skin an apple.

People and animals can be killed by a direct strike. With muscles and nerves paralyzed by electric shock, they stop breathing and die unless they get immediate cardiopulmonary resuscitation. (Since neither people nor pets retain the electric charge of the flash, it is safe to touch them.)

PRECAUTIONS

Experts at the U.S. National Weather Service agree that the best thing to do if you're caught outdoors during a thunderstorm is to go indoors—a house or large building, or inside a closed, all-metal (not convertible) vehicle. If you are in an open area with no shelter nearby, you should try to find a ravine or valley in which to lay low, literally. In a forest the safest spot is under a thick growth of small trees.

Bad places to be include (1) under a tall, isolated tree; (2) in or near open water; (3) on a tractor or other metal farm equipment; (4) on a motorcycle, scooter, golf cart, or bicycle; (5) next to a wire fence, clothesline, metal pipe, rail, or other metallic path that could carry lightning to you; (6) in a small, isolated shed or other unprotected structure in an open area.

HAUNTS

Florida is the U.S.'s most lightning-struck state. The 80-kilometer-wide path from Tampa, on the Gulf Coast, to Daytona Beach, on the Atlantic, is nicknamed "Lightning Alley." For sheer showmanship, however, the lightning displays over Kitt Peak, in Arizona, are unparalleled. In general, lightning is common in the tropic and temperate zones and most infrequent at the poles.

Orbiting satellites are being used to track worldwide lightning frequency. Studies with Vela satellites have revealed "superbolts" of lightning. The superbolts appear to have one hundred times the power of ordinary lightning, but occur only rarely—once in two million strokes. So far, most of them have been seen in conjunction with winter storms over Japan.

IN MANY FORMS

Always associated with the sky, bolts of lightning have actually been preserved in sand and rock. These "fulgurites," or "petrified lightning," are fragile, glassy tubes formed when lightning strikes in sand, melting the particles around its path and fusing them together. The hollow fulgurites, self-portraits of the lightning channels that made them, range from 1.5 to 5 centimeters in diameter. Some fossil fulgurites date back as far as 250,000,000 years.

In addition to the jagged forked bolts that fulgurites preserve, lightning takes many other shapes. Ball lightning, often the source of UFO reports, is the most bizarre. In fact, some scientists have tried to dismiss these balls of fire as afterimages left on the retina by lightning flashes, but they seem to have a reality of their own.

"The reports describe them as luminous spheres ranging in size from a tennis ball up to that of a basketball, usually moving at a moderate pace," Walter Sullivan wrote in *The New York Times*.

"Bead" or "chain" lightning is the term used to describe an ordinary lightning channel that appears to break up into persistent fragments, each one many meters long. Whereas some say the beads are chains of ball lightning, other theories ascribe them to strange magnetic effects that pinch the bolt into a sausage-string shape, or the obscuring effect of clouds and rain, or the result of viewing the lightning from an unusual angle.

The Saint Elmo's fire often seen on airplane noses and wing tips is caused by the same kind of charge difference between earth and sky that precedes a lightning flash. The glow may tip steers' horns or form a halo about people's heads—harmless, except that it highlights areas of intense electrical activity where lightning may strike. The burning bush of the Bible that smoldered but was not consumed has been explained as an instance of

Saint Elmo's fire. The name derives from Saint Erasmus—Italian bishop of the fourth century A.D. and patron saint of Mediterranean sailors, many of whom interpreted a glowing mast or spar as a sign of his presence.

"Sheet lightning," or the broad glow of a whole cloud lit up by an internal stroke of lightning, is often overshadowed during storms by the flashier bolts running cloud to ground.When sheet lightning is seen at a great distance on a summer's night as "heat lightning," however, it is usually impressive enough to talk about.

Ribbons of lightning, seeming to trace identical paths side by side in the sky, are

25 lightning strokes per second over one limited region.

Frank Drake, director of the U.S. National Astronomy and Ionosphere Center, at Cornell University, says that radio astronomers have found the kinds of clouds and convection patterns that should produce lightning on Jupiter, Saturn, "and possibly Mars, because of the dust storms." He says that this extraterrestrial lightning would come in different colors, since the atmospheres of the other planets are so different from earth's. Jupiter, for example, should have reddish pink flashes, because of its hydrogen atmosphere.

Robert M. Butterfield

The whole sky is lit up—with cloud-to-cloud and cloud-to-ground lightning.

caused by wind and illusion. An observer sees ribbon lightning when gusts blow the channel a good distance sideways. He or she perceives two or more component strokes, which are really separated in time, as though they were occurring simultaneously. When there's no wind, a photographer can simulate on film the appearance of ribbon lightning by moving the camera.

EXOTICA

Since lightning is an atmospheric phenomenon, we shouldn't be surprised to learn that it commonly occurs in the atmospheres of other planets. In February 1979, data from the *Pioneer* Venus spacecraft indicated abundant lightning in the clouds of Venus. Soviet spacecraft also encountered intense atmospheric electricity on Venus—as many as

RESEARCH

Only a few scientists are engaged in full-time lightning research. A group, forming the Thunderstorm Research International Project, or TRIP, now does joint research. It is headquartered in Socorro, New Mexico, where the New Mexico Institute of Mining and Technology has covered a whole mountaintop with appropriate instrumentation. Other research projects involve an experiment scheduled to fly on the second space shuttle mission □

 SELECTED READINGS

"The frightening mystery of the electrical storm," by Henry Lansford. *Smithsonian,* August 1979.

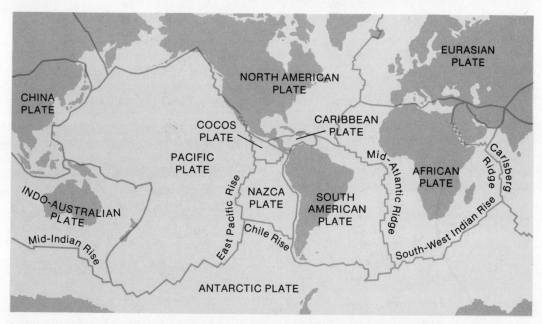

The theory of plate tectonics holds that the earth's crust is broken into six large and several small rigid plates that move slowly relative to one another, carrying the continents.

PLATE TECTONICS

by J. Tuzo Wilson

JIGSAW PUZZLE—that's what many people think of when they look at a map of the world. Push Europe and Africa over across the Atlantic and the coastlines fit—fit very well—against the coastlines of the Americas. Move India, Australia, and Antarctica around and you find that their coastlines also fit together. Like pieces in a giant jigsaw puzzle.

After the Americas were discovered and mapped centuries ago, several learned men noticed that the opposing coasts along the Atlantic had shapes that would fit together. They proposed that early in earth's history the continents had been joined and that later they had been violently torn apart. In the 19th century this idea was supported by studies of the geology and life forms on both sides of the Atlantic that revealed many similarities—some dating from times long after the origin of the earth and indeed as recently as the age of dinosaurs some 150,000,000 years ago.

Studies such as these led Alfred Wegener, a German meteorologist, to propose in 1912 the theory of continental drift.

CONTINENTAL DRIFT

Wegener believed that the opening of the Atlantic, Indian, and Southern oceans was not due to any early cataclysms but rather had occurred slowly and gradually in the center part of geologic time. He supported the admitted similarities of shape, geology, and some living forms on opposite coasts with arguments from surveys that purportedly showed that Greenland was moving relative to Europe at a measurable rate. He further theorized that because the earth is a rotating sphere there exists a force that pushes continents toward the equator. The continents, he believed, plowed through rocks of the sea floor like a ship through water.

LITTLE SUPPORT

While biologists in particular agreed that the similarities were real, geologists and physicists disagreed with Wegener's other arguments and suggested that the similarities might have a cause other than continental drift. Some, for example, proposed that land bridges had once crossed oceans and were responsible for the similarities of life forms. Geologists also showed that the surveys were in error and that the forces on a spheroid are small and act in the wrong direction to explain Wegener's ideas. They further argued that even if the Andes in South America were formed like low waves before continents advancing westward, there were no signs of any break or disturbance along the eastern coasts of the Americas where the wake of the continents should have been seen. While these arguments did not entirely destroy the possibility of drift, they took away support for the theory. When Wegener died in 1930 very few geologists had accepted his ideas.

The chief exceptions were some geologists in the Southern Hemisphere who were impressed by the particularly good match of coastlines across the oceans there. Some Alpine geologists were also impressed by the tremendous compression of hundreds of kilometers indicated by the folding and thrusting of some rocks over others in the mountains. The rest could see little need for the theory and no mechanism to explain drift on a solid earth.

EARLY CLUES

About the time of Wegener's death several geologists made observations that suggested a mechanism for and provided an explanation of continental drift. They realized that the slow radioactive decay of several naturally occurring elements in the earth produced much heat—enough so that the earth, although largely solid, is white hot inside, hot enough to deform rocks. The rocks could then be slowly deformed to generate convection currents in the earth's interior. The currents would be like those in a pan of water heated on a stove, but incredibly large and slow. These geologists further proposed that these currents might be rising under ridges then known only vaguely to occur along the central axes of oceans; that they might be turning down again under active mountains and deep ocean trenches like those off Chile, Peru, and East Asia; and that they might carry the continents along at rates of about 5 to 10 centimeters a year.

These suggestions were vague and little regarded, and most scientists continued to reject the theory of continental drift. But then in the decade between 1956 and 1967 new discoveries revived it in a new form called plate tectonics.

MAGNETIC CLUES

Around 1956 two discoveries turned the tide in geological thinking. One was the finding that the past motions of continents could be traced through an analysis of the magnetism of the rocks on the continents. The second discovery was that there is a continuous mid-ocean ridge throughout the world's oceans.

Since ancient times it has been known that a few rocks, chiefly iron ores, are natural magnets and can be used as compasses. As time went on, instruments improved and it was found that most all rocks are magnetized—though more feebly than iron ores. Further it was discovered that rocks acquire their magnetism from the earth's magnetic field at the time of their formation and that they retain this magnetization tenaciously thereafter.

Thus lavas poured out near earth's magnetic poles are magnetized as they cool in the same vertical direction as the field at the poles. Sediments accumulating in an ocean near the poles are similarly magnetized. On the other hand, rocks forming near earth's equator where the magnetic field is horizontal are magnetized in that direction. And so through other areas of the earth. Rocks are magnetized in a direction appropriate to the latitude of the place where they form, and they retain that direction of magnetization thereafter.

Around 1956 it was discovered that rocks of recent origin on several continents were magnetized in directions corresponding to their location, but that rocks known to have been formed at successively older times showed progressively different magnetic orientations. Further it was found that the orientation changes were just what would be expected if the continents had been moving in the way Wagener and his few followers had proposed. This was striking proof for the theory of continental drift.

MID-OCEAN RIDGE

The second discovery—of a continuous mid-ocean ridge throughout the world—pointed to a possible mechanism explaining the movement. In 1956 U.S. geophysicist Maurice Ewing and others began detailed investigations of the ocean floor. Evidence accumulated over several years suggested that a great broad mountain system lay down the center of the Atlantic Ocean from the Arctic to the Southern Ocean. There, this system, called the mid-ocean ridge, turns to the Indian Ocean. In the middle of the Indian Ocean it branches, one branch going into the Gulf of Aden and the Red Sea and the other passing mid-way between Australia and Antarctica to cross the Pacific and enter the Gulf of California. There it forms the San Andreas fault and emerges again off the coast of Canada as far as Alaska. A faulted, or cracked, valley—a rift—follows the crest of the mid-ocean ridge in most places. Shallow earthquakes occur all along the axis in all oceans.

SEA-FLOOR SPREADING

By 1960 ships had surveyed all of this ridge. Based on accumulated evidence, geologist Harry Hess of Princeton University revived the idea that the crest of the ridge is where the ocean-floor spreads apart. He proposed that as the two sides spread apart intrusions of hot lava from beneath the crust create new ocean floor. He combined this with the idea that the surface crust, being cool and brittle, could slide, carried by very slow currents in the earth's hot interior, until it breaks again. Then one piece could be overlapped and carried down beneath the other side of the break.

This activity occurs under active mountains, ocean trenches, and island arcs. The theory explains why a second great belt of earthquakes marks these areas around the world, rimming the Pacific and following the Himalayas and Alpine Mountains across Eurasia. In places where the brittle crust is forced down deep into the interior it may break. This explains why the only earthquakes observed to occur deep in the center are beneath these areas to depths as great as 700 kilometers.

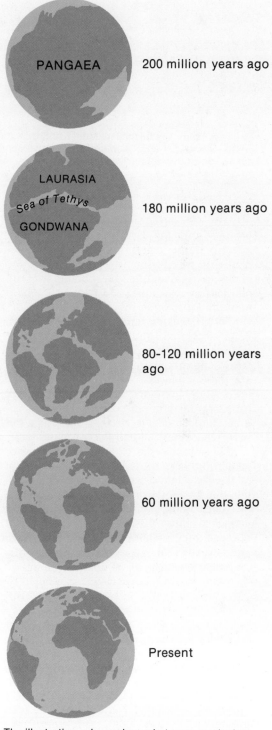

The illustrations above show what some geologists think may have occurred as one giant landmass broke apart during geologic time.

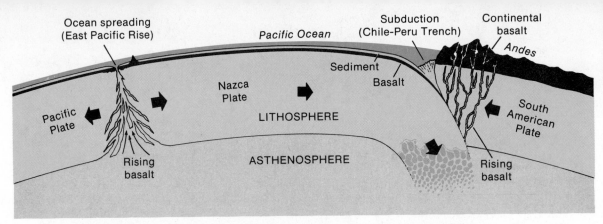

Geologists think that molten material rising from the earth's mantle at mid-ocean ridges creates new crust and "powers" plate movement, and that older ocean floor is then pushed down beneath colliding plates into deep trenches like those off Peru and Chile.

SIX LARGE PLATES

By 1965 further investigations led to the proposal that the earth's surface is broken into six large plates and several smaller plates. It was further suggested that these plates are rigid and that their boundaries are marked by earthquakes where the plates move and also often by volcanoes.

Where plates separate and new ocean floor is created, mid-ocean ridges are the boundaries. Where plates collide and overlap, young mountains and arcs and trenches are the boundaries. Where two plates slide horizontally past one another, a boundary called a transform fault occurs. The San Andreas fault system is a transform fault between the American and Pacific plates.

The three types of boundaries join together in a network to break the whole crust of the earth into a series of plates. This system and its motion is called plate tectonics.

One should point out that a theorem in geometry shows that the relative motion of one part of the shell of a sphere relative to another part is always a rotation about poles and an axis which can be defined. Therefore the plates move relative to one another.

RAFT CONTINENTS

The theory of plate tectonics differs somewhat from that of continental drift. Continental drift suggests that each continent moves like a ship through the ocean floor. Plate tectonics holds that the continents are like rafts frozen in the ice of a flowing stream, carried along with surrounding ocean floor in huge plates.

There are six major plates: the American, the African, the Eurasian, the Antarctic, the Indian, and the Pacific. The American plate comprises North and South America and the floor of the western half of the Atlantic. The African plate contains Africa and much surrounding ocean floor. The Antarctic plate has Antarctica and surrounding sea floor; the Eurasian plate, Europe, Asia, and nearby sea floor. The Indian plate has India, Australia, and all the sea floor between them. The Pacific plate underlies the Pacific.

MAGNETIC STRIPES

Studies of the oceans continued, and new discoveries allowed the theory of plate tectonics to be further developed. Magnetic surveys over ocean basins revealed a regular pattern of stripes of alternately stronger and weaker magnetization on the floors of the oceans. In the early 1960's British oceanographers F. J. Vine and D. H. Matthews showed that these stripes are oriented parallel with the axes of mid-ocean ridges and, in fact, follow the ridges around the earth. They recalled that the earth's magnetic field is known to reverse at irregular intervals of time from a few thousands to a few million years long. This reversal means that the earth's field, without changing its direction, becomes weaker and weaker until it fades away to nothing—and then returns in an exactly reversed direction. What had been the north magnetic pole becomes the south magnetic pole and vice versa.

Vine and Matthews pointed out that the lavas coming up along the crest of the mid-ocean ridge to form new sea floor would be magnetized as they cooled in the direction of the earth's field when they formed. These lavas would be added to the separating plates and carried away equally in either direction. When after a period of thousands to millions of years the field reversed, the lavas injected following the reversal would be magnetized in the reversed direction. This reversing magnetization would alternately strengthen and weaken the magnetic effect measured in surveys and would appear as a symmetrical striped pattern around the spreading seafloor axis.

TIME SCALE

Enough measurements have now been made to provide a time scale of reversals and to date all of the ocean floors. The scheme is like that by which tree rings mark the stages of growth in a tree. It turns out that northwestern Africa began to separate from the eastern coast of the present-day United States about 180,000,000 years ago; that Africa began to move relative to South America about 160,000,000 years ago; and that no part of the present oceans are more than 200,000,000 years old.

MOUNTAIN BUILDING

The theory of plate tectonics also explains much about when and how active mountains like the Andes in western South America and the Cascades in western North America were built at the converging boundaries of plates. As two plates collide parts of the earth's crust are uplifted and folded with great compression and thrusting of rocks occurring. Earthquakes and volcanoes frequently occur. But what about older mountains—mountains no longer characterized by volcanoes, severe earthquakes, and other signs of young life, mountains like the Urals and Himalayas that lie in the middle of continents?

Magnetic studies suggest that the continents did not separate just once with the breakup of a gigantic landmass. Rather, continents have been breaking apart and separating and coming together and joining in different patterns for much of geologic time. This suggests that older mountains like the Urals and Himalayas may have once been on the edges of continents and may have been formed when different plates came together in the past. In other words, older mountains

may mark the sites where plates once converged in the geologic past.

The Atlantic Ocean started to open about 180,000,000 years ago. It opened nearly along the line of closure of an earlier ocean. The sides of this earlier ocean—usually called Tapetus after the father of oceans in Greek mythology—came together some 600,000,000 years ago and raised up a mountain range. The opening of the Atlantic millions of years later tore this range into fragments. These fragments are now part of the Appalachian mountains in eastern North America, the mountains of western Morocco across the present Atlantic, mountains farther north in East Greenland, and the Caledonia Mountains of Scotland and Norway.

VOLCANOES

The theory of plate tectonics can also explain other geological occurrences—volcanoes, for example. Most volcanoes occur, as we have noted, along plate boundaries. They occur at separating ridges—for example, in Iceland, the Azores, and Tristan da Cunha, along the mid-Atlantic ridge. Or they occur along converging plate boundaries, as in the Andes where the American and Antarctic plates are converging. A few, however, have erupted in the middle of plates: those in Hawaii, for example, and the hot springs and

Iceland straddles the Mid-Atlantic Ridge and is the site of much volcanic activity, evidenced here when Helgafell on Heimaey, off Iceland, erupted.
Wide World

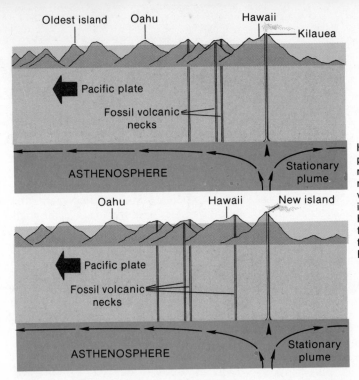

Hot spots—rapidly rising plumes of molten material—are thought to be responsible for mid-plate volcanoes, such as those in Hawaii. The older Hawaiian islands—and their volcanic origins—trace the motion of the Pacific plate.

now-dormant volcanoes of the Yellowstone Park area in western North America. What causes these?

It has been suggested that, besides great, slow convection currents that carry plates about the earth, there are also smaller, somewhat more rapidly rising jets or plumes of hot material rising in the mantle of the earth. (The earth is believed to be composed of an inner solid core; middle mantle that is at least partially molten; and an outer crust.) These plumes, often called hot spots, can be likened to smaller and more active thunderheads or tornadoes associated with a much larger advancing weather front.

Most of the isolated, mid-plate volcanoes like those of Hawaii and the Yellowstone area lie at one end of a line of extinct volcanoes, which get steadily older with distance from the active center. Thus Hawaii itself with its two active volcanoes, Mauna Loa and Kilauea, is at the extreme southeastern end of the chain of the rest of the Hawaiian islands, which become steadily eroded and older to the northeast. Likewise Yellowstone is at the east end of a line of extinct volcanoes extending into the Snake River and Mountains of the Moon in Idaho. These chains of extinct volcanoes have been likened to smoke that the wind is carrying away from a chimney.

The theory of plate tectonics, with the aid of magnetic imprinting, allows the rate and direction of movement of any plate to be found relative to any other plate. If one plate—say the Antarctic—is considered stationary relative to the deep interior of the earth, the date and direction of all other plates can be determined. An analysis of sea-floor spreading has been used to do this. It turns out that the motions of the Pacific plate are compatible with the direction of the Hawaiian chain and the ages of the islands. Plate motion has slowly moved the volcanoes—and islands—away from the hot spot that created them. In other words, the Hawaiian island chain traces the motion of the Pacific plate.

In some spots mid-ocean ridges produce more lava than in other parts and island volcanoes form—as in Iceland. These spots may also be hot spots. In these cases, however, two ridges may form, one on each of the two separating plates. Ridges extend from Iceland, which straddles the Mid-Atlantic Ridge, westward to Greenland on the American plate and eastward to the Faeroe Islands in the North Atlantic on the Eurasian plate. Similarly, ridges extend from the active volcanic island of Tristan da Cunha westward to South America and eastward to Africa.

Hot spots also occur at the junction of some plates. Examples are the Azores where the American, Eurasian, and African plates meet, and Macquerie Island south of New Zealand, where the Pacific, Antarctic, and Indian plates meet. Some geologists find this significant. They propose that, although hot spots do not drive plates about, they may perhaps help to determine the lines along which plates fracture and separate.

ARCS AND TRENCHES

If the theory of hot spots and relative motions is correct, it has other possible consequences. Where ocean floor is being carried down freely into the interior, it is likely to do so along circular arcs. This is so for the same reason that if one pushes one's thumb into a dead tennis ball the depression is circular. Geometry dictates this pattern. This may explain the origin of the dozen or so circular island arcs on the earth—such as the Aleutians.

If, on the other hand, a continent overrides an ocean floor, which is itself stationary, it will force down the floor in a trench directly off the coast. An example of this may be the deep trenches off Peru and Chile.

PRACTICAL USES

The theory of plate tectonics, which has now been generally accepted by geologists, has several practical applications. It tells, for example, much about the cause and distribution of earthquakes and where they can be expected to occur. Although no one has yet been able to predict the exact time of a major earthquake, intensive research in earthquake prediction is going on and such forecasts may become possible.

The theory also throws light on where and in what way many mineral deposits may have formed. Many important petroleum deposits lie near coasts, both on and off shore. These deposits can be seen to have begun to accumulate when the particular ocean started to form, so the oldest rocks—and the chances for petroleum finds—can be predicted even before drilling begins. Knowledge of plate motions can also explain many other features of petroleum basins.

Exploration of mid-ocean ridges has

Ontario Science Center

Canadian geophysicist J. Tuzo Wilson—author of this article—proposed the theory of hot spots, which explains the distribution of some volcanoes and provides further evidence for plate tectonics.

disclosed streams of hot waters bearing abundant metals in solution pouring out of the rift in some places—in the Red Sea, off the Galapagos Islands, and in the Gulf of California, for example. These discoveries have helped explain the source of elements found dissolved in sea water or precipitated from it such as manganese nodules on the sea floor. They also help explain how ore bodies form. More underwater mineral sources will undoubtedly be found and some may be exploited either as sources of minerals or as sources of heat and energy.

AND SO THE PUZZLE FITS

And so the pieces of the jigsaw puzzle fit—and we know why. In a few years the theory of plate tectonics has for the first time provided a comprehensive theory of the behavior of the earth—an essential to understanding our home in space □

 SELECTED READINGS

Continents in Motion by Walter Sullivan. McGraw-Hill, 1974.
Earth Science, Winter 1978, Spring 1979, and Autumn 1979 issues.
"Spotlight on hot spots" by K. Frazier. *Science News,* September 22, 1979.
"Tracking the continents from an ice cube" by K. Bruhm. *Macleans,* June 18, 1979.

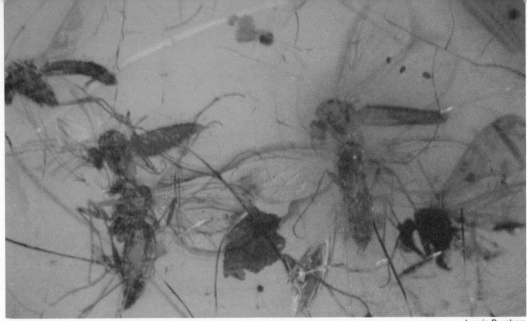

Laurie Burnham

A swarm of midges was trapped in this Baltic amber as it hardened.

AMBER

by Laurie Burnham

ENTER the dark, quiet recesses of a pine forest and you are at once surrounded by tall, gaunt trees whose crowns thrust skyward as if attempting to break free from the closeness below. Their trunks are covered in brown bark, marked here and there with myriad patterns of color. A closer look reveals sticky bubbles and rivulets of sap oozing from wounds and cracks in the bark.

Looking yet again, one may see the delicate legs and antennae of insects struggling against the viscous resin that has trapped them. Anyone who has placed a hand on fresh pine sap knows how undeniably sticky this plant secretion is and how only after the most devoted scrubbing can it be removed from the skin.

Similar processes were taking place on earth as far back as 100,000,000 years ago, and insects, or rather their ancient ancestors, were ensnared in the sticky secretion much as they are today. One difference, however, between the plant resins of prehistoric times and those of today is that the former, secreted long before humans first appeared on earth, have become fossil resins and are collectively called amber. It is this distinction, the millions of years of preservation, that separates amber from a similarly hardened but recent resin we call copal.

VARIETY OF RESINS

Amber is a common, catchall word used when referring to a wide range of fossil resins produced by a large number of different types of trees. Amber, a plant product, originates as a tree resin. It is synthesized in special tree tissues and then stored in vesicles and channels in the tree until periods of increased growth such as in the spring. At this time cracks develop in the bark. The resin flows from these cracks. Syrupy and soft when first secreted, the resin eventually transforms itself into the hardened end product that we call amber.

Some 39 varieties of amber have been recognized, most of them produced by three genera of trees: *Pinus* (pines), *Picea* (spruce), and *Abies* (fir). Although the varieties of amber differ in both chemical and physical properties, the basic ingredients are the same, a complex mix of organic constituents: terpenes, resin acids, alcohols, esters, aromatics, and resins.

Most amber has a translucent, golden-yellow hue, but some has been discovered in various shades of green, red, or blue. White amber has thousands of tiny air bubbles trapped inside. Typically, amber is lightweight, and will float in salt water. It is also a relatively stable substance known to be insoluble in organic solvents.

Amber is, however, extremely susceptible to desiccation, or drying out, and this presents the greatest obstacle to its preservation. Oxidation or exposure to air will dry the outside of amber faster than the inside, culminating in cracking and eventual disintegration of the piece. As a consequence, amber is found only in deposits where it has been well protected—either deep in the soil, buried in clay beds, or in water. Such deposits have been found throughout the world, and some have yielded great quantities of amber. The most notable of these was first discovered hundreds of years ago on the edge of the Baltic Sea. Another famous site currently being mined for amber is in the Dominican Republic. Other less productive deposits have been found in Italy, Burma, Denmark, England, Lebanon, and the Soviet Union. In the United States, amber has been found in Wyoming, North Carolina, Kansas, Alaska, Arkansas, and along the East Coast—particularly in New Jersey.

MYSTICAL APPEAL

Early humans who found golden drops of amber near the sea believed them to be sunlight solidifying on the ocean waves. Amber is, after all, golden and translucent. Others disagreed and pointed to the remains of animals and plants entombed within the resin. Aristotle claimed that these remains proved that the substance must be derived from living trees. However, in the 16th century, the German mineralogist Agricola disputed Aristotle's claim by pointing to the Baltic amber and asking, "How can amber be derived from trees, seeing that it is thrown forth from the sea?"

Such skepticism over the origin of amber only added to its popular, mystical appeal. Many regarded it as a defense against witchcraft. Such attitudes stemmed from the belief that these powers were generated by the plants and animals entombed within the amber, organisms so perfectly preserved that each individual almost looked alive.

EARLY PRODUCTION

Most of the amber harvested at this time came from the edge of the Baltic Sea and for this reason is known as Baltic amber. This is, in fact, a misnomer of sorts, because Baltic amber was actually produced inland some 40,000,000 years earlier by what is thought to have been the extinct conifer *Pinus succinifera*. Rivers and ice gradually transported the amber piece by piece over millions of years from its origin to its present location at the edge of the Baltic Sea. There it was deposited in clay beds on land or washed into the sea.

During storms large amounts of amber were tossed upon the beaches and subsequently collected by basket-carrying women and children. Fishermen brandishing long-handled nets hauled masses of seaweed to shore and then disentangled enormous amounts of amber trapped in the slimy matrix. In more modern times explosives were hurled into the sea to produce the same effect as natural storms. Then in the 19th century, mechanized equipment modified from the mining industry was put to use. This highly

Amber comes in all shapes and in several colors. Most is suitable only for chemical processing.

Laurie Burnham

efficient technique boosted the amber harvest to unprecedented levels of production. During the height of production some 500,000 to 600,000 kilograms were said to have been collected per year.

In all, an estimated total of 4,500,000,-000 kilograms of Baltic amber has been recovered so far. One must realize, however, that this total does not refer to mounds of beautiful, jewellike amber. Amber is generally sorted into three categories: that— about 80 per cent of the total harvested— good for chemical processing only; that clean but too small for anything but making melted, reconstituted amber; and finally, that for jewelry—the type we are most familiar with. Large quantities of chemical grade amber were melted for use as lacquer, particularly as a finish for the steamboats and sailing vessels of the day. The larger pieces of

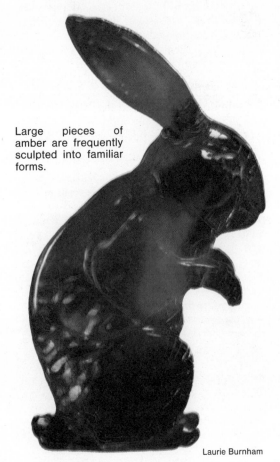

Large pieces of amber are frequently sculpted into familiar forms.

Laurie Burnham

amber were sculpted by local artists. Other pieces were made into jewelry such as necklaces, earrings, and cufflinks.

ENTER SCIENCE

In these early days of amber production, amber was sought primarily for aesthetic and mystical reasons. Since then our fascination with fossil resins has become increasingly scientific in its emphasis. Amber is unquestionably attractive—but no more so than a host of other semi-precious gems. What then makes it so uniquely appealing?

Without a doubt, amber is a special substance because of its inclusions—the countless vestiges of life that existed long ago but remain preserved forever inside their golden sepulchers. Biologists and geologists are drawn to the substance for the invaluable information it provides about the now-extinct animals and plants entombed within it.

Because much amber is translucent, the plants and animals trapped inside can be clearly seen. Even such delicate structures as the legs on a crane fly, the antennae of an ant, or the tiniest gnat wings are visible. In terms of absolute purity of preservation, amber is far superior to other fossil materials. An insect preserved in shale, for instance, is often nothing but an indistinct blur. In contrast, amber tends to contain exceptionally well-preserved insect inclusions. Even such details as body hairs and bristles can readily be seen and studied.

Amber does, however, have one drawback: unlike mineral matrices that preserve either already dead organisms or entire communities (as in catastrophic burial), amber traps its victims selectively. As a consequence, not all organisms are preserved in amber, but only those that are too small or weak to escape the sticky, viscous resin. This is why there is a preponderance of very small invertebrates such as tiny insects, spiders, and ticks in amber.

Plant material is also trapped in amber. Not-yet-hardened resin falling onto the ground probably resulted in the inclusion of fragments of moss, leaves, and other detritus.

Amber also has provided valuable data on the ecological and environmental conditions at the time of its deposition. For in-

Laurie Burnham

Even the delicate structures of this dark-winged funfus gnat are visible in the translucent amber.

stance, we know that the majority of resin production today takes place in the tropical and subtropical regions of the world and is only minimally important in temperate ecosystems. Furthermore, on the basis of plant remains, we can equate fossil flora with comparable flora of today. From this we can draw inferences about climatic conditions in the past.

A good example involves the amber from the Baltic region. Analysis of this amber has revealed no fewer than 15 varieties of oak, as well as beech, chestnut, maple, holly, and a dozen species of pine. Evidence that the climate of the area 40,000,000 years ago was warmer than it is today is provided by the presence of cinnamon, palmetto, date palm, cycad, olive, and sandalwood—all vegetation currently found in the more tropical areas of the world.

CANADIAN AMBER

Canadian amber was virtually unknown until well into the 20th century. Although collected for hundreds of years by the Chemahawin Indians of northern Manitoba for jewelry, fuel, and medicine, its existence was, for the most part, hidden from the rest of the world.

It was January 1935 when Professor Frank M. Carpenter, eminent scholar of insect evolution at Harvard University, noticed a short abstract in the bulletin of the Mineralogical Society of America, which mentioned an amber deposit in northern Canada and the presence of "possible insect inclusions." Professor Carpenter took immediate steps to contact the author of the abstract. One hundred pieces of the Cedar Lake amber, containing an astonishing total of 87 insect inclusions, were sent to Carpenter. The following summer an expedition of five persons brought back 180 kilograms of amber to the Museum of Comparative Zoology at Harvard University. Several hundred insect specimens were identified, and substantial information about the diversity and type of insects living in the area at that time was provided. The amber was a particularly important find, because at 100,000,000 years old, it was roughly 60,000,000 years older than any previously discovered amber.

U.S. AMBER

Not until 1967 did a similarly exciting discovery take place—this time in the United States. For years paleontologists and amateurs had explored the amber deposits along the eastern seaboard of the United States. Much was found of interest to botanists, but it was not until 1967 that a specimen, collected by amateurs along the beach bluffs at Cliffwood, New Jersey two years earlier, was recognized as having insect inclusions, most likely ants. Professor Donald Baird of the Princeton Geology Department, who recognized the inclusions, thought that Frank Carpenter might be interested and suggested that the piece be lent to him for study.

Frank Carpenter was more than interested. While waiting for the amber to arrive in Cambridge, he vacillated between being skeptical and tremendously excited. If the inclusions really were ants, they would be the oldest ants yet discovered, and therefore of extreme importance to an understanding of ant evolution. Questions long unanswered might now be resolved. Questions such as: were ants as fully social 100,000,000 years ago as they are now? To an ebullient trio of scientists—F. M. Carpenter and E. O. Wilson at Harvard, and W. L. Brown at Cornell University—the answers were soon forthcoming.

The ants were instantly recognized as worker ants and therefore provided proof that sociality had indeed evolved in the ant family by 100,000,000 years ago. Equally interesting was the discovery that the ants were very primitive in form and closely related to wasps. These workers were formally described and given the name *Sphecomyrma freyi—Sphecomyrma,* which means a wasp-like ant, and *freyi* in honor of the Freys, the amateurs who discovered the amber. According to Frank Carpenter, the discovery was "without question, the century's most outstanding find in elucidating our understanding of ant evolution."

FORGERY PROBLEMS

Because inclusions like *Sphecomyrma* contribute so much to the value of amber for both scientific and aesthetic reasons, forgery has become a pervasive problem. Copal, a modern-day resin containing insects and other organisms, has been passed off as amber, and unfortunately in some cases, the inclusions have been described as being much older than they really are. This, in turn, can lead to a false representation of flora and fauna species in the fossil record. A different but equally odious type of forgery is effected by softening pieces of genuine amber and inserting present-day organisms into this softened matrix.

Fortunately, neither of these fraudulent methods is flawless. Special laboratory techniques can determine the source and age of a particular resin and can reveal if amber has been softened.

TREASURED COMMODITY

Fossils provide the only concrete evidence by which we can follow the course of evolution and reconstruct the history of life. Amber, because of its unique clarity, has been particularly important in providing a glimpse into the past, an opportunity to study the smaller organisms, such as insects. Sustained analysis of amber inclusions will broaden and deepen this knowledge. Without understanding the diversity of life in the past, we cannot begin to appreciate fully life in the present, nor can we unravel the complexities and magnitude of the evolutionary process □

 SELECTED READINGS

The Magic of Amber by Rosa Hunger. Chilton 1979.

Plant material is also frequently trapped in amber. Here a flower calyx.

Laurie Burnham

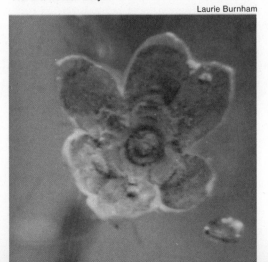

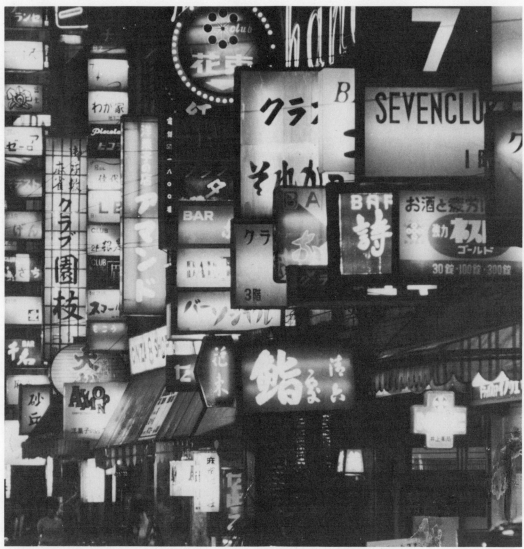

Peter Gridley/FPG

Japan is the world's largest oil importer (after the United States) and its energy costs are skyrocketing. Recent conservation measures include turning down the lights in the famous Ginza district.

ENERGY

ENERGY
REVIEW OF THE YEAR

UPI

Increased oil prices, agreed to at OPEC meetings such as the one shown above, continue to create an energy problem throughout much of the world.

Gasoline shortages continued in some areas and prices rose—and rose.

UPI

"Our nation's energy problem is serious—and it's getting worse," said U.S. President Jimmy Carter in his April 1979 energy address to the nation. No issue conveyed the magnitude of that message during 1979 more than the year-long spiralling increase in the price of crude oil.

Rising Oil Prices. The Organization of Petroleum Exporting Countries (OPEC), a cartel from which the United States purchases most of its imported oil, hiked the price per barrel roughly 130 per cent during the year. Owing to the net shortage of oil on the world market, some noncartel countries like Canada, Great Britain, and Mexico were able to maintain their crude-oil prices above OPEC ceilings for much of the year without jeopardizing sales. The result was an exorbitant balance-of-payments problem for oil importers, with developing nations among those hardest hit. But even industrial giants like the United States were left staggering. Importing roughly 6,000,000 barrels per day, or about one half of the oil it uses, cost the United States more than $50,000,000,000 in 1979.

The higher oil prices had widespread effects. They accounted for a 46 per cent rise in national energy prices from January through July. In addition, increased spending on imported oil contributed to a decline in the purchasing power of the U.S. dollar against foreign currencies. It was, however, President Carter who best outlined one of the most serious and, for the most part, subtle costs. He said, "Our national strength is dangerously dependent on a thin line of oil tankers stretching halfway around the earth originating in the Middle East and around the Persian Gulf—one of the most unstable regions in the world."

Response: New Policies. To reduce dependence on foreign oil, Carter proposed several major revisions to his national energy policy. June 1, 1979, marked the beginning of a phased decontrol of domestic oil prices to allow them to reach world levels. Controlled domestic prices were $6.00 per barrel for oil in production before 1973 and $13.00 per barrel for oil in production later. By the end of 1979 world prices were about $30.00 per barrel for contract sales from OPEC and up to about $50.00 per barrel on the spot market.

Chief among Carter's other proposals was enactment of a windfall-profits tax to recover the unearned money which Carter claimed oil companies would reap under decontrol. Revenue from the tax would go toward credits to reimburse low- and moderate-income families for investments in energy-saving measures. To encourage rapid development and commercialization of renewable-energy sources and energy-efficient technologies, Carter proposed an energy mobilization board. U.S. federal programs approved by the board would get speedy and preferred treatment by government agencies. By the end of 1979 legislation for both proposals was in Congressional committees. ∎ Carrying out new energy policy became the job of Charles W. Duncan Jr., who, on August 24, became the second U.S. Energy Secretary, replacing James R. Schlesinger.

Nuclear Energy. No single event dominated energy news in 1979 more than the catastrophic crippling of the Three Mile Island #2 nuclear power plant near Harrisburg, Pennsylvania, which threatened to release massive amounts of radioactive material into the environment. The drama began shortly after 4 a.m. on March 28, 1979 and continued into 1980 as investigations continued to turn up new data on the causes of the accident—the worst in U.S. nuclear-power history—and on ways to prevent a recurrence at any of the other 71 nuclear plants operable in the United States. Unquestionably the most influential study was conducted by a 12-member panel convened by President Carter and chaired by Dartmouth University President John Kemeny. (See also "The Kemeny Report," starting on page 312.) The President announced that he intended to implement 43 of the Commission's 44 recommendations. Among the changes implemented were a reorganization of the NRC, the replacement of its chairman, and the formation of a five-member expert advisory committee to inform both the government and the public of progress in carrying out the "laundry list" of safety-related changes called for by the Commission. Largely as a result of the Three Mile Island accident, there was increased public opposition to nuclear power, and attempts were made in several states to halt the opening and construction of nuclear power plants.

DOE

Tankers, sometimes traveling halfway around the globe, provide an energy lifeline for many nations.

Synthetic Fuels. Attention again turned to the development of synthetic liquid fuels and gases from coal, shale, and grains. By June 1979 "synfuels fever" had struck many legislators and some 40 bills were proposed. Environmentalists mounted a counterattack, charging, among other things, that synfuel development was unnecessarily costly. As data about costs and potential environmental effects of a major scaling up of synfuels development became available, the fever waned. However, two areas continued to generate interest: coal gasification and grain alcohol. In November the Federal Energy Regulatory Commission approved the construction of the first commercial-scale coal-gasification plant in the United States. The North Dakota plant will manufacture synthetic natural gas (SNG) from lignite and water. (See also the article "Synthetic Fuels," starting on page 178.)

Test drilling along the Atlantic Coast revealed higher-than-expected ground water temperatures—and raised hopes for possible use of the geothermal energy to heat buildings.

DOE

Attention also centered on gasohol, a mixture of nine parts gasoline to one part of octane-boosting ethanol. In July Amoco became the first major U.S. company to test market the hybrid fuel. Later other companies joined and by year's end the U.S. Department of Energy was planning a major salvo of tax incentives and loan guarantees to spur the commercial market for this petroleum-stretching fuel. By December 1979, the U.S.'s annual production capacity for ethanol as a gasoline additive had increased from near zero to 80,000,000 gallons. (See also "Gasohol," starting on page 165.)

Other. DOE drilling of a series of test wells along the Atlantic Coastal Plain revealed higher-than-expected ground water temperatures. This water, heated by radioactive decay in underground granite, could possibly be used for heating and cooling buildings and for some industrial uses, according to some experts in geothermal energy.

Janet Raloff

Arco Solar

In a preliminary step to produce today's standard silicon wafer solar cell, an ingot of single crystal molten silicon is removed from a furnace.

SOLAR PHOTOVOLTAIC ENERGY

by Charles G. Burck

ALL through its brief modern history, solar energy has carried a heavy freight of wishful thinking and extravagant hopes. Now it has been propelled into the mainstream of energy planning by the Carter Administration's pledge that the nation will be getting 20 per cent of its energy from the sun by the year 2000. *Energy Future,* the authoritative report of the Harvard Business School Energy Project, declares that goal—and more—to be attainable.

The broad goal of 20 per cent by 2000 should be reachable, if only because definitions of solar generally include energy from every renewable source for which the sun can be held accountable. The Administration lumps in its definition much more than power derived directly from sunlight. Biomass energy is included, and so are wind power, hydroelectric power, and even power

that can be generated by temperature differences between the surface and depths of the ocean.

When the definition of solar is narrowed, the outlook grows cloudier for use of the sun's energy in ways that would touch directly, and soon, on our lives. Here we're talking about systems for individual homes, factories, and office buildings. These direct solar applications are supposed to make up 35 per cent of the overall 20-per-cent-by-2000 goal. That rather modest sounding share adds up to a lot of energy—some 6.6 quads (6.6 quadrillion British thermal units), the equivalent of more than 1,000,000,000 barrels of crude oil.

About a third of those quads would come from equipment installed for heating and cooling. To achieve this goal could require, at today's prices, some $200,000,000,-

000 worth of solar collectors. This would represent a capital investment in energy production equivalent to some $10,000,000,000 a year.

THE PRESENT STATE OF THE ART

The present-day costs of most direct solar equipment, however, are too high to offer much hope of competing economically with other forms of energy. Solar hot-water heating systems are now competitive with electric heat in many parts of the country. Since the last OPEC price increases, solar hot-water heating is also competitive with oil in some areas. The picture changes for space heating, however.

Solar energy space-heating systems, which typically cost between $10,000 and $20,000 for an average-size home, aren't as competitive. And photovoltaic cells, which convert sunlight directly into electricity, are still expensive. Up to the present, they have been useful only for specialized purposes, such as powering remote radio towers and space vehicles. Consumers today can get far more for their energy dollars by investing in insulation and other conservation measures.

Yet, paradoxically, the prospects for making direct use of the sun's energy have never looked better. Capturing the sun's energy through design techniques, without the use of collectors, plumbing, and pumps, is already here. Such construction design adds little to the cost of a new house. It simply requires plenty of glass on the southern exposure and an overhanging eave to keep the high summer sun out but admit the low winter sun. Judicious plantings to screen off northern winds also helps. This form of construction, called *solar passive,* has limits. A glass-faced Trombe wall (named for its designer), which stores heat during the day in its bulk of masonry and releases it at night, can cost as much per square meter to build as some active solar systems.

The solar thermal industry, which builds active systems relying on heat collectors and other paraphernalia is not as far along. It stands today about where the automobile industry did in 1910. It is just now developing the design and production techniques to make its products competitive.

FROM SUNLIGHT TO ELECTRICITY

Makers of photovoltaic cells are struggling to bring down costs. A rich variety of photovoltaic technologies is now beginning to benefit visibly from years of intense research and development in many laboratories. These systems hold the promise of bringing off a full-scale revolution within the next decade. But they cannot become competitive in the consumer market through incremental improvements. Nothing less than a major breakthrough is required.

Today's bread-and-butter solar cell is a semiconductive silicon wafer that's a close cousin of the microprocessor chip. It is made by drawing a crystalline rod from a molten crucible of silicon, sawing it into thin wafers, and doping it with minute amounts of impurities to give it semiconductor properties. Then an antireflective coating and a metal grid to draw off the current are attached. The finished cell—typically a seven-to-ten-centimeter disk—is assembled with other cells into a module. The average cell is capable of converting about 13 per cent of the solar energy that strikes it into electrical energy. The theoretical conversion efficiency is 22 per cent.

Costs have come down drastically since the first modern photovoltaic cells were sent

Mobil Tyco's Edgedefined Filmfed Growth Process has produced long ribbons of silicon.

Mobil Tyco

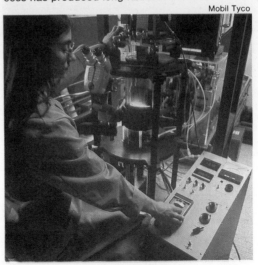

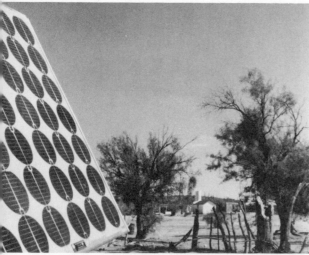

Above: solar energy is used to produce electricity in an Arizona village. Below: solar energy supplements a space-heating system in Danbury, Connecticut Hospital.

aloft to power space satellites. Skylab's array was designed to generate twenty-four kilowatts, which is about enough current to meet the needs of three typical homes. It cost some $23,000,000. Present-day arrays cost between $10 and $15 per peak watt (that is, a watt of electricity generated under peak solar conditions, such as high noon under cloudless skies). This means that three houses could now be supplied with electricity by about $210,000 to $315,000 worth of solar cells.

GETTING THE COST DOWN

The downward cost curve of a technology so closely related to the computer has misled many solar advocates into assuming that solar-cell costs will drop in the same fashion as those of integrated circuits. That is, however, not likely. Integrated circuits came down in price because manufacturers were able to cram more and more circuitry onto a single wafer. Nobody has yet found a simple and cheap way to get more sunshine onto a photovoltaic cell. Therefore, large numbers of cells are needed for any energy-generating system.

The raw material of the cells is expensive. The manufacturing process is slow, exacting, and wasteful—half of the silicon rod is lost in sawing. Furthermore, it takes immense amounts of heat. A typical solar cell will have to work nine to fifteen years to pay back the energy used in its manufacture.

Costs will come down, of course, with volume production of single-crystal silicon cells. Further reductions will be achieved by making solar cells of less highly purified silicon. (Semiconductor-grade silicon is within a few parts per million of perfect purity.) It will also help to improve sawing methods— for example, by using lasers to cut the rods— and by more efficient module assembly.

Solarex Corporation of Rockville, Maryland, is starting work on a plant that could, by 1981, be turning out solar cells at a price of $5 a peak watt or less. The new cells are "nothing like what's on the market today." They are polycrystalline cells cast from molten silicon in a process that takes less than a fifth of the time needed to make single-crystal cells. If the market justifies it, the new plant could turn out enough cells annually to produce up to five megawatts a year.

Companies like Solarex expect to see a demand for cells to be used at remote sites where power is now provided by batteries or small generator sets. This so-called intermediate market includes installations for lighthouses and buoys, and rural railway crossing signals. It also includes cathodic protection systems, which generate low-voltage currents to help prevent corrosion in pipelines and oil and gas wells. As prices fall, the market will eventually grow to include remote rural villages in less developed countries.

RIBBONS OF SILICON

The ultimate market, of course, would be residential and commercial buildings. Generating power on rooftops will require photovoltaic modules delivering electricity for cents per peak watt, rather than dollars. The Department of Energy (DOE) will spend more than $135,000,000 in fiscal 1980 on its low-cost photovoltaic research and development program. It will involve dozens of corporations and research institutions. The program's aim is to get the cost down to 70 cents per peak watt (in 1980 dollars) by 1986. At that price, electricity from photovoltaic systems would be competitive with that from new coal or nuclear power plants.

Most of the advanced research is still in laboratories. This research runs the gamut from efforts to develop cells with vastly higher efficiencies than today's cells, to experiments with low-efficiency materials that are orders of magnitude cheaper. Among the front-runners in the race to make direct-solar energy realize its promise are companies attempting to develop continuous processes for fabricating long ribbons of single-crystal silicon material. The contenders include I.B.M., Motorola, Westinghouse, and several research laboratories.

Nobody has made more meters of silicon ribbon than Mobil Tyco Solar Energy Corporation, a joint venture of Mobil and Tyco Laboratories. In its "Edgedefined Filmfed Growth" process, molten silicon rises through a die by capillary action and is crystallized as it emerges. Mobil Tyco has managed to grow ribbons as long as 45 meters. The company is now confident that it can eventually produce the 160-meter ribbons it regards as adequate for commercial production. The company has worked out the means for drawing up to five 5-centimeter-wide ribbons simultaneously. It is now developing machinery to produce 10 centimeter ribbons. However, minute quantities of impurities picked up from the dies hold down average efficiencies to between 10 and 11 per cent. Also, the growth rate of 7 centimeters per minute is well below what the company eventually hopes to achieve. To do this it must overcome the tendency of ribbons to buckle at higher growth rates.

If the sun's rays can be concentrated enough, even a conventional silicon cell becomes markedly more efficient. Motorola has been working on a DOE-sponsored demonstration project to provide power for the Phoenix airport in Arizona, using concentrating collectors. Present plans call for a 225-kilowatt system drawing its power from 5,624 75-centimeter reflecting concentrators spread out over a 3-hectare field. The arrays will swivel to follow the sun.

NEW BREAKTHROUGHS COMING?

The great photovoltaic breakthrough that everyone hopes for may come with use of "thin film" solar cells that can be made cheaply in vast quantities. Honeywell corporation is working on a DOE contract to coat ceramic tiles with thin films of silicon. And a company called Photon Power has built a pilot plant for making cells with a compound of cadmium sulfide and copper sulfide sprayed on hot glass. The average efficiency of Photon Power's cells today is between 5 and 6 per cent, with the theoretical efficiency not much more than 10 per cent.

The search for cheaper, more efficient solar cells continues. Here cadmium sulfide cells are inspected.

Libbey-Owens-Ford

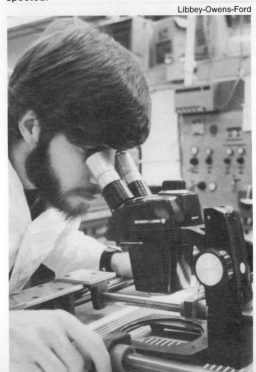

The potential cost, however, is low enough to offset the penalty.

Other thin-film researchers are concentrating their efforts on a class of compounds called amorphous semiconductors, which can be made to do many of the things crystalline silicon wafers do, such as switch on and off. Stanford Ovshinsky first found uses for amorphous semiconductors and started Energy Conversion Devices, Incorporated. His company is presently developing silicon-fluorine-hydrogen-alloy film photocells. RCA has patent rights for a technology based on hydrogenated amorphous silicon spread in a thin film on glass or steel plates.

ELEGANT BUCKSHOT

The most radical—and exciting—photovoltaic concept to date was developed by Jack Kilby, an inventor of the integrated circuit, for Texas Instruments. In the T.I. system, the silicon cells are tiny spheres that look just like buckshot. The cells are immersed in a electrolyte of halogen acids (a family of compounds including chlorine, iodine, and bromine). When sunlight strikes the cells, the current they generate breaks the electrolyte down into the hydrogen and halogens of which it is composed. These are piped separately to a fuel cell. In the fuel cell, the hydrogen and the halogens are recombined to generate electricity. As a bonus, the electrolyte is circulated through a heat exchanger to capture thermal energy that would otherwise be wasted.

The system is an elegant technical *tour de force* because it deals simultaneously with several of the major problems that remain unresolved in other photovoltaic technologies. The silicon cells are cheap to manufacture, and the system tolerates defects easily because each tiny sphere is independent of all others. Most important, any hydrogen not used immediately is drawn off to a tank filled with hydrides. These are inexpensive compounds that combine easily with hydrogen and release the hydrogen when they are heated slightly. Thus, the system has the inherent ability to store energy during peak generating periods and release it after the sun goes down, when it is most likely to be needed. Storage is a problem generally unaddressed by other photovoltaic technologies.

T.I. has much to do before the system is ready for commercial production. It must find the right hydride and develop a fuel cell with useful performance and service life. Then T.I. must conduct long-term corrosion tests and work out many details of construction and controls. Halogen acid is highly toxic. Therefore, T.I. will have to ensure that it does not constitute a hazard in operating systems. "But we've established proof of the principles in the important areas," says George H. Heilmeier, vice president for corporate research, development, and engineering. That may be an understatement. T.I.'s original proposal to the DOE included a "milestone chart" with steps leading toward a dramatic goal: "Attain full production in first plant—March, 1985."

WITHIN REACH AT LAST

To date, the history of solar—especially solar photovoltaic—has been the story of Tantalus: year after year the prize has remained, maddeningly, just beyond reach. Each new rise in the price of conventional energy has been accompanied by fresh revelations of seemingly unsolvable problems. It has proved harder than the pioneers imagined to overcome the difficulties of harnessing an energy form that is stupendous in the total but dilute in any given setting. The kind of progress that is evident today suggests that the period of solar-photovoltaic frustration is drawing to a close □

SELECTED READINGS

"Despite problems, solar cell advances" by P. Schuyten. *The New York Times,* December 11, 1979.

"Solar photovoltaic energy" by H. Ehrenreich and C. Miller. *Physics Today,* September 1979.

"The photovoltaic generation of electricity" by B. Chalmers. *Scientific American,* October 1976.

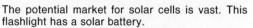
The potential market for solar cells is vast. This flashlight has a solar battery.

Solarex

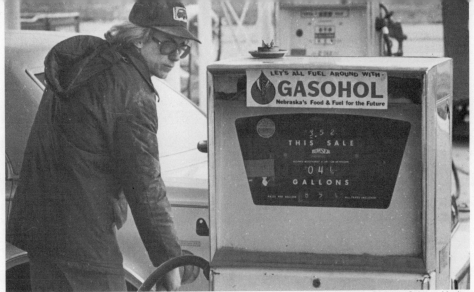

R. Norman Metheny, Christian Science Monitor

During 1979 many service stations, particularly in the grain-growing Midwest, started selling gasohol to supplement dwindling gasoline supplies.

GASOHOL

by Benedict A. Leerburger

**NO GAS
PUMPS CLOSED AT 3 P.M.
CLOSED SATURDAYS AND SUNDAYS**

SIGNS such as these at gas stations in many parts of the United States in recent years have led many to wonder about an alternative to gasoline—something that could replace or reduce U.S. dependency on gasoline. The limited world supply of crude oil—from which gasoline is refined—and its increasing cost make finding alternative fuel sources very important. Gasohol may be one solution.

Gasohol is a blend of 90-per-cent unleaded gasoline and 10-per-cent ethanol, also known as grain alcohol since it is derived from grains such as corn. The United States refines about 110,000,000,000 gallons of gasoline a year from both domestic and imported crude oil. A complete switch to gasohol could then theoretically save approximately 11,000,000,000 gallons of gasoline annually.

Sounds simple. However, there are many questions that have to be answered before a major, national effort can be devoted to putting gasohol in our cars' tanks. Is gasohol as efficient as gasoline? Will it damage car engines? Does the United States have the industrial capacity to produce enough ethanol to meet the demands of the consumer? Is gasohol economically attractive?

NOT A NEW IDEA

The use of alcohol as a motor fuel is certainly not a new concept. When Henry Ford designed one of his first automobiles, the quadricycle, alcohol was to be its fuel. Ford's famous Model T was built with an adjustable carburetor that could easily be modified to use pure alcohol in the engine.

In the period from 1935 to 1939 service stations in Missouri, Nebraska, Illinois, and parts of Kansas sold a gasoline-alcohol blend. In 1938 alone more than 18,000,000 gallons of ethanol were produced for distribution to some 2,000 independent service stations in the region. In those days the gasoline-alcohol mixture was called Agrol. The makers of Agrol went out of business because they couldn't sell their blend as cheaply as gasoline, which sold for six cents a gallon in the late 1930's.

Gasoline-alcohol blends are not new. In the late 1930's such blends were sold as Agrol—but they couldn't compete with cheap gasoline.

During World War II alcohol again came into prominence as a motor fuel. Hitler converted much of Germany's war machinery to alcohol fuels after his East European refineries were destroyed.

Brazil has been producing ethanol from sugarcane since 1920. Since that country imports more than 80 per cent of its oil, it has been actively seeking alternative fuel sources. Today Brazil is one of the world's major producers and users of alcohol-blend fuels, producing more than 200,000,000 gallons of alcohol annually. Experiments are underway to extract alcohol from locally grown cassava, or manioc, which thrives in the Brazilian climate. This starchy tuber promises to yield twice as much alcohol per ton as sugarcane.

This limited experience with gasohol plus ongoing research provide some answers to how gasohol acts in cars and the problems it raises.

CAR ADJUSTMENTS

A car using blends of alcohol and gasoline such as gasohol does not need major carburetor adjustments. A minor adjustment is, however, necessary to decrease the amount of air mixed with the fuel since alcohols need less air than gasoline to form the proper mixture for combustion. If gasohol is used as the major fuel, a single simple adjustment is all that is needed. If, on the other hand, gasohol and gasoline are used interchangeably, an adjustment should be made each time a different fuel is used. The use of

pure alcohol would require still another carburetor adjustment.

Older cars with high-compression engines probably benefit most from gasohol, according to Harry B. Weaver of the Motor Vehicle Manufacturing Association's engineering division. "Since gasohol has a higher octane rating (90 for gasohol *vs.* 87 for regular, unleaded gasoline) it is better suited for older engines designed for use with premium fuels. Gasohol might also improve slightly the fuel economy and overall performance of these vehicles."

EMISSIONS

When the carburetor is properly adjusted, gasoline and gasohol produce the same amount of carbon monoxide during the combustion process. Nitrogen-oxide emissions are lower with gasoline-alcohol blends than with gasoline. But gasohol emits slightly more hydrocarbons than gasoline. Thus the use of gasohol or any alcohol-gasoline blend will not eliminate the widespread need for catalytic exhaust-gas treatment devices. And a General Motors study details a potential problem: alcohol may damage some emission filters and engine gaskets.

FUEL ECONOMY

Does gasohol give better fuel economy than gasoline? Although this sounds like a simple question, there is a great deal of controversy over the answer. In a widely publicized study by Nebraska's Agricultural Products Industrial Utilization Committee, it is claimed that "gasohol-fueled vehicles consumed 5% less fuel than vehicles fueled with no-lead gasoline in the . . . [200,000,000 mile] . . . road test. In other terms, 6,000 miles of driving expands to 7,000 miles when converted to gasohol." Unfortunately, a final report has never been released and, at present, no scientifically defensible road tests have been completed for gasohol.

The energy potential contained in equal units of gasoline and gasohol indicates that gasohol should produce an approximate 4 per cent decrease in miles per gallon compared with gasoline. This conclusion appears to be supported in a report issued by the American Petroleum Institute, which concludes that for alcohol-gasoline blends as vehicle fuels, "fuel economy measured in miles per gallon generally decreases, approximately in proportion to the alcohol content of the blends."

Recent tests comparing gasohol with indoline, a fuel comparable to gasoline, indicated that there is an approximate 2 per cent average decrease in miles per gallon with gasohol. In a 1977 report presented to a U.S. congressional subcommittee E. E. Ecklund of the U.S. Department of Energy concluded that "most researchers agree that with regard to fuel economy ... there is no significant technical advantage or disadvantage to the use of 10 per cent (by volume) alcohol-gasoline blends compared to gasoline."

WATER PROBLEM

A significant potential problem with gasohol is related to the mixing of alcohol and water. It is not uncommon for small amounts of water to contaminate gasoline during the process of distributing the fuel over long distances from the refinery to the service stations. If such contamination were to happen with gasohol, serious problems could result.

When water is added to a container of gasoline the water, being the heavier substance, sinks to the bottom of the container. The very small amount that can blend with the gasoline causes no serious problem and can pass through an engine without causing damage. This is not so with gasohol. The ability of ethanol to mix with gasoline to form a solution is affected if water is added to the mixture.

Theoretically this problem could be overcome by shipping the gasoline and alcohol separately and storing them in separate containers at service stations. They could then be blended at the last possible moment during vehicle refueling. For this, however, new transportation, storage, and blending facilities would have to be built throughout the country—at very high costs.

VOLATILITY

A further potential problem with gasohol involves its volatility. At ordinary temperatures some liquids, including alcohols, tend to evaporate quickly. These liquids are said to be volatile. Gasoline is a relatively volatile liquid—it tends to evaporate rather quickly. With the addition of even small amounts of alcohol, its tendency to vaporize becomes abnormally high. In order to remain within volatility standards certain chemicals such as butane and pentane would have to be removed from the gasoline-alcohol blend. Failure to do so might lead to the formation of a pocket of vaporized fuel in the fuel line blocking the normal flow of fuel. This vapor-lock problem can be solved—but only through costly modifications of fuel delivery and engine systems.

EROSION

Gasohol may also cause erosion problems—so say researchers who have conducted laboratory tests on the effects of gasohol on auto parts. They report that rubber and plastic fuel-system components can show signs of erosion, and that tubing can swell, elongate, and lose strength when in contact with alcohol additives. Consumer complaints have not been heard, however—not even in the midwestern United States where gasohol is growing in popularity.

THE LARGER PICTURE

Even if all the problems associated with gasohol use in present-day cars were solved, is gasohol the answer to fuel shortages? Is it economical? Can the United States produce enough to meet demands at an energy and dollar cost that make it worthwhile? Can, in other words, the grain-to-alcohol process yield more energy than it consumes?

The fuel distribution system is a wet one, using tankers, pipelines, barges, etc. If water contaminates gasohol, serious problems result.

ADM

Sugars released from ground and cooked grain are fermented in plants such as this to yield an ethanol-containing brew.

During the gasoline shortages and accelerating oil-price increases of the late 1970's President Carter called on the United States to search for alternative-energy sources. In October 1978 the U.S. Congress approved the National Energy Act, which included a provision exempting gasoline containing at least 10-per-cent alcohol produced from agricultural products or wastes from the four-cents-per-gallon federal gasoline excise tax.

By early 1979 more than 1,000 service stations nationwide were selling gasohol. In Iowa alone, gasohol sales increased from 600,000 to 5,600,000 gallons in just five months. This tremendous jump in the sales of gasohol was undoubtedly the result of Iowa Governor Robert Ray's move to reduce the price of gasohol by cutting the state's excise tax by eight cents a gallon. Thus gasohol sells in Iowa as a premium fuel within pennies of the price of regular gasoline. Governor Otis R. Brown of Indiana quickly followed Ray's lead and reduced his state's excise tax on gasohol.

FROM FARM WASTES

In July 1979 President Carter announced a new program to provide $11,-000,000 in financing for 100 small plants to produce alcohol from farm wastes. The President also issued a directive to federal agencies to streamline their procedures for approving the construction of plants designed to produce alcohol for fuel use. In 1979 the U.S. Department of Agriculture spent more than $5,000,000 to develop methods of converting corn to ethanol for gasohol and has provided $43,000,000 in loan guarantees to four pilot projects.

A National Gasohol Commission has been established in the Midwest, with 16 states participating. Since corn is one of the major grain sources of alcohol it is natural for the major states in the U.S. corn belt to take an active interest in gasohol production. One of the commission's leaders is Dr. William Scheller, Chairman of the Department of Chemical Engineering at the University of Nebraska and President of the Nebraska Grain Alcohol and Chemical Company. According to Dr. Scheller, "One gallon of anhydrous-grain alcohol mixed with nine gallons of unleaded gasoline will move a car as many miles as 10.324 gallons of unleaded gasoline. When one gallon of grain alcohol is used to replace unleaded gasoline there is a savings of 1.106 gallons of crude oil." According to Dr. Scheller's research, "by producing about 4 billion gallons of grain alcohol annually approximately 178 million barrels of crude oil would be saved."

ENERGY COST

Unfortunately these computations do not consider how much energy it costs to produce corn. A study by researchers at Louisiana State University at Baton Rouge concluded that "with current practices it would require the energy equivalent of two to three gallons of high-grade petroleum fuel such as gasohol to produce enough alcohol energy to replace a gallon of gasoline."

The energy required to produce grain is expended in the production of fertilizer and the powering of trucks, tractors, harvesters, and other farm machinery. The process of converting grain to alcohol also requires energy. The LSU study noted that in Brazil, unlike in the United States, alcohol-fuel production is profitable energywise. This is because the farmers in Brazil use less farm machinery and fertilizer in producing sugarcane than do U.S. farmers in producing corn and their energy input is therefore less in terms of what they produce.

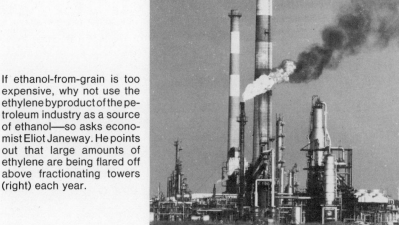

If ethanol-from-grain is too expensive, why not use the ethylene byproduct of the petroleum industry as a source of ethanol—so asks economist Eliot Janeway. He points out that large amounts of ethylene are being flared off above fractionating towers (right) each year.

Paolo Koch/Photo Researchers

PROFIT AND LOSS STATEMENT

Is the energy value of the ethanol produced from grain greater than the energy put into the whole process of production? Is there, in other words, a net profit?

Several researchers have developed a profit-and-loss statement to try to answer these questions. Dr. James Kendrick, an agricultural economist from the University of Nebraska, believes that there is a net energy loss in the production of a gallon of ethanol. He balances the energy needed for corn production and for the processing of corn into ethanol against the energy content of the resultant ethanol and comes up with a net loss—a considerable loss.

Others calculate in the energy value of process byproducts—chiefly cattle feed—and still see a loss, though a smaller one. Says W. Gordon Leith of Farmland Industries, blending alcohol with gasoline "is like stretching hamburger with filet mignon."

Others, however, disagree. Some find ways to minimize the energy input—burning corn wastes to provide energy for ethanol processing, for example—and thus making ethanol production profitable from an energy standpoint.

Furthermore, net energy content and expenditure may not be the only way to look at the problem. The form the energy takes should be considered. If the energy used for processing grain into alcohol comes from coal and not liquid fuels, then the whole strategy makes more sense since it then produces more liquid fuel than it consumes. And it is liquid fuel that is in the shortest supply.

BURNING AWAY?

The noted economist Eliot Janeway has suggested another way to obtain ethanol at less energy cost. He notes a 1978 report by The Stanford Research Institute claiming "the oil industry was still flaring off 10 billion pounds of ethylene a year into the smog above its fractionating towers." According to Janeway, if this gaseous byproduct in all oil-refining and petrochemical operations were hydrated, or added to water, approximately 2,500,000,000 gallons of ethanol could be produced each year. Says Janeway, "The United States has ethylene to burn. In fact, that is exactly what we are doing: wasting it in many ways in the refineries when it could be converted into ethanol."

SEARCH CONTINUES

Research in producing gasohol at a lower cost in dollars and reduced energy use may tell us if gasohol is one step in solving the energy problem. Perhaps another fuel substitute will be developed to replace gasohol. One thing is known for sure: with continuing oil shortages and price increases the need to take advantage of all scientific and technological know-how grows more critical each day □

SELECTED READINGS

"Gasohol: solution to the gas shortage" by Eliot Janeway. *The Atlantic Monthly,* November 1979.

"Gasohol: does it or doesn't it produce positive net energy?" by R. S. Chambers and others. *Science,* November 16, 1979.

"The use of gasohol" by Jerry E. Berger. *Ecolibrium,* Spring 1979.

DOE photo by Schneider

Dr. Melvin Calvin thinks he may have one answer to the energy problem—fuel-producing plants.

FUEL FROM PLANTS

by Melvin Calvin and Gene Elle Calvin

Introduction: Melvin Calvin, who received the Nobel Prize in 1961 for his work in photosynthesis, has started an experiment he believes may open the way to literally growing petroleum, or at least a petroleum substitute. The scientist, a professor emeritus of chemistry at the University of California in Berkeley, is cultivating a common plant called a "gopher" or "mole" plant that yields a hydrocarbon that the chemist believes could be put to the same uses as coal, petroleum, and other present-day hydrocarbon fuels.

The basic transformation in this energy-trapping process has long been known. Through the agency of green plants, sunlight transforms carbon dioxide and water into carbohydrates and free oxygen. Calvin and his colleagues achieved a far deeper understanding of what actually happens in the chloroplasts of green plants. In order to do that, they needed two laboratory tools that did not become available until after the mid-1940's. One was the nuclear reactor, which could produce radioactive isotopes of various chemical elements in practical quantities and at reasonable costs. The second was paper chromatography, a method for analyzing tiny amounts of highly complex mixtures of organic compounds.

These tools, then, coupled with a highly imaginative experimental approach, provided Calvin and his associates with the means of probing the innermost secrets of the single cells of green plants. But, let's let Prof. and Mrs. Calvin tell the story in their own words.

Ritchie Ward

FOR the past several decades, we have studied how green plants capture sunshine and use it to store the energy of the sun in the form of chemicals. These chemicals are mostly carbohydrates—the substance of wood, cotton, sugar, and many of the other macroscopic things that plants make.

The fossil fuels, which we have been using over the last 100 years (coal, oil, and gas), are all stored products of the sun's action on ancient green plants. These plants lived and died and were buried in mud. Eventually they were converted from cellulose into the various fossilized materials, which we use so freely today. What the fresh photosynthetic product became depended upon the geological construction of its storage chambers.

It takes tens of hundreds of millions of years to convert the primary product of the sun's energy fixation into these conveniently useful fossil forms. The fraction of the annual solar energy fixed in the form of carbohydrate material is perhaps one per cent. Of this, surely no more than one per cent finds its way to coal, oil, or gas. This would mean a net of perhaps .01 per cent.

If we can directly use the sun in some way as a source of energy and materials, it may be possible to substitute the energy of the sun for the fossilized fuels. Consider the capacity of solar energy on earth. Firstly, the amount of solar energy falling on the earth's surface in ten days is equivalent to all the known fossil fuel reserves on earth. Secondly, the present average energy demand per person can be met, with ten per cent recovery, by an area about three meters square between latitudes $40°$ N and $40°$ S, where 80 per cent of the world's population lives and where the greatest needs are found. Thirdly, an area of only 330 miles square is sufficient to supply all present-day energy needs.

COLLECTING SOLAR ENERGY

There are two processes by which solar energy can be collected: They are heat collection and light, or quantum, collection. With the first process, we degrade the energy and use it as heat. This is what the more conventional methods of solar radiation collection do. But the methods that are dependent on light, or quantum, conversion are still waiting for scientific development.

Photosynthesis is the process in which the green plant uses light and makes food and materials—for example, fuel in the form of wood. The photochemical method of quantum conversion is largely unknown, and this is an area that needs a great deal of basic scientific effort.

The conversion of light energy in the green plant occurs in a minute machine, called the chloroplast. The chloroplast is composed of many membranous layers. The quantum conversion occurs in the parallel membranes of the chloroplast by means of a complex chemical called chlorophyll. It is believed that the oxygen is evolved inside the membrane envelope, and the carbon dioxide is combined with hydrogen, forming glucose ($C_6H_{12}O_6$), on the outside.

How do the energy levels (quanta) of the sunshine work on the chloroplast membranes? Apparently, two large quanta are in-

volved in a complicated system of photosynthetic electron transfers. The second quantum of light raises the electron to a high enough state so it will combine carbon dioxide and hydrogen. Then the positive charge, which is left, generates the oxygen.

LATEX—A HYDROCARBON

Most plants use sunlight, water, and carbon dioxide to produce carbohydrates. These are chemicals made of carbon, hydrogen, and oxygen, called sugars. Hydrocarbons are composed only of carbon and hydrogen. Sugarcane is one of the most efficient plants in producing carbohydrates. Large-scale efforts already are under way, particularly in tropical Brazil, to extract fuels from the carbohydrates-producing plants. This is done by taking the sugar and fermenting it to produce alcohol, which can be used as a fuel.

Some plants carry photosynthesis further and produce hydrocarbons. A well-known example is the rubber tree, known as the *Hevea* tree. The latex that seeps out when the rubber tree bark is "tapped" is an emulsion of one-third hydrocarbon and two-thirds water. The main difference between the hydrocarbon of the rubber tree and that of petroleum is the length of the molecule of carbon and hydrogen atoms. The tree hydrocarbon is much longer, giving it its rubbery consistency.

There are thousands of species of plants that produce latex emulsions made of hydrocarbons. These have never been exploited as

Some plants, such as *Euphorbia tirucallii*, produce latex, a possible source of hydrocarbon fuels.

a possible source of hydrocarbon fuels. One genus of such latex-producing plants is known as *Euphorbia.* This genus includes a treelike shrub from Africa that grows in arid regions. However, I discovered one species—an annual called *Euphorbia lathyrus,* or gopher plant—on my ranch in California. Like the rubber tree, it produces a latex emulsion composed of about one-third hydrocarbon that I believe could be used as a petroleum substitute.

Right now, we have grown experimental plots of the plant *E. lathyrus* for experimental use and to produce seed. We expect to get enough seed to grow about 0.4 square kilometers in a year or two. Then we will have enough of the plants to get some realistic ideas about their yields of hydrocarbons and the cost of making fuels from them.

Rough estimates of $20 a barrel for petroleum from the plants is based on just picking the plants out of the wild and growing them. Rubber plantations in Malaysia made spectacular increases in the yield of latex from rubber trees, going from 100 kilograms per 25,000 square meters in 1945 to 1,800 kilograms on some experimental plots, and even 4,000 kilograms with experimental trees.

A laboratory assistant tries to find ways to extract petroleum from the *E. lathyris* plant in a practical and economical way.

DOE photo by Schneider

ARTIFICIAL PLANT CELLS

One of the main thrusts of our efforts in Berkeley is to construct synthetic membranes. Such membranes would be capable of performing some of the same photochemical reactions that occur in the natural system of the green-plant cell. The natural membranes of the plant are exhaustible. Therefore, part of the reason we want to construct synthetic membranes is to create a system that will last indefinitely.

Natural membranes make carbohydrate, protein, fats, and nucleic acids. We would hope that the synthetic "photosynthetic" systems could make hydrogen, hydrocarbons, or other more directly used materials. These membranes should be capable of using the sunshine to break up water, and make hydrogen, which can be stored for use as a fuel. We have constructed a theoretical artificial membrane in such a way that the oxygen and hydrogen could be made separately on opposite sides of the membrane. Thus the separation of hydrogen and oxygen is achieved.

We have reached a stage where we can, in principle, create such an artificial membrane. However, we do not yet know in detail the molecular nature of the positive and negative charges produced, so that one will go out as hydrogen and the other as oxygen, with this their sole function.

We feel, however, that the development of efficient artificial photosynthetic membranes, capable of generating renewable materials for fuel and materials production, has much potential. I believe it will take less than 25 years to attain commercially adequate efficiency of the photochemical cell with its artificial membrane. This will be able to use the sun's energy to store usable, renewable energy for the use of people everywhere □

SELECTED READINGS

"Petroleum plan: perhaps we can grow gasoline" by T. Maugh. *Science,* October 1, 1976.

"Petroleum plantations for fuel and materials" by M. Calvin. *Bioscience,* September 1979.

"Synthetic chloroplasts" by M. Calvin. *International Journal of Energy Research,* January–March, 1979.

"Solar energy by photosynthesis" by M. Calvin. *Science,* April 19, 1974.

Warm, cozy, and old-fashioned—yes. But also one modern answer to the energy crunch.

WOOD STOVES

by Vita West-Muir

"THEY burn not only wood, but the gases from the wood. They are highly efficient, have automatic thermostats, and two or three oak logs or hardwood logs will last for as long as eight to ten hours."

Does that sound like a pitch from the burgeoning ranks of wood-stove salesmen? Guess again. The enthusiastic spokesman is the President of the United States and the product he is touting is the modern, airtight wood stove. The White House is now equipped with six of them.

America's 250-year-old stove industry is setting the world of big business on fire. With its acquisitions, the White House has joined the five million other American households that now use wood stoves for heating and cooking. Conservative estimates put sales at a quarter of a billion dollars a year. Fully half the homes in frigid northern New England rely on wood heat.

Before you purchase a stove of your own, however, consider carefully: almost nothing is "cheap enough to burn" nowadays. Between 1978 and 1979, the cost of a cord of wood (4 ft. x 4 ft. x 8 ft.) doubled in most parts of the United States, and now sells for $85 to $100. At these prices, wood burning may be picturesque, but it is hardly economical. The current rule of thumb used by the U.S. Department of Energy is that, at $100 a cord, wood becomes cheaper to use than oil when the price of oil tops the dollar-a-gallon mark.

If you live near a cheap source (some state forests even allow free wood cutting), heating with wood may make good sense for you, provided you have the time, energy, and equipment to cut, haul, split, and stack the wood and the space to dry and store it.

Once you buy and install a stove, you must tend it, loading wood at least two or three times a day, carrying away ashes, cleaning the chimney, sweeping the floor, and dusting the furniture to remove the ubiquitous white ash generated by woodburning. All this is more time-consuming and more irksome than dialing a thermostat.

CHOOSING A STOVE

If heating with wood suits your budget and inclinations, a choice has to be made among the hundreds of models of wood stoves available from as little as $100 to over $1,000—and these prices do not include installation.

Size is probably the single most important factor to consider. Too large, and you can slow-cook quail in the ambient air; too small, and the stove must be tended con-

Wood stoves have been used for centuries and come in many models, including ceramic ones.

Kachaturian

stantly to operate at full capacity. As a general rule, the stove should be rated at 20,000 BTU's to heat an average-sized room. Ceiling height, windows, and other factors that make a space hard or easy to heat must be considered.

For efficient burning, the stove must be "airtight." That term is, however, a misnomer. If these stoves admitted no air, combustion would be impossible. Airtight construction describes a stove with seams and joints sealed, with doors precision-fitted, and sometimes gasketed.

Airtight stoves are made of cast iron or steel. Cast iron absorbs heat and radiates it even after the fire had died. This feature makes it more attractive than steel, but cast iron is expensive and can crack from thermal shock.

Most stoves provide heat by radiation from their outer surfaces. A few circulate heat between the stove and an outer shell. This type of heater is safe to touch even when fully fired.

If you understand the dynamics of wood burning and the principles that govern the function of the stove you are considering, the choice will be a little easier. The basic assembly consists of a stove, stovepipe, flue, and chimney. A draft, which delivers oxygen for combustion, is provided by the chimney and regulated by a damper.

When wood begins to burn, its water content—even the driest wood is about 20 per cent water—boils off. (This accounts for the hissing sound.) At 300 to 400 degrees Fahrenheit, wood starts to break down into charcoal, tars, resins, hydrogen, and volatile gases. These gases must not be allowed to escape up the chimney before they burn, or some 60 per cent of the heat potential of the wood will be lost.

At 600° Fahrenheit, the wood itself burns and is transformed into charcoal, which in turn burns to form ash. An efficient stove, therefore, burns gas as well as "solid fuel" and it does so at temperatures of 1,-100–1,400° Fahrenheit. If these temperatures are not reached and the gases are not burned, they condense inside the stovepipe or flue to form a tarry liquid, which then solidifies. This substance, known as creosote, blocks the free flow of air, causes the stove to burn inefficiently, and creates a serious fire hazard.

INSTALLATION

It is best to leave wood stove installation to a competent contractor if you are not qualified to do the job yourself. Building codes and insurance regulations vary, so your fire department and insurance agent should be contacted before and after you install your stove. You will not have effected much of an economy if you save on your fuel bill by using wood, but burn your house down through faulty installation or careless use of a stove.

If an existing chimney is to be used, it should be inspected to see that flue tiles and masonry are not cracked. Ideally, the wood stove should not share a flue with a conventional furnace. In some states, this arrangement is mandatory.

When a masonry chimney is not available, a prefabricated metal one may be used. This should be an Underwriters Laboratories-listed, double-walled, non-corrosive steel chimney with one inch of insulation. Tripled-walled or other air-cooled chimneys will chill the flue gases, creating poor draft and excessive creosote build-up.

The stovepipe conducts smoke and fumes from the stove into the flue. It should be made of at least 24-gauge metal, and have a short horizontal run and as few elbows as possible, to minimize accumulation of creosote.

The stove itself should have durable weldings, inside and out. Check the welds in a second-hand stove, and look for broken parts and cracks. The seams in cast-iron stoves are usually sealed with stove putty, which needs periodic replacing. Any gap in a seam could permit embers or sparks to escape. The door latch must open and shut securely. Finally, the casting thickness must be at least 1/16 of an inch to preclude cracking and warping.

FIRE PREVENTION

Although statistics for fires related to wood stove use alone are not yet available, the United States Fire Administration esti-

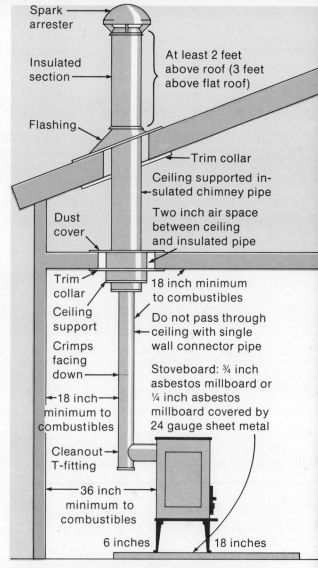

Wood stove installation is best left to the experts so that all building, fire-code, and insurance regulations are met.

mates that approximately 6,700 fires annually are related to wood-burning stoves and other fixed local heating units such as room heaters. This number is bound to increase with the skyrocketing sales of wood stoves if owners are not informed and are not cautious. The New York State Division of Fire Prevention and Control advises that you:

• Check the stovepipe and chimney periodically for creosote build-up. Do this at least once a month during periods of heavy use.

• Never use a flammable liquid in the same room with a wood stove.

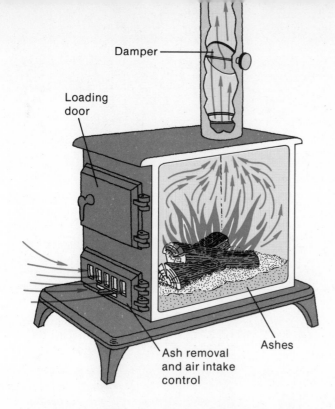

Damper

Loading door

Ash removal and air intake control

Ashes

Wood stoves require careful use and maintenance. Dampers must be kept open when there is a fire; ashes must be carefully removed; logs should be added a few at a time.

• Never use a flammable liquid to start a fire.

• Remember to keep the damper open when there is a fire in the firebox.

• Use a metal container with a tight-fitting lid for ash disposal.

• Keep children away from the stove. The surface of a convection-type stove is hot enough to cause severe burns.

In case of chimney fire, the doors of the unit should be shut and the damper closed to cut off oxygen. The fire department should be called immediately. Baking soda or salt continually thrown on the fire creates a gas that helps control the fire in the chimney. After a fire, the chimney should not be used without an inspection for damage. Cold water should never be thrown on a fire: it will crack a cast-iron stove.

CREOSOTE PREVENTION

Keeping the flue and stovepipe free of creosote is the surest way to prevent chimney fires. The higher the temperature inside the firebox, the closer the wood comes to complete combustion. Remember, creosote is a product of incomplete combustion. Creosote build-up can be reduced by operating a hot (but not roaring) fire for about 15 minutes once or twice a day. The fire should be started with paper and kindling. Larger pieces of wood should not be added until the fire has caught. Then, the fire doors should be closed but not latched. This will cause a rush of air, making for a hotter burn than would be possible by leaving the doors fully open. After this quick blaze, the stove may be operated in the damped-down mode. Adding logs a few at a time is preferable to refilling the stove infrequently with large loads of wood, which sharply lowers the temperature inside the stove. When loading the stove for overnight use, wait until all the wood has caught fire before damping it down.

Small fires should be built in a new stove until there is a one- to two-inch bed of ashes. Maintaining an ash bed will help conserve live coals for easier fire starting.

Paradoxically, efficient wood burning creates the greatest creosote problem. Efficient burning is slow burning, and slow burning is cool burning. The cooler the fire, the greater the creosote formation. Baffles and secondary air inlets are all designed to ameliorate this problem, but there is a trade-off. If you operate your stove for long-lasting, slow-burning fires, you will have to perform maintenance more often.

Creosote can be removed from the

A second-hand, old-fashioned black stove may seem like just what you want. However, it should be checked carefully for cracks, open seams, or other defects that might make it inefficient or dangerous.

Kachaturian

stovepipe by wire-brushing or scraping. Tapping the pipe hard with a fingernail should produce an echo. A muffled thud means there is a build-up in the pipe that should be removed. The chimney should be rid of creosote once a year.

POLLUTION

"Where there's smoke," said an official of Maine's Department of Environmental Protection, "there's pollution." And that pollution lies like a heavy gray blanket over many towns in Maine, Vermont, New Hampshire, Oregon, and Colorado. In a recent study on a winter day in Portland, Oregon, 36 per cent of the inhalable particulates came from wood burning, compared to 5 to 10 per cent from road dust, 8 per cent from automobile exhaust, and only 2 per cent from oil burning. (Even efficient wood-burning stoves are no more than 50–60 per cent efficient, whereas a well-maintained oil burner generally operates at about 80 per cent efficiency.)

Most of the particulate material is harmless enough. It may soil the draperies, but it poses small hazard to your health, since the nose filters much of it out of the air before it reaches your lungs. In addition to particulates, wood smoke produces gases that are of greater concern. Some, like nitrogen oxides, produce smog. Others, the POM's—polycyclic organic materials—are known carcinogens. Luckily, wood burning emits only small amounts of these chemicals. How serious this will become as more and more people burn wood is uncertain.

Fortunately, something can be done to decrease this pollution. Burning hardwood rather than the more resinous softwoods, and burning it at higher temperatures or in a wood stove designed for more complete combustion reduces both particulate and gaseous pollution.

In this era of energy crisis, there are no simple solutions. But wood is a fuel we can count on until science and technology give us a better answer □

 SELECTED READINGS

"Clean burn: air pollution for woodstoves" by R. Deis. *Country Journal,* October 1979.

"How to control creosote for safer wood burning" by E. Powell. *Popular Science,* October 1979.

"Many ways warmed: wood stoves" by J. N. Cole. *Organic Gardening,* October 1979.

"Return to wood heating." *Family Handyman,* October 1979.

"Wood heat safety guidelines" by J. W. Shelton. *Organic Gardening,* October 1979.

A handful of energy—a sticky, tarlike mixture with the consistency of coarse brown sugar—that may provide one answer to the energy crunch.

SYNTHETIC FUELS

by Corliss Kristensen

IN mid-1979 President Carter, faced with continuing shortages and increasing prices of imported oil, called for intensive efforts to develop synthetic fuels. Excitement mounted over a possible way to decrease U.S. dependence—8,500,000 barrels a day—on foreign oil for liquid fuels. Numerous bills for synthetic fuel development were proposed in Congress, some calling for the expenditure of vast sums.

The excitement waned somewhat as projected costs and possible harmful effects to the environment of such a big push became better known. High interest in synfuels, as they are sometimes called, continues, however. With the proposed Crash Synfuel Program now before Congress, the United States may be using 500,000 barrels of home-produced synthetic fuels per day by 1985 and 2,000,000 barrels per day by 1990.

What is causing all this excitement? Just what are synthetic fuels?

Synthetic fuels is a broad term for substitute liquid fuels derived from indirect sources. Synthetic fuels are not artificial; they are derived from natural sources—tar sands, oil shale, and coal.

BIG PUSH NOW

Crude methods for obtaining fuels from indirect sources have been known for centuries. A technique of forcing rough crude—kerogen—out of shale was patented in England in 1694. Over the past century, industry has devoted major efforts to synfuel research in attempts to refine production technologies. Practically every major U.S. oil company has an ongoing research and development program on at least one synthetic fuel. A few projects have even reached the pilot-plant stage. However, no major synfuel development plans have been pursued in the United States before now. Why?

In general, synfuels were largely ignored because they were too costly, environmentally damaging, and in general a risky investment in an inexperienced industry. Cost estimates for producing synfuels have always been a few dollars above the cost of importing oil or natural gas. When crude oil cost

$3.50 per barrel back in 1973, synfuels estimates started at $4.50 per barrel.

Now things have changed. Foreign oil supplies are no longer dependable, and they are very costly. In early 1980 imported oil cost about $22.00 a barrel. Predictions for producing synfuel now run about $25.00 to $30.00 per barrel of oil, depending on the process used. Many economists expect synfuel production costs to stabilize while oil costs continue to soar. If this occurs, synfuel prices will become competitive in the very near future. Estimates vary, however, with some economists multiplying any synfuel cost predictions by 1.5 to cover unexpected costs confronted in untested technologies.

Given that the fuels are there and that the United States has the technology to use them—untested though it may be—the main question boils down to: Can the United States afford to go after them? Or perhaps more appropriately: Can the United States afford not to pursue any major fuel alternative?

The United States is not alone in seeking greater self-sufficiency in energy supplies. Canada is extracting an average 100,000 barrels of oil a day from its tar sands deposits in Alberta. In Johannesburg, South Africa, you can fill your tank on gas made, in part, from coal. South Africa's coal conversion program is now meeting 10 per cent of that nation's energy needs.

If the United States proceeds with the Synfuel Crash Program or any other synfuel development plans, efforts will concentrate on three sources: tar sands, oil shale, and coal.

TAR SANDS—BETWEEN THE GRAINS

The creation of tar sands began over 200,000,000 years ago with the depositing and compacting of decaying terrestrial life. The sands today are beds of a mixture of sand, water, and bitumen, a natural hydrocarbon that is the raw material for oil production. The water and bitumen form a film around each grain of sand. The black, sticky tarlike mixture has the consistency of very coarse brown sugar.

An estimated 967,000,000,000 barrels of oil are trapped in four Athabasca deposits in Alberta and Saskatchewan, Canada. But only about 26,500,000,000 barrels are thought to be recoverable with present-day technology. By comparison the largest U.S. tar-sand deposit—a site in Utah—is estimated at 28,000,000,000 barrels of oil. As we said earlier, Canada is already exploiting her huge deposits—currently through Syncrude Canada Ltd.

Tar sands cannot be removed by conventional drilling methods. First, 15 meters of topsoil from overlying soggy bogs are removed by immense bulldozers, some as tall as a 12-story building, to expose the underlying sands. The sands are then scooped up and dropped onto conveyor belts, which feed the sands into giant tumblers. As the tumblers roll, steam, hot water, and air are used to separate the sand from the tarlike bitumen. The bitumen is then chemically treated to remove some carbon, nitrogen, and sulfur. The net product—syncrude—is a heavy viscous oil.

The Canadian operation has run into production snags. Machinery has sunk into the sands during the summer and been caught on frozen chunks in winter. Added to this is the fact that even under the best conditions present-day technology can recover only about five per cent of the total tar sands. The rest is too deep for profitable removal. Intensive research is underway to find ways to reach more deposits and to speed their removal.

Environmental concerns also pose significant problems. The industry must replace the topsoil and restore the natural vegetation to disturbed sites. Many potential problems exist with this land reclamation—and even if it is successful, will wildlife return to their former homes or will the entire ecological balance of the area be permanently disturbed?

There is also the problem of sulfur dioxide emissions when bitumen is treated. And then there are oil leaks. Despite cautious management, oil leaks have already spilled onto a drainage pond in Canada. The company has not been able to clean up the spill, but has diverted migrating birds from landing.

In Canada Syncrude cost estimates vary

from $15.00 to $20.00 a barrel. Many economists believe that a U.S. installation like Syncrude's, but without the government subsidies received by Syncrude, would cost about $30.00 per barrel. One thing is known: if and when the United States embarks on an intensive tar-sand project, it will benefit from the Canadian experience.

OIL SHALE—SQUEEZING ROCK

American Indians called it "the rock that burns." It is formed from marine materials that were deposited 40,000,000 to 50,000,000 years ago. Centuries of compaction have resulted in limestone formations laced with oils, primarily kerogen.

Oil shale offers some exciting prospects for obtaining large quantities of crude oil. The largest known oil-shale deposit in the United States is the Green River Formation which covers 4,400,000 hectares of Utah, Colorado, and Wyoming. It is estimated to contain 2,000,000,000,000 barrels of oil, about one-third of which lies in exploitable rock shelves. Oil shale produces a high quality oil that can be readily burned in industrial boilers. Only one additional step is necessary to turn shale into gasoline or jet fuel.

Securing the oil does, however, present many problems. Approximately 1.7 metric tons of shale are required to produce one barrel of oil. Two processes are proposed for removing the oil from the shale. Surface retorting involves deep mining the oil shale and breaking it into chunks. The chunks are then cooked in retort chambers at 425° to 540° Celsius, using gases to force the kerogen out of the shale. Variations of the basic method involve crushing the shale into small pieces before heating.

In the other method the oil shale is heated *in situ*—that is, where it is, underground. First, wells are dug into and under the shale formation. Then, huge chambers, 85 meters high and the width and length of a football field, are created by blasting or chemically crushing the shale between the wells. This increases the porosity of the shale. The chambers are then sealed from surrounding rock and compressed air is pumped into them to facilitate combustion. The shale is then heated to 480° Celsius, and the kerogen oozes out. Free kerogen and other bituminous oils are then carried to the surface. The *in situ* process bypasses the mining step, which accounts for 60 per cent of the cost in surface retorting, and eliminates the degradation of large tracts of land.

There are serious problems with both methods—problems that must be solved before any large-scale industry can proceed. Could kerogen, for example, seal its own chambers, preventing further removal of kerogen? Of four pilot plants two are no longer in operation because of technical difficulties. (One *in situ* plant collapsed.) At every step of the way, oil shale technology has proved more difficult and expensive than forecast.

The major concerns are, however, environmental. With surface retorting, large tracts of land would be littered with piles of shale tailings. With *in situ* burning there may be serious effects on ground water. The process could affect nearby water tables, possibly altering their levels or even causing contamination. In addition, heating could hypothetically cause leaching of surrounding soils and consequent further contamination and disruption of underground streams and wells. The possibility of disrupting the entire Colorado River basin is not out of the question, according to some geologists.

Serious dust and water-pollution problems also attend both methods. And with any present oil-shale technology there are the serious consequences of heating shale to high temperatures to be considered. Such heating is known to release carcinogenic, or cancer-causing, compounds. An interesting method involving the use of acid-producing bacteria to increase rock porosity and thus allow the release of oil at lower temperatures has been proposed, but so far not extensively tested.

COAL CONVERSION

No doubt about it, coal is the most abundant source of energy in the United States. As President Carter once commented, "Coal is to the United States what oil is to Saudi Arabia." An estimated 215,000,000,000 tons of coal are accessible for mining in the United States. At our current rate of coal consumption this represents about 300 years of use. The Carter synfuel plan, calling for increased mining of 1,500,000 tons a day, or about 250,000,000 tons a year, will, naturally, reduce the number of years coal can be used.

Coal can be converted into several products. It can be made into gas—syngas. It can be liquefied into synoil—either directly or indirectly from syngas. And it can be converted into methanol. Oil companies are scrambling to come up with feasible technologies for these conversion processes. The earliest date estimated for coal-based synthetic fuels to make a dent in the U.S. market is 1990.

TO GAS AND LIQUID

The ancestral coal gasification process is the Lurgi method, developed and first used in Germany in the late 1930's. All other techniques are variations of this method.

In coal gasification, golf ball-sized pieces of coal are loaded into a pressurized vessel and treated with steam and oxygen. Methane, the main component of natural gas, and synthetic gas, or syngas, are produced along with several other chemicals. Further processing removes sulfur, carbon dioxide, and other byproducts.

The syngas product has a medium-range heating value. It can be upgraded to levels acceptable for blending with natural gas by the addition of methane. Or it can be used for the indirect process of coal liquefaction.

Indirect coal liquefaction uses syngas as its essential building block. The Fischer-Tropsch method first used in 1925 is the parent of all indirect liquefaction technologies. The syngas is passed over a catalyst and a combination of methane, waxes, and other products results. A conventional refinery then reduces this product to an assortment of liquids, including jet fuel, diesel fuel, and gasoline.

Direct coal liquefaction is, however, preferred. There are now four major ways to liquefy coal. All basically add hydrogen to the coal, then remove carbon, break down the coal compounds into individual carbon atoms, and then rebuild the compound in liquid form. Direct liquefaction is theoreti-

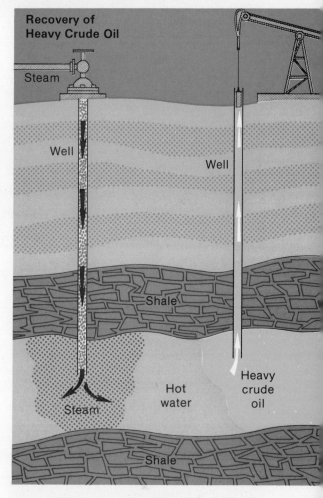

In the *in situ* method, compressed steam is forced down deep wells. The heated shale then gives up its oil which is pumped up to the surface.

cally more economical than indirect methods; however, indirect methods have the advantage of 25 years on-stream experience in South Africa.

The greatest excitement over coal-energy substitutes seems to be focused on methanol produced via liquefaction methods. Coal-based methanol can be used as an additive or gas extender, and better yet, is a ready replacement for valuable natural gas as a feedstock in the production of plastics, synthetic fibers, and glue.

AGAIN PROBLEMS

In theory, all the coal conversion techniques are simple, self-contained processes, but in practice, they may be as messy, expensive, and environmentally hazardous as the production of other synthetic fuels. In

There are serious environmental problems associated with most methods of synfuel production. As shown here, large tracts of land are often degraded, with the vegetation uprooted and the animal life disturbed.

Alan Orling/Black Star

addition to the main products of coal conversion—synthetic gas, oil, coke, pitch, and ash—more than 200 other chemicals have been identified, including some, such as 3,4 benzo(a)pyrene, known to be carcinogenic.

Aerial emissions from coal liquefaction plants include coal dust, sulfur dioxide, nitrogen oxide, and carbon monoxide. The wastewater looks no better: it includes toxic chemicals. Escalated mining efforts result in degradation of large tracts of land. And environmentalists caution about the enormous drain of using several hundred tons of water each day for each ton of coal refined.

And if production and environmental constraints are not enough: oil produced from coal now runs at least $30.00 a barrel.

COST TOO HIGH?

As we have seen, the potential for environmental damage is high with all synthetic fuel plans. Large tracts of land may be mutilated by processing and mining. Fragile, pristine back reaches of public lands may suffer most. Extraction and refining procedures add to air and water pollution. Increases in sulfur dioxide and toxic chemicals in water are greater from synfuel production than from natural gas or oil production. In addition, mining and processing of all the synfuels requires enormous amounts of water. Ironically the western states which are the most likely targets for most synfuel industry are already stressed for water.

The greatest danger may, however, lie in an odorless, colorless gas product of synfuel production and use—carbon dioxide. Production and consumption of synfuels releases more than twice as much carbon dioxide per unit of energy as natural gas. Carbon dioxide acts like the glass or plastic roof of a greenhouse, trapping heat beneath it. An increase in the amount of carbon dioxide in the atmosphere would result in an overall increase in the temperature of the earth's atmosphere. Such a global warming trend could have dire consequences for mankind—drastic agricultural upheavals and massive flooding in some areas, to name just a few.

AND SO—CAUTION

While many scientists recognize the need for the United States to become more energy self-sufficient, they urge extreme caution before and during the implementation of any energy program as untried as synfuels. As Dr. Teh Yen, a synfuel researcher and author of numerous books on the subject, says, "We have to solve the problems [mechanical and environmental] before we put the programs on stream" □

SELECTED READINGS

"Coal conversion technology: some health and environmental effects" by S. C. Morris and others. *Science,* November 9, 1979.

"Enter Buck Rogers with an oil shale extractor" by J. Mattill. *Technology Review,* December 1979/January 1980.

"Geology of the Athabasca oil sands" by G. D. Mossop, *Science,* January 11, 1980.

"Rough road to making oil and gas from coal" by A. Stuart. *Fortune,* September 24, 1979.

"Synthetic fuels at crossroads" by C. A. Stokes. *Technology Review,* August 1978.

"Synthetic fuels: the new saviour" by P. Behr. *Environment,* July 1979.

Gary Gunderson

This diagnostic machine measures the emissions from a car's tailpipe. The test is the result of a Connecticut state law aimed at reducing auto pollution.

THE ENVIRONMENT

THE ENVIRONMENT
REVIEW OF THE YEAR

NBC

The disposal of radioactive wastes—a byproduct of the nuclear-power industry—poses grave threats to the environment and all wildlife.

The blowout of a Mexican offshore oil well in mid-1979 posed an almost year-long threat to Gulf of Mexico fishing and Gulf beaches.

UPI

The year 1979 ended the first Environmental Decade, an epochal era of public awakening to environmental problems and of sweeping action to resolve them. Anniversary stock-taking yielded both a remarkable roster of accomplishments and a formidable, growing array of challenges to be met. On the achievement side stood the 1969 passage of the National Environmental Policy Act, cornerstone of the U.S. quest for environmental quality; a score of laws dealing with air pollution, water pollution, solid waste, noise, toxic chemicals, land use, wildlife protection, and kindred subjects; and years of marked progress in implementing these laws. In the realm of challenges stood the fact that while many problems had been mitigated, few had been fully dispelled; the recognition of vaster dimensions to some dilemmas; and the discovery of some new problems.

The Environment and Energy. Proliferating questions about energy supply dominated 1979. The shrinking flow of foreign oil impelled the Carter Administration and Congress to focus on a multi-billion dollar program of developing synthetic fuel sources, from shale oil and gasohol to coal liquefaction and gasification. As 1979 ended it was not clear how large the synfuel program would be or what environmental concessions might be necessary. Environmental activists were highly critical of envisioned outlays of up to $100,000,000,000 for synfuel development, contending that rigorous energy conservation practices and innovative energy sources would be far more productive. Although President Carter, in his second environmental message to Congress, on August 2, 1979, pledged that energy-development efforts would not change the Administration's "basic commitment to clean air, clean water, and overall protection of the environment," environmentalists' concerns were not allayed. They were, in fact, increased when Carter went on to say that the proposed Energy Mobilization Board should "when necessary for the completion of a critical energy facility" be empowered to override environmental strictures, subject to presidential and judicial review.

The foremost alternative to fossil fuels—nuclear power—sustained a dire setback in the March 28, 1979 breakdown of the Three Mile Island nuclear plant near Harrisburg, Pennsylvania. The accident caused no apparent injuries but stirred widespread fears of a disastrous radiation release. It also brought the development of nuclear power virtually to a standstill and exacerbated controversy over the disposal of radioactive wastes. (See also "The Kemeny Report," on page 312.)

In May 1979 another accident—the blowout of a Mexican offshore oil well in the Gulf of Mexico—dramatized U.S. vulnerability to water pollution from sources beyond its borders. Spewing millions of gallons of tarry black crude, history's biggest oil spill posed a threat to hundreds of kilometers of ecologically-precious wetlands along the Texas and Louisiana coasts and to the multi-million dollar Gulf fishing industry.

Air and Water Pollution. While the U.S. Federal Council on Environmental Quality in its 1979 report noted continued progress in abating air and water pollution generally, it admitted that the advances were slow and fraught with obstacles. A dozen big cities, including New York, Chicago, Washington, and Los Angeles, were said to have air that, by the latest measurements, was essentially "unhealthful" much of the time. ▪ A new problem, on an international scale, was identified in acid rain, the precipitation of atmospheric contaminants that has exterminated or impaired aquatic life in many lakes in both the United States and Canada.

Seven years after the passage of the Water Pollution Control Act, 85 per cent of major industrial dischargers of fluid wastes were found to be in compliance with cleanup requirements, through privately financed improvements. Community sewage systems, beneficiaries of federal grants for 75 per cent of their outlays, were found only about 40 per cent in compliance. The Environmental Protection Agency (EPA) announced a crackdown on dilatory municipalities.

Toxic Substances. Toxic substances continued to bulk ever larger in the environmental picture. An EPA report estimated that there are as many as 50,000 disposal sites in the United States containing hazardous wastes, and that 2,000 of them may pose "significant risks" to human health. President Carter asked Congress to create a $1,600,000,000 fund to help clean these up. EPA administrator Douglas Costle said toxic problems were "like a thread" running through all the agency's regulatory activities and that emphasis in most programs was being shifted to deal with this "legacy of the chemical revolution." ▪ The issue that to a large extent focused attention on the problem—the discovery in 1978 that chemical dumping at Love Canal in upstate New York in the 1940's and 1950's was responsible for ailments in area residents—continued to be the subject of much attention. Early in 1980 blood tests revealed chromosome damage in some area residents, prompting more evacuations.

Land Use. Environmentalists counted as perhaps their biggest victory of 1979 the mustering of a 277-to-31 vote in the House of Representatives in May to put a large portion of Alaska—more than 500,000 hectares—in protected, non-developable status as national parks, national forests, wilderness areas, and wildlife refuges. However, action by the Senate was blocked until the 1980 session. Meanwhile, the land remained temporarily untouchable by executive order.

Worry for the 1980's—and Hope. Environmentalists viewed 1979 as a decided contrast to the heartening sequence of achievements in previous years, and environmental questions loomed as a bigger issue than ever in campaigning for the 1980 election. President Carter lost the support of some environmentalists because of a series of actions, some obviously politically motivated. Among these were his backing of increased logging in national forests, his acquiescence to Congress's overriding of the Endangered Species Act in connection with the snail darter fish to allow completion of the Tellico Dam in Tennessee, the sidetracking of his "hit list" of questionable water projects in the western states, his proposals for the Energy Mobilization Board, and the proposed weakening of the 1977 strip-mining control law. Environmentalists did, however, find consolation in the general invulnerability of basic environmental legislation and in sustained grass-roots support for environmental quality. While some observers mused about an Armageddon-like showdown between the Environment and Energy, a more realistic prospect seemed to be more case-by-case confrontations, resolved individually with a consideration for environmental values that was unknown a decade ago.

Gladwin Hill

UPI

The toxic waste problem encountered in New York's Love Canal region continued—and spread "like a thread" through many areas of the United States.

Proponents of the Tellico Dam won—and the five-centimeter snail darter fish lost—in one of the decade's most widely publicized environmental issues.

Tennessee Valley Authority

Steve McCutcheon

THE ESKIMO AND THE BOWHEAD

by Kathryn Karsten Rushing

THE bowhead whale and the Inupiat Eskimos of northern Alaska lived for centuries in harmony with their environment and each other. They might have continued on the same way forever except for the encroachment of white civilization. Now, though white whalers have long since left the Arctic waters, the whale and the Eskimo are still trying to cope with the effects of that alien influence.

The whale is fighting for its survival as a species, and the Eskimos are fighting for their way of life. The survival of each depends on the other. In their struggles, both Eskimo and whale have caused an international controversy. The controversy involves the United States government, the other member nations of the International Whaling Commission (IWC), and conservationists. Some, fearing the extinction of a species, would take away from the Eskimos the right to hunt the bowhead. Others support a more moderate course.

AN ANCIENT RELATIONSHIP

The relationship between Eskimo and bowhead dates back to prehistoric times. Some time around 900 A.D., Siberian Eskimos invented the seal-skin float, which enabled them to keep large animals buoyant after they were killed. Until that time, however, the bowhead was probably the only whale the Eskimos could hunt. Like other right whales, the bowhead, or Greenland right whale, will float when dead, making it the "right" whale to catch.

This quality, combined with its relative slowness and high oil content, made the bowhead whale the central figure in Eskimo subsistence and culture for centuries. A winter without the meat and oil of the bowhead could mean starvation or at best living on the brink of survival for an entire village. Reliance on the meat of smaller animals required daily and exhausting hunts. No wonder the bowhead came to dominate the legends and festivals of the northern Eskimos, who owed their existence and way of life to the animal.

WHITE PEOPLE IN THE ARCTIC

Life for the bowhead and the Inupiat Eskimos, however, began to change in the late 1500's, when the bowhead was discovered by the Dutch in Arctic waters. The discovery was significant because the Dutch and other Europeans had already hunted the Atlantic black right whale to scarcity. The right whale's baleen was highly prized for its length and was used to make such articles as whips, stays, and umbrellas. Its oil-rich blubber lit the lamps of Europe for hundreds of years.

During the mid-nineteenth century American vessels took some 400 arctic whales yearly. In 1886, the Americans established their first whaling station along the Arctic coast, which came to be known as Jabbertown because of the many tongues spoken there. When the white whalers abandoned Jabbertown, the whales had practically disappeared, and the surrounding Eskimo villages were in a state of chaos. For some 50 years, until the early 1960's, bowhead hunting was minimal, with only about ten bowheads taken each year.

HUNT PREPARATIONS

The season for hunting the bowhead starts when the offshore ice begins to move some time in April. This is the signal that the bowheads will soon make their annual northward migration through the channels between the ice.

Almost every Inupiat Eskimo has a role in the yearly hunt. Whaling crews check their paddles, inflate sealskin floats, and clean and prepare their harpoons and guns. From rooftops children scan the horizon for a glimpse of the whales. Women sew new covers of bearded sealskin over driftwood frames. And when the skins dry, they fit tightly to the frame. Then the *umiak,* as the boat is called, is ready for the hunt.

Before the actual whaling operation can begin, the crew must establish a base camp

Whaling crews carefully prepare for the yearly hunt: loading the harpoons (left) and checking the traditional sealskin-and-driftwood *umiak* boat.

Glen A. Seaman   Glen A. Seaman

The hunt is successful—but the work continues. The whale must be brought ashore.

on the ice next to open water. This might be several kilometers away from the village. The camp consists of a tent with a chimney for a stove, with whale blubber providing the fuel. It creates a sweltering oasis in sub-freezing temperatures and biting winds. The camp serves as a lookout point for whales and a retreat for cold, weary, and hungry whalers.

The crew at the base camp keep the fire stoked, cut blubber for the stove, melt snow for drinking and washing, and cook. A typical meal might consist of chopped whale skin and blubber, cooked with onions and water, and thickened with flour. Fried bread, caribou meat, and coffee also fuel the hunters.

THE HUNT

What is clear from accounts of bowhead hunting is the incredible endurance, patience, and stamina required by all members of the crew to catch even one whale. Seas can be rough, winds difficult to paddle against, and snow blinding. And the whale can be a formidable prey, capable of smashing small boats or dragging vessels long distances after being wounded.

Then there is the frustration of sighting whales but being unable to reach them through the ice. Then come the long periods of waiting and watching. If the hunt is successful the crew must then tow a whale that weighs as much as 40 metric tons, or more, ashore. This requires the back-breaking efforts of some 50 people, tugging and pulling for hours. Butchering then requires an additional ten hours of labor.

THE WHALE-BASED SOCIETY

In Eskimo society the whaler is the most respected member. The courage and strength necessary for the hunt are obvious reasons. But the roles of the captain and his crew in maintaining social stability and in providing the community with most of its yearly protein needs are even more important.

The economy of northern coastal Alaska has been described as a modern subsistence culture. The natives have been able to strike a successful balance between their ancient social network and the contemporary monetary culture.

Everyone in the community, as well as inland relatives, receives a share of the bounty. Intangible rewards such as social cohesiveness and stability and community welfare are of overwhelming importance.

The annual whale hunt provides the

Some fifty or more people help to pull a bowhead ashore—sometimes for hours.

only communal subsistence opportunity for the coastal towns. This is essential to the preservation of the traditional cultural values and social bonds. In the whale hunt no one person supports his or her family alone— community members support each other.

THE ESKIMO DIET

The whale, along with seals and caribou and fish, birds, and walrus to a lesser degree, is an important component in the diet of the northern Eskimo. This traditional diet supplies all essential nutrients because whale blubber is a good source of vitamins A, D, and C. Eskimos obtain their calcium requirement by consuming the cartilage and soft bones of the native animal species. Therefore, importation of alternative food sources from the lower forty-eight states not only would be costly but would not provide the basic diet to which the Eskimos seem to be metabolically adapted.

Replacement of the whale by other native species is not a viable alternative either. Caribou and the Beluga and gray whales are also protected species. Smaller native species such as seals, walrus, waterfowl, and fish could not substitute because of the time and effort that would be required to hunt them.

THE BOWHEAD WHALE

The Eskimos' traditions, social structure, relationship with the sea, and rhythm of life have an appeal that pleads for their preservation. The bowhead, however, cannot speak for itself. In addition, it is perhaps the least understood of the great whales. What little we know of it is related to its importance to humans. We know what it looks like. We know of its value as a food source. We know that it was once of utmost economic value. We know it was hunted almost to extinction. We know where to hunt it today, and that it floats when dead. But do we know how to save this species?

The massive, slow-moving bowhead reaches lengths of up to 20 meters and weighs as much as 46 metric tons. Its curving, cavernous mouth holds the longest baleen found in any species of whale—the average measuring three meters in length— which extends from its palate in fringed plates. For humans, the bony baleen plates at one time represented a ton and a half of whalebone. For the whale, they function as a sieve through which pass sea water and plankton—its primary food as far as we know. Its 50 centimeters of blubber is the thickest developed by any species of whale. It yields about 23 metric tons of oil and, by the way, protects the whale from its harsh Arctic environment.

The bowhead has a limited migration pattern, never straying far beyond Arctic regions. Females give birth in Arctic waters. Presumably in adaptation to living in ice-filled waters, the bowhead can remain underwater one hour, which is longer than any other species of whale. Scientists have yet to discover its whereabouts in summer and winter, though they presume that it keeps to the edge of pack ice. Except for subsistence hunting by Eskimos, the species has been protected by international convention since 1935.

INTERNATIONAL DECISIONS

In June 1977 the IWC banned all hunting of the bowhead. This decision was based on an admittedly inexact population estimate of between 600 and 2,500 individuals. This action also came after an alarming increase in the number of bowheads struck and lost during recent years—82 in 1977. The decision caused a storm of controversy among Eskimos, conservationists, and American officials. Furthermore, it placed the United States in a double-bind situation. The United States government has long been a leader in whale conservation. But it also has legal and moral obligations to its native people.

In the summer of 1978, a majority of the IWC member nations present voted to adopt a compromise quota for the spring 1978 hunt: 12 whales taken or 18 struck, whichever came first. Calves and nursing mothers were completely protected for the first time.

SELF REGULATION

The compromise pleased no one. Conservationists who had supported the complete ban were outraged. The Eskimos predicted that the low quotas would not meet their nutritional needs and would result in violations.

Little is known about the bowhead whale despite its long association with man.

Whale meat, blubber, and cartilage supply most essential nutrients for the Eskimo.

All villagers help in the hunt—here Eskimo women carefully store whale parts for later use.

The natives then began to take a long look at some of the reasons for the recent heavy losses of bowheads. And they took steps to modify their weapons and procedures to eliminate as much waste as possible. This action resulted in only five lost bowheads in 1978.

The Eskimos have long contended that government estimates of the bowhead population were low. And, actually, a truly comprehensive census has never been made. Therefore, during 1978 the United States used more accurate census techniques. Biologists also studied the population dynamics and acoustic techniques of the bowhead. Ice- and land-based observation points plus aerial surveys yielded a count between 1,783 and 2,865 whales. This was a larger population than had been believed to exist.

The 1979 quota for bowheads was set at 18 landed or 26 struck and lost—whichever came first. The result of the most recent IWC meeting was, again, to please no one. The Eskimos would still like a higher quota. And many conservationists would like to see a complete moratorium on hunting of the bowhead.

MORE RESEARCH NEEDED

On one fact both sides have agreed: more research on the natural history and population of the bowhead is needed.

Even a Solomon would have found it difficult to make a completely acceptable decision on the bowhead controversy. A definitive answer may never settle this environmental problem. If it does, it will be only after many more years of accumulation of data and a continuation of the intensive research that has just begun. In the meantime, we can only hope that the bowhead population will not be decreased by subsistence hunting. And we also hope that the whalers will continue their efforts to increase their efficiency and adhere to their own stringent regulations.

If this does not happen, we stand to lose two irreplaceable resources: a cultural tradition both of intrinsic value and of value as a model of individual commitment to the community and a little-understood giant of a species. The world would be much poorer for the loss of either one □

 SELECTED READINGS

"Black water, red death" by R. Rau. *Sports Illustrated*, November 1, 1976.

"Right whale" by R. Reeves. *Conservationist*, August 1975.

"Whale of a problem: eskimo hunting of the bowhead whale" by J. Walsh. *Science*, October 8, 1977.

"Issue of survival: bowhead vs tradition" by J. R. Bockstoce. *Audubon*, September 1977.

CLEANLY FLOWS THE THAMES

by Trevor Fishlock

WHEN I was a boy, my father took me to London to see the sights. We walked over Westminster Bridge and gazed at the swirling Thames. I asked my dad if he would buy me a rod so I could do some fishing. He gave a short laugh. "A fish would need a diving suit to live in that lot," he said. He was right. Old Father Thames, Britain's greatest river, its praises sung by poets down the centuries, was a very dirty old man, indeed. It was a dead, oxygenless sewer in which any fish would most surely have choked to death. It was a national scandal.

FROM SALMON TO SEWAGE

When Queen Elizabeth I reigned in the sixteenth century, she enjoyed banquets of luscious salmon, caught in her own sparkling Thames. Indeed, Elizabethan poet Raphael Holinshed wrote of "fat sweet salmon dailie taken in this streame . . . such plentie as no river is able to exceed it. What store also of barbels, trouts, roches, daces, gudgings, flounders, shrimps."

How different it was when the second Elizabethan Age started in 1952. In the dank Thames, life was virtually extinct. A few eels swam with heads above the reeking water.

Some worms inhabited the foul mud, and a few gulls pecked at the garbage strewn along the banks.

AND BACK TO SALMON?

Today, though, Queen Elizabeth's Father Thames has been given back its self-respect. The river has been restored in an astonishing environmental rescue operation. And its rescuers reckon it to be the world's cleanest metropolitan river. It has a thriving fish population the year round, and even salmon may return in large numbers some day.

Since 1964, when pioneer fish began to venture back to the Thames, 91 fish species have been recorded. An occasional seal has been seen casting an exploratory eye. With the fish have returned the fish-eating birds. Large stretches of the river that were recently without birds now provide homes for them. Furthermore, there is a wintering population of 10,000 wild-fowl and 12,000 waders.

The Thames measures about 270 kilometers from its source in the soft Cotswold Hills to its estuary on the North Sea. It is tidal from Teddington, about 95 kilometers from the sea. Its basin covers about 13,000 square kilometers and in this region live 12 million people. The river's well-being is part of their well-being.

SOME HISTORY

The great Thames cleanup needs to be viewed in historic context. The Romans, those cleanest of conquerors, appreciated the river for its fish and oysters. During their 300-year occupation, they filtered its waters through sand to ensure good drinking supplies. But, as London grew, the river was used increasingly as a dump and a sewer. King Edward III, riding beside the Thames in 1357, noticed "dung and abominable stenches" and enacted simple environmental laws to try to improve matters. People ignored them, but for more than three centuries the broad-backed Thames was able to sustain its wildlife.

After the Great Fire of London in 1666, Sir Christopher Wren, was called in to rebuild the ravaged city. He also planned a drainage system to keep London free from dirt and plague. His magnificent St. Paul's Cathedral was built, but his sewers weren't. And from then on, the river began to die. London apprentices, who once grumbled because they were given salmon too often, found the delicacy disappearing. The Thames fishing industry, with oysters bringing a penny a dozen, started to dwindle.

The reality of "the good old days" was that Londoners lived in, or close to, filth. There was hardly any sanitation and disease was rife. Invention of the water closet in 1810 simply accelerated the flow of sewage to cesspools, then to street sewers and into the long-suffering Thames. London's importance as the center of the expanding British Empire increased and the industrial revolution brought factories. The population swelled. And with the Thames an open sewer carrying diseases, there were horrific outbreaks of cholera.

The year 1856 was known to Londoners as Year of the Great Stink, so bad was the Thames. Two years later, Queen Victoria and her consort Albert attempted a pleasure cruise, but the malodorous waters drove them back to land after a few minutes. Thousands of Londoners were dying of infectious fevers, and Prince Albert himself died of typhoid in 1861, a victim of bad sanitation.

AT LAST—SOME ACTION

Action was needed urgently. A board of works was set up to stop sewage entering the Thames—and also the waste from gas works, chemical plants, breweries and paper mills. Sewers were built to take waste from the city center and out to sea. This led to some improvement in central London, but deterioration in the out-fall areas. The problem had been moved from one place to another.

More sewers were built but they could not keep up with the pollution. In the 1930's, large treatment works were constructed, but still pollution worsened. During the wartime blitz, there was bomb damage to treatment works and sewers—and no time or money for repairs.

ANOTHER START

In the 1950's, the government appointed a committee, under Professor A. J. Pippard, to examine the Thames pollution. The job

Since clean-up operations began in 1964, many species of fish and birds have come back to the Thames. Herring (left) and pintail duck (right) are now permanent residents.

Jeff Goodman/N.H.P.A.   Kenneth W. Fink/Photo Researchers

Queen Victoria's gilded barge sailed over an unsavory stew of a Thames in 1843.

was complex and took ten years. There were talks with scientists, industrialists, and environmental groups. Even as the committee investigated, a new pollutant was attacking the river. Detergents foamed and scummed and reduced what little oxygen there was even further. Deadly to fish, the detergents also ruined the waterproof plumage of birds.

At last, though, the rescue master plan was made. The Pippard report came out in 1961 and was implemented by act of Parliament three years later. It set out steps that should be taken to render the Thames inoffensive and to ensure at least 10 per cent dissolved oxygen content. Daringly, it said the river should be made fit for salmon.

First to be done was large-scale improvement to sewage works—one important sewage project in 1964, another in 1974. The most up-to-date pumping, screening, and processing equipment was installed. The final fluid now discharged into the Thames is virtually pure water. Solid waste is rendered non-toxic and dumped at sea from tankers. Inefficient sewage plants have been closed.

Industry has played its part, too. There

are strict pollution controls, and companies have become much more pollution conscious. Firms pay for the conveyance and treatment of effluent in proportion to its volume and toxicity. Generating stations use traps to make sure oil does not get into the Thames. At docksides, modern loading methods have almost eliminated spillage accidents.

FISH IN THE RIVER

The effect has been inspiring. At a time when environmental danger signals were being sounded throughout the world, fish started swimming in the Thames again. Here was proof that, with determination, tough laws, goodwill, and a sense of responsibility, aquatic pollution could be overcome. Of course, the action had to be backed by large funds.

In 1965, there was dramatic evidence of the river's comeback when live fish were caught for the first time on power-station cooling screens. A regular survey of trapped fish was started at seven stations. Included in the list of 91 types are uncommon sea fish like scad, dory, and Nilsson's pipefish. Around the Dartford area are whiting and sprats. Herring are numerous. Flounders abound and plaice, dab, brill and sole are becoming common catches. There are grey mullet and bass—the young bass, especially, being attracted to the warm water flowing from power stations.

Alwyne Wheeler, noted marine biologist and author of "Fishes of the British Isles and North West Europe," finds the presence of haddock in the lower Thames intriguing. He writes: "As many pollution control officers have discovered, the presence of a percentage of dissolved oxygen in water is a nebulous concept, being invisible and odorless. But a live fish in the same water is a measure of the river's health, which everyone can understand."

AND NOW—BIRDS

The return of the birds is just as exciting to naturalists and others. Large flocks of mallard, teal, pintail, tufted duck, pochard, shelduck, dunlin, lapwing, and redshank have been counted. And the Thames is now rated in the top category of sites of international importance to wildlife conservation.

A report by two naturalists, Dr. Jeffrey Harrison and Peter Grant, says that the Thames is an example to other polluted regions of the world. "Presence of these birds is constant and visible proof that all is well with the river. It is hoped that this achievement is not wasted by thoughtless riverside development in the future."

The last salmon caught in the Thames was taken in 1833. The idea that the river could once again be host to salmon is exciting, even romantic. But the conditions are now about right. The average dissolved oxygen content is about three times what scientists predicted ten years ago. And the catching of sea trout in recent years at Deptford and Teddington has increased optimism. A London paper is now offering a prize for the person who catches the first salmon.

CONSTANT MONITORING

So Father Thames breathes again, as do the people who live and work beside him. It

Tom Hollyman/Photo Researchers

A newly pristine Thames rises in the Cotswold Hills and flows cleanly to its estuary in the North Sea.

would be wrong, though, to give the impression that the Thames Water Authority, set up in 1973 to manage the river, is sitting back complacently. Far from it. There is constant monitoring of the river. Scientists take frequent samples for testing. And the engineers watch over the Thames with all the care of doctors treating a patient on the mend after a long illness and a tricky operation.

Many people now think about the re-established wildlife. You can see this interest reflected in the newspapers and in the schools. Recently, the Thames authority suspended pumping at a sewage treatment works for eight weeks while a little ringed plover successfully hatched four eggs it had laid in a drying bed. A small story, but it illustrates the true affection that now exists between the river's managers and the much-prized wild residents.

Such examples show, too, some of the pride in a wrong righted. Maybe it won't be too long before "fat sweet salmon are dailie taken in this streame" to grace a Queen's table once more □

Diesel cars are at present more widely used in European cities, including Rome, pictured above, than in U.S. cities, but serious health hazards resulting from diesel emissions have not yet been found there.

FPG

CANCER AND THE DIESEL CAR

by Charles G. Burck

THE energy-environment conflict has a new battlefield—diesel cars. The Environmental Protection Agency (EPA) has been under pressure to consider economics and energy conservation. The feeling is that it must base its standards on what the auto industry is capable of achieving with available technology. At the same time, it must protect the public health. In December 1979, the EPA made a compromise decision, allowing General Motors and two foreign car manufacturers to install four diesel engines in 1981 and 1982 that will not meet nitrogen oxide standards for those years.

GENERATORS OF ANXIETY

Diesels produce copious clouds of particles—microscopic specks of carbon. The particles contain compounds that are known to cause cancer. No one is certain that they are concentrated enough to be dangerous, but there is no question they can generate high levels of anxiety. Cancer from synthetic chemicals—so-called environmental cancer—has come in recent years to rival, if not replace, nuclear holocaust as the major specter of technology gone amok. Voices both within the EPA and without are urging a temporary freeze on new industry commitments to the diesel, while more conclusive information is assembled.

At the same time, diesel automobiles are so popular today that some buyers are waiting months for them, or paying hundreds of dollars over list price. Diesels get, on average, about 25 per cent better mileage than comparable gasoline-engine cars. By the late 1990's this could cut total automobile fuel consumption by about six per cent.

For this reason diesels may offer the only practical hope for the continued production of full-size, six-passenger cars and station wagons that many people in the United States regard as necessities. EPA decision-makers must thus grapple explicitly with what is becoming the central regulatory dilemma of the age: choosing between how much safety is possible and how much is practical.

ENERGY EFFICIENT

Concerns about the diesel's emissions have emerged almost overnight with the explosive growth of diesel-auto sales in the United States. The engine itself, of course, has been around since the beginning of the 20th century. Diesel-powered cars have been on the market since 1936, when the first one rolled out of Mercedes-Benz's factory. Diesels account for four to seven per cent of automobile registrations in Europe.

The diesel's economy is due in large part to its high compression ratio and the large amounts of air it gulps. Its compression ratio is about 20 to 1, against the 8 to 1 typical of gasoline engines running on unleaded fuel. Unlike a gasoline engine, the diesel has no throttle to regulate the fuel-air mixture. Only the fuel, which is directly injected into each cylinder, is controlled. An unthrottled engine does not waste energy trying to pull air past the physical obstruction of a throttle. More important, extra air means that more of the fuel is burned instead of escaping through the exhaust pipe. The engine's relative efficiency is greatest in city driving, when it is idling or decelerating a great deal of the time. Under such conditions, a diesel can be 40 to 50 per cent more efficient than a gasoline engine.

Until recently, few people in the United States had any reason to buy diesel cars. It is true that diesel engines eliminate ignition-system problems since they have no spark plugs. High compression alone ignites the fuel. But this advantage is offset by some penalties—sluggish acceleration, cranky starting in cold weather, noise, odor, smoke,

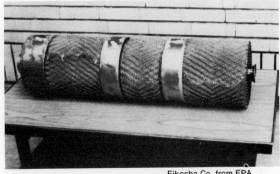

Eikosha Co, from EPA

Diesels emit copious amounts of particulates. Above, the filter used to collect the very tiny but potentially very hazardous specks (below).

Eikosha Co, from EPA

higher initial cost, and the need for more frequent oil changes.

SUDDEN BANDWAGON

In 1976, only about 25,000 diesel cars were sold in the United States, 80 per cent of them Mercedes and the balance Peugeots.

But as demand rose along with gasoline prices, the mass-market automakers responded. In 1977, Volkswagen began importing diesel-engine Rabbits; in 1978 it added a Dasher diesel. Oldsmobile brought forth the first U.S.-made diesel in 1977. In 1979 it was available from all General Motors divisions and standard in the Cadillac Seville. Chrysler Corporation is getting ready to produce a diesel version of its workhorse slant-six engine, provided it can come up with the money needed.

Ford is resting its hopes for high efficiency on its so-called PROCO engine, a stratified-charge gasoline engine that burns fuel so efficiently it does not need a catalytic converter and so rivals the diesel in economy. Ford expects it to be lighter, more powerful, and cleaner. But questions remain about whether the engine can be mass-produced.

Manufacturers have done a good deal to minimize the diesel's drawbacks. Current engines are noticeably less smoky and smelly than their predecessors. They are also generally easier to start when cold. The newer ones—that is, those from General Motors and Volkswagen—are derived from existing gasoline engines and provide driver performance approximating that of conventional cars. But the biggest reason for the diesel's upsurge in popularity was the gasoline shortages of the 1979 summer. Many current buyers are enamored not just of the diesel's higher mileage but of its greater range between fillings. Thus, at present, it seems that a strong market for diesels will continue.

The future of the six-passenger automobile is probably tied to the diesel. There seems to be no other cost-effective way to build such a car capable of getting the sort of mileage that will be required by government regulations by the mid-1980's. General Motors calculates that it would have to take some 900 pounds out of a full-size gas car to get equivalent economy. It would take very expensive materials to keep the resulting vehicle from being structurally frail.

Both General Motors and Mercedes-Benz are counting on diesels to meet government regulations for corporate average fleet economy. These averages rise from 20 miles per gallon in 1979 to 27.5 in 1985. While the diesel is now about four per cent of General Motors' total sales, it amounts to seven per cent of its full-size car production.

DIESEL SOOT

Ironically, the diesel itself was once regarded as an exemplary nonpolluter. With

The EPA is testing diesel engines and their emissions under various operating conditions.

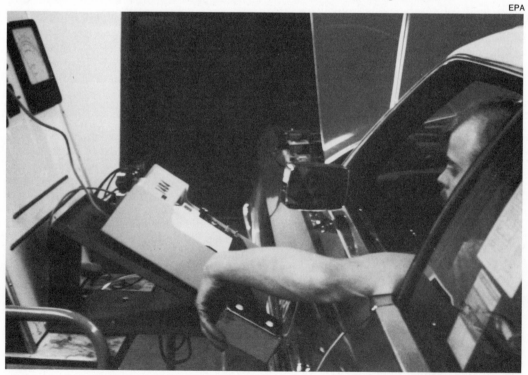

The 1980 Audi 5000 with a diesel engine can cruise over 600 miles on one fill-up.

no emission controls at all, it emits fewer hydrocarbons and less carbon monoxide than today's tightly muzzled gasoline engines. Back in 1973 the EPA was hailing it as a possible alternative to the conventional engine. By the time the Clean Air Act was amended in 1977, however, diesel soot had come to be recognized as a potential, if distant, problem.

Diesel soot consists of microscopically fine carbon particles that measure less than one-half of a micron in diameter. (One micron is equal to 1/1,000,000 meter.) The EPA has estimated that a fleet of uncontrolled diesels equivalent to about 17 per cent of the estimated 1990 total automotive population could produce some 280,000 tons of particulates annually.

Spread out over the total area of the lower forty-eight states, that amount does not sound especially disturbing. Even in dense urban settings, the diesel's contribution to total airborne particulates would amount to perhaps five per cent. The trouble is that those extremely fine particles tend to float in the air for hours or even days, especially in urban canyons. In the long run, a pronounced swing to diesels of the uncontrolled type could be expected to create a persistent gray haze over large cities.

The EPA's currently proposed regulations for particulate emissions pose serious problems. Some automakers can meet the standards proposed for the 1981 model year—0.6 gram per mile—with no trouble. Others can do so only with immense difficulty and expense. But none knows how to meet the standards proposed for 1983, which would limit particulates to 0.2 gram per mile.

The difficulties are greatest in big cars, since particulate emissions tend to increase directly with an engine's size. According to EPA tests, a 5.7-liter Oldsmobile V-8 engine puts out about 1 gram per mile, and a 3-liter Mercedes 0.8 gram. A 1.5-liter Volkswagen Rabbit, by contrast, emits less than 0.4 gram.

The problem is compounded by standards already laid down for oxides of nitrogen that apply to all cars. By 1981, nitrous-oxide emissions are to fall from 2 grams per mile to 1 gram. Nitrous oxide is a key component of smog. The only practical way to control it down to 1 gram in a diesel is by recirculating small quantities of exhaust gas back into the engine. Unfortunately, exhaust-gas recirculation sharply increases the production of particulates.

Even Volkswagen, with its low particulate emissions, has told the EPA it sees no hope of meeting both the nitrous oxide and particulate standards together in 1983. In December 1979, EPA granted waivers of up to four years from the nitrous oxide standard for diesel engines emitting no more than 1.5 grams per mile. General Motors, Mercedes, and Volvo won waivers for four engines but for only two years.

THE "BRILLO-PAD APPROACH"

It's likely that the auto industry will eventually be able to meet fairly tight emission standards, but not by 1983. Many approaches, none costly enough to price diesels out of the market, hold promise. Among them are changes in combustion-chamber design, and new exhaust-treatment devices.

The catalytic converter won't work on a diesel because the temperature of a diesel's exhaust is too low to sustain the converter's chemical reactions. Some kind of filtering system may well prove the answer. The most likely solution is what some engineers scornfully call the "Brillo-pad approach." A fine metallic mesh in an insulated canister collects the particles. When the metallic mesh is fully laden with them, it is brought to a high-enough temperature to burn itself clean.

When it proposed its particulate standards, the EPA was operating on some faulty assumptions. It picked out fragments of promising technology and concluded that automakers would be able to both maximize the diesels' potential and mass-produce them. The EPA's estimates for the costs of control technologies were also low. In fact, the agency's basic computer model for calculating atmospheric particulate levels is now also open to question.

During the controversy over possible emissions of sulfuric acid from cars with catalytic converters in 1975, General Motors and the U.S. Department of Transportation separately conducted tests in which they monitored particulate emissions at roadside locations. Both found levels to be significantly lower than those predicted by the EPA dispersion model. With only minor modifications, this test is the one used to calculate diesel emissions.

INTO THE AIR . . . AND LUNGS

For several years there have been suspicions about carcinogens in diesel exhaust. The EPA began its own investigations in 1977. The compounds in question are a group of several thousand chemicals called polynuclear aromatics. Some—for example, benzo(a)pyrene—are known carcinogens, and others are suspect. A great many are found in the smoke from other petroleum-based fuels besides diesel fuel, and from coal. Before the advent of the catalytic converter, they were present in the exhaust of gasoline-engine cars. So, for that matter, were significant quantities of particulates, mostly lead.

The aromatics themselves would probably not be a concern if they simply dissipated into the atmosphere, as they did after leaving the tail pipe of the pre-catalyst gas auto. But diesel particulates are specks of carbon that tend to adsorb many of the compounds in question onto their surfaces. These particulates not only remain suspended in the atmosphere but—because they are so small—seem to bypass most of the body's defense systems, such as the cilia in the nostrils, for screening out larger particles. They can be sucked into the deepest recesses of the lungs, and may remain there for considerable lengths of time.

Extracts of diesel soot have caused mutations in bacteria exposed to them in the so-called Ames test. This test is widely used to screen potential carcinogens. Substances that prove mutagenic in this test often turn out to be carcinogenic. The diesel flunked its first Ames test in 1977. Since then it has flunked tests using yeast cells and mammalian cells. The production of mutations in all three types of cell tests constitute "suggestive evidence" of a carcinogen. This is according to criteria established by the Interagency Regulatory Liaison Group, which includes the EPA. Precatalyst-gasoline exhaust, as well as extracts from its particulates and extracts from heating-oil smoke, yield the same results in these tests.

The automobile industry, the EPA, the U.S. Department of Energy, and the U.S. National Institute for Occupational Safety and Health are researching diesel engines in a variety of ways. Efforts to assess the effects of diesel use on animals range from painting diesel-soot extracts on the skins of mice to exposing rats to diesel-exhaust fumes for their lifetimes. Researchers are also testing specific parts of diesel exhaust. This includes particulates produced under different operating conditions—for example, during acceleration versus steady cruising.

GUILTY UNTIL PROVED INNOCENT

One of the most important questions is whether adsorbed aromatics remain on soot particles once they enter the lungs or enter surrounding tissues. If they stay on the particles they are eventually expelled, and the likelihood that they are dangerous diminishes greatly.

There will be relatively few long-term observations of groups of people who are exposed to high levels of diesel exhaust because of the time and expense involved. But investigators do hope to pinpoint differences and similarities between diesel exhaust and several other products, such as coke-oven emissions and cigarette smoke, that have been linked with cancer.

Because there is as yet no compelling evidence that the diesel poses a new threat to health, the EPA is officially obliged to be sci-

A diesel engine has no spark plugs and works on the principle of compression-ignition. The engine's power depends on the amount of fuel delivered by the pump.

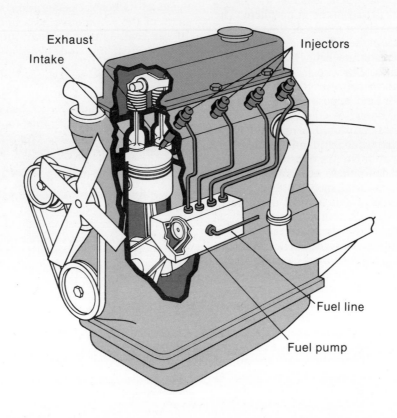

Exhaust

Intake

Injectors

Fuel line

Fuel pump

entifically circumspect about any fears it may have. Unofficially, though, the agency is badly worried. During the past few years, environmental cancer has become such a powerful and emotional issue that any suspected carcinogen is now judged by a particularly severe version of the Napoleonic code: until proved innocent, it is guilty of the worst imaginable effects upon human health.

Society is learning that it must pay more attention to the subtle menaces of the industrial age. Hitherto unsuspected dangers are being unearthed almost daily in entire classes of chemicals now adrift in the environment. One recent study suggests that there are perhaps 30,000 different compounds in diesel exhaust. The apparent wholesale collapse of past easy assumptions about what is safe demands that potential new hazards be scrutinized as sharply as possible.

THRESHOLD

There are, however, questions about how much light laboratory results can shed on the way compounds behave when they are widely dispersed in the atmosphere. The questions are related to one of the great scientific debates of the day: Is there a threshold level of concentration below which cancer-causing agents are harmless?

The laboratory-test procedures, like others of their kind, expose cells and animals to massive doses of the suspect compounds—doses that would never be even remotely approximated in quantity or duration in the real world. No one questions the economic rationale for these techniques—testing a suspect chemical at small doses could require thousands of animals and many years before it yielded any useful information.

But debate rages on about the meaning of it all. Zero-risk scientists believe there is no such thing as a safe dose. Even the tiniest exposure increases the risk of cancer, they say, so that any sign of carcinogenicity in the laboratory is cause for alarm. Other scientists argue that the body can, in fact, defend itself against low doses of most suspect substances. They argue that this is so even against multiple carcinogens if the quantities are not so great that they overwhelm the body's natural defense mechanisms.

NO PANIC IN EUROPE

It does seem noteworthy that European governments have not voiced alarm over the problem. Concentrations of diesel vehicles in many cities there would appear great enough to have laid bare by now any significant health risks. A number of epidemiological studies conducted in working environments rich in diesel fumes have failed to turn up positive evidence. Critics of the diesel dismiss the studies because of various methodological flaws and say, moreover, that they do not rule out the possibility that cancers with long latency periods may develop many years later. But ruling out long-term possibilities seems beyond the purview of a federal regulatory agency—if, indeed, it is not beyond human capability itself.

A DILEMMA STILL

The case against the diesel today rests on strongly intuitive suspicions, and EPA decision making must be an exercise in probabilities. Under the most extravagant assessments of its market penetration, the diesel's share of the automotive fleet will not reach 10 per cent until some time around 1990. Thus, even if the worst fears about its exhaust come true, its potential for causing significant health problems will remain minimal for about a decade. This is ample time for the conclusion of health studies. Also it gives the industry time to develop effective and cost-effective control technologies on the basis of need, rather than suspicion.

On the other hand, there is the fear, expressed by some within the EPA, that no future findings of danger would be able to stop the spread of the diesel once the industry had sunk substantial sums of money into it. That scenario seems improbable. The investments involved would not be all that large by auto-industry standards □

 SELECTED READINGS

"How we got into this mess and why diesels won't get us out." *Popular Science,* September 1979.

"The diesel dilemma" by Lois Ember. *Environment,* March 1979.

Dave Foreman

ORV'S THREATEN A WILD CANYON

by Dave Foreman

ALONG the side of Sundial Mountain in the remote Gila National Forest in southwestern New Mexico, the San Francisco River boxes into a precipitous canyon and turns abruptly west. Roadless and uninhabited for about 50 kilometers, eventually the canyon crosses into the Apache National Forest of Arizona. At one point the south canyon wall, known fittingly as the Angel's Roost, rears more than 500 meters above the river.

Tributary canyons are so rugged and intricate that the most intrepid wilderness explorers in the Southwest have yet to find a way up them. Cliff dwellings, petroglyphs, and other reminders of the ancient Mimbres people are scattered like potsherds throughout the canyon. During spring runoff, river runners find common habitat with black phoebes and mergansers.

Lower San Francisco Canyon possesses a healthy herd of bighorn sheep, javelina, mule and white-tailed deer, mountain lion, turkey, and pronghorn on the mesas above.

However, the essential wildlife values of the Frisco are more subtle than this. It is the primary route through which the Lower Sonoran biota enters New Mexico. It also attracts species from Mexico's Sierra Madre, introducing them to the Rockies.

HOME OF ENDANGERED SPECIES

Dr. John Hubbard, supervisor of the endangered species program of the New Mexico Department of Game and Fish, estimates that there are more than 200 breeding species of birds within an 80-kilometer radius of the canyon. This represents a quantity that few other temperate non-marine areas can boast. Of these, 23 are on the periphery of their range.

This canyon is the hunting habitat for the bald eagle, peregrine falcon, and Mexican black hawk. Important habitat is also provided for other species that are rare or threatened in New Mexico, including the zone-tailed hawk, osprey, loach minnow,

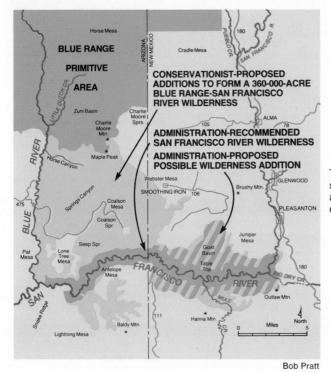

This map shows the wild canyon area in southwestern New Mexico where wildlife and their habitat are threatened by increasing use of off-road vehicles.

Bob Pratt

Sonoran Mountain king snake, narrow-headed garter snake, Arizona coral snake, lyre snake, and Gila monster.

This exceptional display of species is explained by the fact that the canyon embraces the largest undisturbed tract of remaining Lower Sonoran riparian (riverbank) woodland in the United States. Some 32 species of broad-leaved trees and shrubs, dominated by cottonwood, sycamore, willow, and walnut, are found in the canyon—an exceptional number for the West. In the arid Southwest, the riparian zones around the few permanent watercourses are the most critical of all habitats to a wide variety of wildlife. Unfortunately, the riparian areas have also proved most attractive to people. Human intrusion has reduced these fragile riverine woodlands—never extensive—to a fraction of their former area.

FOUR-WHEEL-DRIVE CARAVANS

As with many non-forested areas in New Mexico and Arizona, the greatest threat to the wilderness of the Frisco is posed by recreational off-road vehicle (ORV) use. The canyon has become a favorite challenge for four-wheel-drive caravans consisting of dozens of heavily equipped rigs. A decade ago such use was minimal. It has grown, however, until now it hangs like a guillotine blade over the natural integrity of the canyon.

There have been many pleas that the canyon be closed to vehicles to protect it. The U.S. Forest Service, however, has responded that significant damage has not yet been done and that floods do more damage than vehicles. The protectors of this area reply: "Floods renew, they are natural, they don't come at breeding and nesting season. They don't poach or jacklight or change their oil in the canyon. Neither do they pilfer Indian artifacts or come close to running over people sleeping on the beaches."

Dr. Hubbard has shown that the ORV tracks in the canyon greatly intensify the impact of the periodic floods. They do this by channeling the flood waters into the vehicle tracks and causing them to eat away the flood terraces above the river and create more channels along the tracks.

ORV DAMAGE

Perhaps the most vivid testimony regarding vehicle damage to the canyon comes from Steve Zachary, a naturalist. Last year he led a small group down the river. In a subsequent letter, he reported as follows to the Gila National Forest supervisor:

"We stayed in the canyon seven days. It was a delightful experience. We saw many birds (including a merganser with six ducklings and a nesting least bittern), bighorn sheep, and many wildflowers. As Memorial Day weekend approached I noticed that the cattle down in the canyon were herded out. Then I began to see why: four-wheel drives. ORV's of all kinds started coming down the canyon. They turned a beautiful river into a noisy motorized playground, with no concern or sensitivity for the environment.

"It was a real challenge for the ORV's to cross the river. We saw ORV's stuck in the river dripping oil into it. Some of the people had guns and were shooting at anything that moved. Over the weekend we saw that common merganser again but with only three young and eventually with none. With motorized vehicles going up and down the river canyon, it's hard for something like a merganser to keep her family together. The least bittern nest was completely destroyed, tire tracks going right over the nest. I was really worried about the birds of prey since some people had big rifles.

"We started seeing litter throughout the canyon, and the beautiful riparian habitat destroyed. We camped along the river at night and people would come by in their vehicles, shining their spotlights on the canyon cliffs. There were a group of bighorn sheep in the immediate area. The ORV'ers began to fire shots. I believe they were poaching or trying to poach the sheep. I can see now why the rancher removed his cattle. We saw a camp of ORV'ers drinking beer and throwing the cans in the river, then shooting them as they floated by.

"What seemed so ironic was that I was made to place a $500 bond to lead a group of three backpackers into the canyon. This performance bond was in case of any damages to the national forest. Yet all these vehicles were down in the same canyon destroying the canyon, river, and wildlife, and do you think they paid a performance bond? When I

A hiker inspects ORV damage to riverbank vegetation.

Bob Langsenkamp

returned to the Glenwood ranger station, the secretary wasn't going to give my $500 bond back until someone went down the canyon to see if my three backpackers had done any damage."

DAMAGE NOT AN UNACCEPTABLE RESOURCE LOSS

The Forest Service replied to Zachary: "The Lower San Francisco is presently managed under the multiple use concept. This permits recreation use in all forms that do not present unacceptable resource loss. Off-road vehicle use in the San Francisco River bottom is not at present presenting unacceptable resource loss." This insensitivity to the natural values of the canyon dates back to the first roadless area review (RARE I) in 1972. At that time the Forest Service did not even inventory a roadless area in the canyon. Later, in response to the President's order on ORV's, the service launched a study to determine which areas of the forest should be closed to vehicular use. Conservationists, alarmed at the rapidly growing ORV damage in the lower canyon, urged the closing of the area. They were ignored. Officials stated that ORV use in the canyon would have no detrimental effects.

In the Southwest, RARE II was a vast improvement upon RARE I. Three times the roadless acreage was identified by the Forest Service, including a 34,500-hectare Lower San Francisco Canyon roadless area contiguous to the Blue Range Primitive Area on the Arizona-New Mexico border. Moreover, the Forest Service found no resource conflicts with wilderness designation. In the 1978 environmental statement, the Southwest regional forester's recommendation proposed wilderness designation for the entire Lower San Francisco area. Conservationists were jubilant.

Conservationists remained hopeful that the Forest Service would continue with the new direction indicated. But in its final RARE II action, the service failed to recommend the canyon as wilderness. It stated that the canyon is not an ecologically significant area. The service also claimed that public input was against wilderness. It totally disregarded the overwhelming mandate for wilderness in the flood of letters it had earlier received.

THERE IS STILL HOPE

In 1978, President Carter partly reversed the Forest Service decision. He rec-

Riverine woodlands are unfortunately as attractive to people as to wildlife.

Bob Langsenkamp

Roadless for more than 50 kilometers, San Francisco River scenery is often spectacular.

Dave Foreman

ommended to Congress that about 6,000 hectares along the river in New Mexico and Arizona become wilderness and an additional 4,600 hectares in New Mexico be given further consideration for the same protection. Although this was less than conservationists wanted, it did embrace the core canyon, scenically and biologically the most critical area.

Southwestern conservationists understandably expected the Forest Service, as a matter of course, to close this 10,400 hectares to ORV's. But on Memorial Day weekend, 1978, without official interference, some 40 all-terrain vehicles and jeeps invaded the canyon for an annual ORV "event." They ripped out new trails where cottonwoods and willows were reseeding after an unusually severe winter flood, gunned down and ran

over wildlife, drained oil into the river bed, and turned the flat where Big Dry Creek enters the Frisco into a devegetated racetrack for motorized tricycles.

It is plain enough that officials are reluctant to buck that segment of local opinion that is antagonistic to preservation. A hint of the character of this sentiment is provided by an El Paso *Times* report published shortly after the presidential announcement. An anti-wilderness Glenwood realtor was quoted as warning: "It will be unsafe for environmental groups to travel in the area."

The service did not entirely dismiss the conservationists' concerns. Gila National Forest officials have been instructed to "reassess the situation with regard to ORV use." Meanwhile, New Mexico conservationists intend to stand their ground □

Riki H. Kondo

Not even an idyllic country setting is free from air pollution.

THE AIR: UNSAFE AT ANY SITE

by Holcomb B. Noble

CLARENCE Webster gets on the train for Pelham, New York, and by chance finds himself on the smoker. He doesn't smoke, and the initial shock of the air is staggering. He rushes to the next car. The air there is better, and he's O.K. After he gets home, he jogs through his neighborhood—far from the auto congestion of Manhattan, far from heavy industry, or large power plants—and the air seems fine. The breeze blowing in the window at night is refreshing, too, and at some point it occurs to him that the times when he must inhale really toxic matter are, after all, relatively few.

Unfortunately, he may be wrong—very wrong.

There is growing, if inconclusive, evidence to suggest that not only is the air he breathes contaminated by cigarette smoke and auto fumes, and hazardous at industrial sites, but also that large portions of the entire atmosphere over sizable areas of the United States and southern Canada may be dangerous to human health.

UNSEEN MENACE

Scientists are beginning to identify the chief culprits of this environmental assault as fine particles. These remain in the atmosphere for weeks and can be transported long distances on the winds. The particles, or particulates, are so small—one-fiftieth the width of a human hair—that they cannot be seen. Yet they are capable of inflicting extraordinary damage. Moreover, they are slipping right through many of the expensive and elaborate air-pollution control devices that are being installed at industrial sites around the United States. It's not that the heavier, visible particles are harmless—they are not. But scientists are finding that the finer ones, which are at present unregulated and uncontrolled, are in some ways far more menacing.

EXTRA DEATHS

Because of the combination of their size and durability, fine particulates can penetrate the body's physiological defense system. Researchers have drawn some startling conclusions about them. The Brookhaven National Laboratory, on Long Island, New York, estimates that 21,000 extra deaths—primarily respiratory and heart related—are occurring each year in the United States east of the Mississippi River due to the presence in the atmosphere of just one class of these particulates.

That class, referred to as the sulfate complex of particulates, come from coal- and oil-burning power plants. Two Yale University researchers estimate that 140,000 deaths each year in the United States are related to all forms of air pollutants, but principally sulfates. And a report published in September 1979 by Frederica Perera and Karim Ahmed of the Natural Resources Defense Council has intensified environmentalists' concern. The report cites one research project after another that have convincingly incriminated fine particulates in the atmosphere as serious public-health and environmental hazards.

QUESTIONS AND DEBATE

The studies pose fundamental questions. Even though the United States is caught in an energy crisis, is it wise, in light of these findings, to turn toward much greater use of coal or to high-sulfur coal? This is what the Consolidated Edison power company is now proposing to do in New York.

Will damage caused by long-distance-traveling fine particulates touch off a battle between the states? Suppose, for example, that one state has not tightened its air controls and exports its particulates to neighboring states who have? Is it wise to be switching to diesel-fueled cars, which spew out many times more particulates than gasoline-fueled vehicles? And are city dwellers who jog alongside diesel buses doing themselves greater harm than good by gulping down diesel-produced hydrocarbons?

Scientists have now established a correlation between fine particulates and increased deaths and illness. The key question now is whether they will go on to prove a direct link and establish whether the inhalation of specific contaminants is causing specific diseases.

The research has already thrust the

U.S. Environmental Protection Agency (EPA) into a lively crossfire. Some prominent scientists and environmental groups contend that even the preliminary findings now justify immediate action by the EPA to control fine particulates. Some economists are arguing, on the other hand, that new environmental rules are important causes of inflation.

Industry insists that the cost of controlling fine particulates would be far too high. They also insist that all fine particulates in the atmosphere cannot be subjected to a blanket indictment without specific knowledge of what type causes what disease under what conditions.

DAILY POLLUTION FORECAST

The research on fine particulates has been spurred on by two important scientific developments: a revolution taking place in the technical capacity to isolate and analyze airborne particles, and an increased understanding of the connection between environmental factors, including fine particulates, and rising cancer rates.

"For the first time in history, we are beginning to learn the causes of cancer," says Dr. Irving Selikoff, of New York's Mount Sinai Medical Center, who has done important work on asbestos. He adds: ". . . we are learning that there is a possibility of preventing this disease."

The uses of new technology are evident at Brookhaven. Meteorologist Ronald E. Meyers, head of an atmospheric-study unit, evaluated EPA data on sulfur-dioxide emissions in the eastern United States. Meyers said that the major portion of those emis-

Tiny particles in the air—here magnified 42 times—pose an unseen but very dangerous health hazard.

John Gustav Delly/McCrone Associates

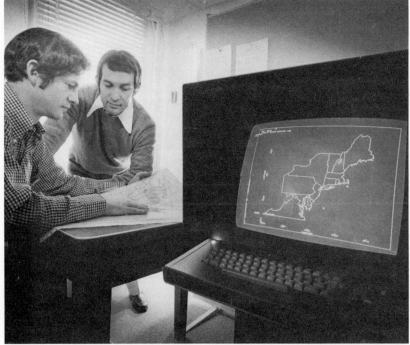

Data on sulfur-dioxide emissions, temperature, humidity, and wind direction and speed are used to prepare pollution forecasts for the northeastern United States.

Brookhaven National Laboratory

sions came from coal-burning plants. Some were also reported from oil-burning facilities. Using EPA-supplied data and information from points all over the world about temperature, humidity, and wind direction and speed, he and his staff developed a computer program to track what happened to the particulates in the atmosphere. They then mapped pollution patterns as they spread out on a day-to-day basis. Meyers hopes in the very near future to be able to produce a national daily pollution forecast. This would predict when and where concentrations of sulfates will move over the United States.

HUMAN-DAMAGE EQUATION

At the same time, Leonard Hamilton, head of a biomedical group at Brookhaven, began to analyze Meyers' traveling sulfate cloud. Aided by EPA data, Hamilton and his staff added mortality statistics to Meyers' information. They found a consistent pattern of higher-than-normal death rates in all areas where Meyers had recorded high concentrations of sulfates. They came up with what they regard as a reasonably accurate

human-damage equation. One microgram of sulfur particulate per cubic meter of air exposed to a population of 100,000 for one year was associated with 3.7 excess deaths.

Hamilton stresses that they have not proved that sulfates caused the 3.7 deaths but, rather, that a statistical connection was established. They used the damage equation to estimate that a median of 21,000 extra deaths occurred each year east of the Mississippi.

The Yale studies referred to earlier, by Robert Mendelsohn and Guy Orcutt, were conducted much the same way. "Remember," Orcutt says, "our figure of 140,000 extra deaths is statistical. We didn't do direct experiments—but the statistics must be taken very seriously."

TOO LIGHT TO MEASURE

Most fine particulates are emitted from industrial sources either as solid particles or as gases. The gases are converted into aerosols—tiny combinations of liquid and solids. This happens by exposure to the sun's radiation, by condensation, or by their attaching

Is this jogger helping maintain his health or is he doing himself more harm than good—breathing in car-emission fumes?

themselves onto other materials already in the atmosphere. Many toxic particulates become even more dangerous once atmospheric reactions take place. A single particulate, for example, may be a mixture of beryllium, nickel, arsenic—all agents that will cause cancer—and converted sulfur oxides, or of nitrogen oxides and hydrocarbons. The mixture can be far more lethal than any of its parts.

Present EPA air-emissions standards group all air particles together, the fine with the heavy. Under these standards, the total weight of particulates per cubic meter of air sampled must not exceed 75 micrograms. But fine particulates are not measured by weight—they're too light. They are classified by size, as being smaller than two micrometers in diameter. (One micrometer is equal to 1/1,000,000 meter.) Thus, millions of fine particulates may enter the atmosphere as long as together they don't weigh more than 75 micrograms per cubic meter of air.

Power plants and steel mills can meet the EPA standards by filtering out the relatively large chunks of heavy particulates in smokestacks. The almost weightless—and often more dangerous—fine particles escape. The heavier particles, ironically, are the ones that can normally be blocked by the body's own filtering system in the nose and mucous membranes. The fine particulates can penetrate deep into the lower lung and many of them eventually work their way into the rest of the body.

AND THEN THERE ARE DIESELS

The problem is especially frustrating with diesel-fueled automobiles, which, most studies agree, produce from 50 to 80 times more fine particulates than gasoline-fueled automobiles. The diesel particulates contain thousands of chemical substances that are known or suspected causes of cancer and other diseases.

The ominous initial findings about diesel emissions came at a time when the auto industry thought it had a perfect solution to both the pollution and energy problems: Diesels offer a 25 per cent mileage improvement over refined-gasoline engines. They can be made to comply with present emission

Air pollution has eroded the hard stone of this statue in Venice. What does it do to the soft tissues of the respiratory system?

UPI

standards. Making diesel cars comply with emission standards proposed for 1981 and 1983 poses serious problems, however.

Environmentalists now warn that auto makers should not be encouraged to increase production of diesels until further studies have been done. Indeed, the federal government has embarked on a large-scale investigation. The auto industry, meanwhile, agrees that the study should be undertaken. Industry spokesmen point out that most of the diesel studies to date have been statistical and have not established direct cause. (For a more detailed discussion of energy and environmental issues relating to diesel cars, see the article "Cancer and the Diesel Car," beginning on page 196.)

There is other statistical work on fine particulates that is equally disturbing. Dr. Bertram Carnow of the University of Illinois and Dr. Paul Meier of the University of Chicago have identified a correlation between cancer and segments of the population living where benzopyrene exists in the atmosphere. Gaseous benzopyrene is emitted from steel-mill coke ovens, among other sources, and converts, in combination with other materials in the air, into fine particulates. Carnow and Meier found that one microgram of benzopyrene in 1,000 cubic meters of air has been associated with a 5 per cent increase in lung cancer.

Another researcher, Dr. Richard Hickey, of the University of Pennsylvania, reports that a study of 38 U.S. cities shows, among other things, a correlation between sulfates and both heart disease and lung cancer. And Dr. Henry Palacios, of St. Elizabeth's Hospital in Washington, D.C., says his statistical research has convinced him that fine-particulate air pollution is now the number-one cause of a whole range of respiratory diseases—chronic sore throats, repeated colds, hay fever, asthma, bronchitis, pulmonary emphysema—and some skin diseases.

THE SMALLER, THE MORE HARMFUL

Experimentation on animals by Dr. Mary Amdur, a toxicologist at the Massachusetts Institute of Technology, has illustrated the destructiveness of the fine particulates. Using guinea pigs, she has found, for example, that a sulfate "one-tenth of one micron [or one-tenth of one-millionth of a meter in diameter] tends to have an irritant effect that is much greater than 0.3 or 1 or 2 microns." Larger particles were trapped in the rodents' noses or blocked by mucous layers, but the smaller ones penetrated deep into the lungs, where they would almost immediately begin to impair the guinea pigs' ability to breathe. Other studies have shown that some particulates may remain in the lower-lung region for months, while others work their way into the bloodstream.

To study the effects on humans, Harvard's School of Public Health has set up monitoring devices in six cities in the eastern and midwestern United States—two with high-pollution concentrations, two with medium concentrations, and two with low concentrations. The devices are taking samples of particulates in public locations and in the backyards and living rooms of volunteer families. Harvard's Dr. John Spengler says the long-term project aims to determine at what levels of pollution specific respiratory problems begin to appear.

WARS BETWEEN THE STATES

The new research has already touched off minor wars between the states. Steubenville, Ohio, and Pittsburgh, Pennsylvania, emit as much pollution as any two communities of comparable size in the country—and they are exporting a good deal of it, via the air, to the East Coast. The extra high smokestacks that have been built by power companies and industrial plants, in the hope of getting pollution up and out of the way, have actually played a major role in transporting a local problem to a larger region. The sulfur dioxide is put up into the winds and converted into traveling particulates.

Studies have shown, for example, that 73 per cent of the sulfates in the air over New York City may have been transported on prevailing westerly winds. Brookhaven's Ronald Meyers says, "Our calculations are showing that Ohio exports more sulfates than any other state, with Indiana and Pennsylvania not far behind."

However, Ohio and some other states whose economy is strongly linked to coal mining and other heavy polluting industries seem reluctant to enforce air-quality regulations.

ACID RAIN AND HAZE

Fine particulates are now regarded as principal villains in two other environmental crimes: acid rainfall and reduced visibility in urban areas.

Rain and snow falling on the United States contain more and more sulfuric and nitric acids. Research has shown that much of the acid results from sulfur dioxide that is emitted when fuel is burned at industrial sites in the middle-western and east-central states.

Visibility, too, is affected by fine particulates. This is explained by the fact that the particulates happen to have the same diameter as the wavelength of light. They scatter and absorb light, producing the effect that one sees when flying into the thick haze over LaGuardia Airport in New York City.

CONTROL POSSIBLE

The technology to control fine particulates emitted from stationary sources exists and, in some cases, is already in use. For example, bag houses—essentially fabric filters, with finer weaves used for finer particulates—can be installed on smokestacks. Electrostatic precipitators charge particles with electricity so that they will adhere to retaining magnets. Scrubbers, roughly analogous to giant hoses inside smokestacks, wash out offending gases, which are then converted into a sludge that is easier to treat.

The cost of installing fine-particulate controls may run into very large amounts of money for large facilities without any existing equipment. Smaller facilities that are able to adapt or augment their present controls would require a much smaller investment. Brookhaven's Leonard Hamilton says, however, that it is possible to strike a reasonable balance between what would be ideal and what is economically feasible. "It's possible with reasonable controls to reduce the levels of fine particulates to a reasonable level without costing too much."

The equipment for reducing fine particulates from diesels is less developed. There is now debate over it among the EPA's experts,

Experiments on the effects of acid rain on various plants are being conducted at the Brookhaven National Laboratory.

Brookhaven National Laboratory

industry officials, and White House inflation fighters. But, as discussed in the article "Cancer and the Diesel Car," starting on page 196, a variety of strategies are under consideration.

NOW OR LATER?

The Environmental Protection Agency says it is re-evaluating its own logic in regulating the gross weight of total suspended particulates across the United States, while having no standard for the often more deadly emissions of fine particulates. But for now, while the incidence and distribution research is still under way, the EPA is not acting. Industry regards this as a correct course.

The Natural Resources Defense Council does not agree. They point out that the Clean Air Act requires the EPA to impose air-quality standards whenever a pollutant is widespread and poses a risk of harm to public health and environment. The risk is there, it says, and the kind of proof that may be re-quired to get action may be the kind of proof none of us wants: continued acceleration of respiratory diseases and cancer rates, for example.

In the meantime, nearly one out of every four persons in the United States is stricken with cancer. Faced with that statistic, many people agree with the environmentalists. Harvard's John Spengler is one, stating, "In the absence of more definitive data on the safety of fine particulates, they must be controlled now" □

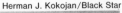 SELECTED READINGS

"Global pollution: is the Arctic haze actually industrial smog?" by R. Kerr. *Science,* July 20, 1979.

"Photochemical air pollution in the northeastern United States" by W. Cleveland and T. Graedel. *Science,* June 22, 1979.

"Smog gets in your psyche: carbon monoxide and nitrous oxide" by M. Slade. *Psychology Today,* June 1979.

The noxious emissions of planes may be carried far from the sites of airports.

Herman J. Kokojan/Black Star

A child with Down's Syndrome, an abnormality which had been thought to be passed on through the mother, but may after all sometimes be due to genetic defects in the father.

HEALTH & DISEASE

HEALTH AND DISEASE
REVIEW OF THE YEAR

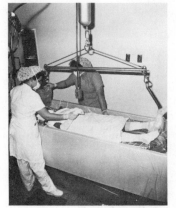

Nassau County Medical
Center Burn Clinic

There have been tremendous improvements in the treatment of severe burns in recent years. Here a patient is being treated at a burn clinic specially equipped to handle the delicate work.

Use of the electron microscope is speeding up the diagnosis of certain viral diseases.

Courtesy DuPont

Microsurgery. Surgeons have operated for centuries and scientists have used microscopes since the 17th century. But it was only in 1921, when a Swedish ear specialist used a simple monocular (one-eyepiece) microscope to help him correct a chronic ear infection, that surgeons began operating with the aid of microscopes. Since then surgeons have increasingly relied on the combination of microscopes, tiny instruments that can easily fit in an average-sized drinking glass, and fine sutures to do a wide variety of operations ranging from reimplanting hands, digits, and limbs severed in accidents to removing tumors from the brain.

During 1979 the microsurgical reattachment of limbs lost in two well-publicized violent incidents in New York City—a teenage flutist's hand that had been severed by a subway car and a policeman's leg severed in an automobile accident—focused international attention on the revolution in microsurgery that has gone on quietly and that has cut across virtually every field of medicine in recent years. (See the article "Microsurgery," beginning on page 243.)

Using microsurgical techniques doctors have devised new operations to do what had hitherto been impossible and have improved traditional operations. Microsurgery's success has been due to improved technology—new lenses allow surgeons to see very tiny areas greatly magnified in bright and shadowless operating fields—and the acquisition of new surgical skills. Restoring a blood supply is crucial in microsurgical work. Because some blood vessels are as narrow in diameter as a paper-clip wire, the sutures that are used to reconnect the ends of the vessels are actually so fine that they are thinner than a human hair. The techniques take considerable practice, and for some surgeons it means learning to operate all over again.

Microsurgeons have reached the point where they can transplant almost any tissue from one place to another in the same body. A dramatic advance has been the transfer of free flaps—that is, a piece of skin with a self-sustaining blood supply. Skin flaps can be transplanted to a new location in the same person by successful reattachment of the small artery and vein of the flap to the recipient blood vessels in the new location. The free flap technique has eliminated the tortured positions—legs sutured together or arms sutured to head, for example—that patients had to endure in the past to maintain blood supply to transplanted tissue. The new technique also cuts down on hospital costs.

Microsurgery is also having a major impact on brain surgery. Not only can neurosurgeons now operate on tiny structures in the brain, but they can also be more precise when they operate on larger structures. At the same time they produce less trauma to brain tissue involved because they no longer need to move and disturb large areas of tissue. One advance is the nasal approach to the pituitary gland. Tumors within the gland can be removed while still leaving the gland intact. The new techniques have also been used to prevent the rupture of aneurysms in the brain. Aneurysms are weaknesses that develop in the walls of arteries and threaten to blow out.

There are many other applications of microsurgery. It can, for example, be used to repair nerve injuries. When the gap between the two ends of a severed nerve is too long to permit pulling the ends together, a nerve can be taken from another part of the body and grafted to fill the gap in the injured area. ■ Sections of colon have been transplanted to the esophagus to make a new gullet for patients with cancer or other diseases of the esophagus. ■ In women infertile because of blocked fallopian tubes microsurgical repair has helped make conception possible. ■ Some vasectomies have been reversed. ■ Many eye operations have been improved.

Diagnostic Tests. The diagnosis of viral illness is a lengthy, complex process that usually involves a series of blood tests and cultures in the laboratory that take several weeks to do. Now, the electron microscope is aiding doctors in diagnosing more rapidly certain viral diseases that affect children—cytomegalovirus, the most common cause of infection in fetuses and newborns, and certain other viral diseases that often occur in children as complications of cancer and transplant surgery. Under certain circumstances, electron-microscope diagnoses can be made in less than one hour. Wider application of this new procedure might help spare patients needle biopsies and other diagnostic tests that are standard procedures in baffling cases, as well as help cut down on some hospital stays and costs.

Diabetes. Yale University researchers are testing a portable insulin injection system to determine whether its use for rigid, long-term control of the amount of sugar in the blood can help prevent the complications of diabetes mellitus. Diabetes mellitus is a chronic disorder of the pancreas that results in too high levels of sugar in the blood. Blindness, heart disease, and damage to the kidneys, blood vessels, and nerves are among the complications of the disease. Whether the complications can be delayed or prevented by rigid control of blood sugar has been debated by diabetes experts for years. One school of thought insists on rigid, yet imperfect, control of blood sugar through diet, insulin ingestion, and other means. The other school of thought takes a more *laissez-faire* attitude toward controlling blood sugar. One reason there has been no resolution of the debate is that until now doctors have not had a means of rigidly controlling blood sugar. The new injection system may provide an answer. It relies on a commercially available portable battery-operated pump that has been adapted to inject insulin through a thin tube kept in place just beneath the skin over the stomach. The pump is programmed to inject small amounts of insulin continuously and larger doses just before meals according to the needs of the individual. It, in other words, provides the rigid control of blood sugar that doctors have long wanted to achieve and evaluate.

In a separate development, researchers at Washington University in St. Louis, Missouri, took a step toward the ultimate goal of transplanting normal pancreatic cells to a diabetic person. The researchers developed an immunologic technique by which insulin-producing pancreas cells transplanted into a rat survived 100 days. The hope—still many years

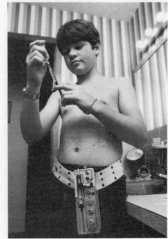

John Senzer for *Medical World News*

A portable insulin injection system worn on a belt may at long last provide physicians with information on how rigid blood sugar control affects the course of diabetes. Below, a close-up of the insulin injection system.

Auto Syringe

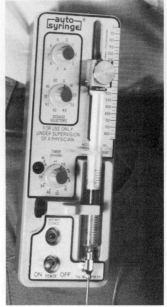

Although the American Cancer Society has revised some of its recommendations about routine checkups and X rays, it still cautions certain persons— smokers like this man, for example—to have frequent checkups.

Cholera—caused by *Vibrio cholerae* bacteria shown here—made a surprise appearance in the United States in 1978-1979.

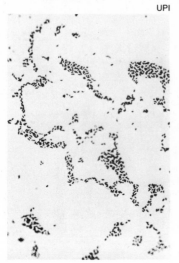

away—is eventually to be able to do such transplants in diabetic humans, thereby regulating their blood sugar levels and eliminating their need for daily insulin injections. (For more on diabetes, see the article "Diabetes in the Early 80's," on page 224.)

Cancer. During 1979 the completion of the largest and longest study of childhood leukemia showed that adequate therapy can be given in 2½ years—less time than previously believed. Also physicians are beginning to use the term "cure" for some cases. In using the term "cure" for childhood leukemia, researchers at St. Jude Children's Research Hospital in Memphis, Tennessee, said the word should be taken to mean that the relapse rate of four years or more after cessation of drug and radiation treatment is extremely low, not that it is zero. Current research results show that modern treatments will "cure" about 40 per cent of childhood leukemia patients.

Physicians' attitudes toward telling patients about a diagnosis of cancer are changing. Many doctors no longer keep the diagnosis secret from their patients, according to a questionnaire survey by doctors at the University of Rochester in New York. The results show a reversal of attitude expressed in a similar study 18 years ago. Among the reasons cited for the change was that more patients need to know the diagnosis of cancer. Patients who agree to participate in research projects at medical centers must, for example, be told their diagnosis to satisfy legal requirements of informed consent. Another reason cited was the dramatic change in the malpractice situation that encourages doctors to minimize their liability by providing more information to patients.

Epidemic Diseases. New outbreaks of old infections occurred during 1979 at the same time that other older diseases were eradicated or nearly vanished. Cholera, for example, which disappeared from the United States at the beginning of the 20th century after having been an important health problem, made a reappearance in 1978 and 1979. Cholera is a potentially devastating diarrheal illness caused by the toxin produced by the *Vibrio cholerae* bacterium. In its severe form it can kill in hours by dehydrating the body and depleting it of vital chemicals, yet many cases are as mild as a simple attack of diarrhea. In 1978 U.S. government health officials traced eleven non-fatal cases in Gulf Coast states to the eating of contaminated crabs; in 1979 three more cases were identified in northern Florida.

Only a few years ago measles was probably the commonest childhood infection. Yet in 1979 the number of cases was the lowest recorded in U.S. history and health officials believe that they will reach the target of zero cases by 1982 if immunization requirements are rigidly enforced. If this proves so, the United States will be the first nation to wipe out the viral infection that is characterized by cough, sneezing, red eyes, and a red rash. Among the complications of measles are brain damage and deafness.

Yaws, a potentially crippling and mutilating disease of children that nearly vanished from the world in recent years, was resurgent in several countries, particularly in western Africa, during 1979. Yaws is caused by a spirochete, *Treponema pertenue,* which is a close relative of the organism that causes syphilis. However, yaws is not a venereal disease. It spreads through skin-to-skin contact, primarily among children under 15 years of age, and can produce mutilating facial and body sores. Yaws cannot be prevented by immunization but treatment with a single injection of penicillin leads to one of the most dramatic cures in medicine.

The World Health Organization is nearing an official declaration of the eradication of smallpox from the world. The year 1979 marked two years since the last case of smallpox occurred by means of natural spread. The last naturally-occurring case appeared in Somalia in 1977. (In 1979 two cases resulted from viruses that escaped from a research laboratory in Birmingham, England, but they were not the result of natural spread of the disease.)

Genetics. During 1979 there were continuing advances in prenatal diagnosis and the detection and understanding of genetic defects. Cells from a fetus were discovered in a pregnant woman's blood as early as the 12th week of pregnancy in research done at Stanford University. Using an instrument called a fluorescent activated cell sorter, scientists determined that from 2,000,000 to 20,000,000 fetal cells appear in an expectant mother's blood; they do not, however, know why the cells are there. The researchers hope to convert the observed phenomenon into a simple blood test that could help detect many genetic defects, including Down's syndrome (mongoloidism). Such a test would be simpler and quicker and could be done earlier in pregnancy than currently used amniocentesis tests in which a needle is inserted into the uterus to collect fluid and cells which are then taken to a laboratory for several weeks of tests to detect potential hereditary disorders and birth defects. ■ The presence of fetal cells in the pregnant woman's blood may also help unravel some of the mysteries of pregnancy, particularly why a woman can bear a child for nine months without rejecting it as a foreign body in the way a transplant patient rejects a new organ. The fetus contains substances foreign to the mother. Accordingly her immunological system should reject the fetus.

Another prenatal diagnostic test—the alpha-fetoprotein (AFP) test—became more widely used during 1979. Between the 14th and 20th week of pregnancy either amniotic fluid or the blood of the pregnant woman is tested for levels of a particular protein from the fetus—the alpha fetoprotein. High levels are believed to indicate major structural defects in the baby's brain and spinal cord. ■ More knowledge of Down's syndrome was also gained during the year. For some time the commonest form of Down's syndrome has been known to be caused by a disorder in the chromosomes of the mother. It is a disorder that increases in frequency with maternal age, particularly after 35. Now, recent studies indicate that a number of cases are due to a chromosome mixup in the father. This finding adds a new dimension to the concerns of some couples about conceiving a defective child.

Endorphins. Since 1975 scientists in several medical centers have discovered a group of chemical substances in the brain that are involved in the body's response to pain and that may have other unknown functions in emotions and mental illness. Endorphins, as these chemicals are known, appear to be the body's internally-produced equivalent of morphine, the pain killer. In 1979, as part of expanding research on the chemical nature of the brain, scientists at Stanford University and the California Institute of Technology discovered a brain substance that is 200 times more powerful in action than morphine and 50 times more powerful than any previously known substance of its kind. The new substance is called dynorphin, and its importance stems from its extraordinary potency. Because it is potent, specific, and selective in its action on nerve cells, dynorphin may become a powerful aid in designing more effective, nonaddictive drugs to combat pain and to produce other useful effects on the brain.

Lawrence K. Altman, M.D.

Protect mommies from German measles (rubella)

Have your children vaccinated now. You'll help prevent birth defects.

The National Foundation-March of Dimes

March of Dimes

The importance of immunizations cannot be stressed too much. Thanks to immunizations the once common disease of measles has almost been wiped out. Intensive efforts to immunize against rubella will, it is hoped, lead to similar results.

Advances in prenatal diagnosis continued throughout the year. Some fetal defects can now be diagnosed through analysis of the pregnant woman's blood.

March of Dimes

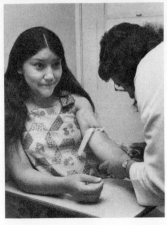

ASPIRIN

by Jane E. Brody

ASPIRIN, hailed as a "wonder drug" when it was first introduced 80 years ago, is today a drug of ever-expanding uses. It has one main drawback—the ability to cause bleeding. But new research has revealed that this drawback has potential life-saving effects for persons in danger of heart attacks, strokes, and other disorders caused by blood clots.

The new studies have shown that, at very low doses, aspirin can block the formation of life-threatening clots. Just half a tablet a day may be sufficient to protect patients from dangerous clots, the findings indicate. The results are not yet in from a $17,000,000 national study of aspirin's ability to prevent heart attacks. However, new discoveries about how aspirin works suggest that too high a dose was used in the test, which might have shown even greater benefits from less drug.

Even without its new uses and despite a number of known hazards, aspirin, as one of the few pharmaceutical miracles that never fizzled, is ranked among the greatest advances of medicine.

"When you think of things that have ab-solutely revolutionized medicine, you have to put aspirin up there with antibiotics, general anesthesia, and digitalis," remarked Dr. J. Richard Crout, director of the Bureau of Drugs of the Food and Drug Administration.

No other drug has been used so safely by so many people for so long and for so many different purposes. The American pharmaceutical industry produces 12,000 tons of aspirin a year for domestic consumption, the equivalent of 150 aspirin-containing tablets for every man, woman, and child in the country. Worldwide, 100,000 tons of aspirin are used each year.

ASPIRIN'S HISTORY

Aspirin's activity is based on chemicals called salicylates, derived from the willow and other plants used as medications since antiquity. More than 2,000 years ago, Hippocrates, the father of Greek medicine, recommended chewing willow bark to counter the pain of childbirth and postpartum fever. In Rome, Pliny the Elder used poplar bark, another salicylate source, for sciatic pain.

Before Europeans landed, American Indians were making tea from willow bark to reduce fever. The Hottentots in Africa prepared a similar brew to counter rheumatic pains.

Aspirin got its start as a "modern" medicine by some contorted logic called the "doctrine of signatures," fashionable among doctors in the 18th century. The doctrine held that nature provided nearby remedies for local maladies.

Thus, in 1763, the Reverend Edward Stone reported to the Royal Society of England that he had discovered the willow's benefits for "the agues." His reasoning was that, since the malady (chills and fever) occurs mainly in wet areas, he looked there for nature's own cure and found the willow.

Not until the 1800's did aspirin move out of the realm of crude folk medicine. Scientists began extracting salicylates from plants. In 1853 a German chemist synthesized pure salicylic acid, the base chemical for salicylates. Salicylic acid and salicylates, however, were extremely irritating to the stomach and had a repulsive flavor.

The father of Felix Hoffman, a German chemist working for Friedrich Bayer and Co., was suffering from rheumatism. He prevailed upon his son to devise a form of salicylate he could tolerate. In 1893, Hoffman came up with acetylsalicylic acid, the aspirin we know today. Six years later Bayer, convinced of its usefulness and safety, devised a system to mass-produce and market the miraculous chemical. Today it is derived from coal tar and petroleum products.

FEVER, PAIN, AND SWELLING

Aspirin is the standard treatment to reduce fever. It is far and away the nation's leading pain killer. In carefully controlled studies it has outranked many prescription analgesics, including Darvon and codeine. Most of the nonprescription competitors to "plain old aspirin" contain aspirin as their main and probably only active pain-relieving ingredient. The newest nonaspirin analgesic, acetaminophen (marketed as Tylenol), may be as good a pain-killer, and it may lack certain of aspirin's side effects. It also lacks some of aspirin's other benefits, Dr. Crout noted.

John Gerard

Willow bark has provided a drug for pain and fever since ancient times. In 1893 Felix Hoffman (below) devised the relatively nonirritating form of the bark's basic ingredient we now know as aspirin.

Photo courtesy of Bayer

Unlike acetaminophen, aspirin is also the front-line treatment for inflammation, whether caused by illness or injury. Despite a wide range of newer potent prescription drugs, aspirin remains the treatment of choice to counter the painful inflammation of arthritis, not only because it is so effective, but also because it can be taken by most people day in and day out for years without serious ill effects.

One of aspirin's drawbacks is its tendency to irritate the lining of the stomach and cause the loss of small amounts of blood. Every two-tablet dose of aspirin produces a loss of one milliliter of blood (about two-tenths of a teaspoon) from the stomach.

In every tissue of the body, aspirin prolongs bleeding time by interfering with the ability of the blood to clot. It can also cause temporary ringing in the ears. Between one and four persons in a thousand are hypersensitive to aspirin and may suffer life-threatening reactions.

THE WAY IT WORKS

Yet for all its long use and well-established effects, the way aspirin works was a mystery until 1971 when Dr. John R. Vane and his colleagues at the Royal College of Surgeons in Britain discovered that aspirin inhibits the synthesis of prostaglandins. These are hormonelike substances produced by cells throughout the body.

Prostaglandins have an extremely wide range of effects. For example, they can cause redness, swelling, fever, and sensitivity to pain-producing substances. Prostaglandins are found in the "ooze" of inflamed tissue. They produce headache when injected into the blood, and cause fever when injected into the brain.

The new understanding of aspirin's action on body chemistry explains how it produces its known benefits. It also explains how it causes many of the side effects associated with its use. The finding has triggered a cascade of research to uncover the detailed workings of both prostaglandins and aspirin-like drugs. It is hoped that this research will show how new and better medications may be custom-designed in the future.

As it is now understood, aspirin inacti-vates the enzyme that changes a certain fatty acid (arachidonic acid) in cell membranes into forerunners of prostaglandin. These forerunners are known as endoperoxides. Endoperoxides can be changed by enzyme action into various prostaglandins, including those that produce fever, pain, and inflammation.

Aspirin, in the 5- or 10-grain doses commonly used, can block the formation of these prostaglandins. It also blocks another prostaglandin called prostacyclin, a clot-inhibiting substance produced in the cells that line blood vessels.

However, in the platelets, the blood's clotting cells, the opposite effect takes place. Aspirin blocks the formation of a potent clotting agent called thromboxane, which is also made from an endoperoxide. It takes only tiny doses of aspirin—a quarter to a half a tablet a day—to inhibit thromboxane formation, and the effect lasts for the week-long life of the affected platelet. At these doses, prostacyclin production in blood vessel walls is believed to be unaffected. The body's natural protective mechanism against clots is left intact.

A CHANCE OBSERVATION

As so often happens in medicine, aspirin's potential role as an anticlotting agent was a lucky rediscovery of an old observation that had originally been rejected. In 1953, a California doctor had observed that, contrary to expectations, no heart attacks occurred among 1,400 overweight, sedentary, middle-aged men who were given two aspirins a day. But the study had no aspirin-free control group for comparison, and the findings were largely discounted.

Then, two decades later, the Boston Collaborative Drug Surveillance Program, a study set up to detect adverse effects of drugs, instead noted a possible benefit. Heart attacks were shown to be less common among frequent users of aspirin than among those who did not take aspirin. This and a study in Britain that found a 25 per cent reduction in deaths among heart patients given aspirin every day for a year triggered a closer look at aspirin's ability to prevent clots.

In 1978, a Canadian study showed that

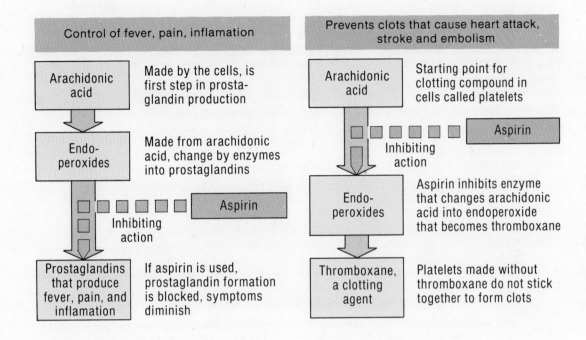

Control of fever, pain, inflamation	
Arachidonic acid	Made by the cells, is first step in prostaglandin production
Endo-peroxides	Made from arachidonic acid, change by enzymes into prostaglandins
Aspirin — Inhibiting action	
Prostaglandins that produce fever, pain, and inflamation	If aspirin is used, prostaglandin formation is blocked, symptoms diminish

Prevents clots that cause heart attack, stroke and embolism	
Arachidonic acid	Starting point for clotting compound in cells called platelets
Aspirin — Inhibiting action	
Endo-peroxides	Aspirin inhibits enzyme that changes arachidonic acid into endoperoxide that becomes thromboxane
Thromboxane, a clotting agent	Platelets made without thromboxane do not stick together to form clots

four aspirin tablets a day could reduce the occurrence of serious stroke in men who suffered mini-strokes called transient ischemic attacks. For unknown reasons, women were not protected.

Similar observations were made in a Boston study the year before of patients undergoing hip replacement. Those who received the equivalent of nearly four aspirins a day for two weeks were far less likely to suffer blood clots in their legs, a common complication of such surgery. Again, the benefit was limited to men.

RESEARCH ON THE BENEFITS OF ASPIRIN CONTINUES

In September 1979, researchers at Washington University in St. Louis reported that just half an aspirin a day could reduce the risk of clots by more than 50 per cent among patients on kidney dialysis machines. Unlike the other studies, at this low dose both men and women were shown to benefit.

Meanwhile, in 1976 the National Health, Lung, and Blood Institute had begun a three-year test of three aspirins a day among 4,524 people who had already suf-

fered one heart attack. The study has been completed, but its findings are still being analyzed. The discovery of aspirin's dual action on clotting—the inhibition at higher doses of the clot-inhibiting prostacyclin as well as the blockage at low doses of the clot-promoting thromboxane—was made after the study had begun.

Dr. Philip W. Majerus of Washington University believes on the basis of his research that the national study is using too much aspirin to show the maximum possible effect. He also believes that the side effects associated with the higher aspirin dose would reduce the ratio of benefit to risk. However, the study and others like it on how aspirin acts and what it does continue to reveal much about this ancient "wonder drug" □

 SELECTED READINGS

"AMIS trial: can aspirin prevent heart attack?" by J. Marx. *Science,* June 3, 1977.

"Aspirin," *Science Digest,* September 1977.

Aspirin Therapy by Paul E. Schindler. Walker and Co. 1978.

John Senzer for *Medical World News*

A belt-worn pump that administers insulin throughout the day and provides far better control of blood-sugar levels than ever before is one of the most recent advances in diabetes management, giving increased hope to young patients like this boy.

DIABETES IN THE EARLY 80's

by David N. Leff

UNCONSCIOUS after three days of flulike illness, a 10-year-old Virginia boy was admitted to a Washington, D.C., hospital with a very high blood-sugar level. A week later he died of diabetic ketoacidosis and brain edema (swelling).

At autopsy, pathologist Marshall Austin of the National Naval Medical Center of Bethesda, Maryland, found inflammatory destruction in the boy's islets of Langerhans in the pancreas. Many of the islets' insulin-secreting beta cells had been destroyed.

The picture reminded Dr. Austin of mouse islets he'd seen across the street in virologist Abner L. Notkins' laboratory. In that laboratory many genetically susceptible rodents develop high sugar (glucose) levels or die of diabetes when inoculated with some viruses. Dr. Notkins is chief of the laboratory of oral medicine at the National Institute of Dental Research.

When the pathologist brought him frozen specimens of the dead boy's pancreas and blood, Dr. Notkins and his associate, virologist Ji-Won Yoon, were able to isolate Coxsackie B4 virus from the islets. Cultured and injected into their sensitive mice, the virus promptly destroyed the animals' islets and gave them lethal ketoacidosis.

Dr. Notkins established that the boy's blood had contained few Coxsackie antibodies when he was hospitalized, but many at his death seven days later. This evidence ruled out any chance that the offending virus was a contaminating latecomer.

Reporting this first-ever evidence of virus-caused diabetes early in 1979, the *New England Journal of Medicine* ran an accompanying editorial declaring that "Prevention of diabetes may be achieved in some patients by immunization." Dr. Notkins himself is more cautious. "Talk of a vaccine is premature," the virologist insists. "It's dangerous to extrapolate from a single interesting case."

DIABETES: A CHRONIC SICKNESS

This all recalls the enthusiasm that welcomed insulin's discovery in Canada 57 years ago. The new hormone, besides saving lives, suddenly made sense of a baffling disease. Diabetes could be seen as a simple metabolic defect with a single cause—failure of islets to make insulin. There was a simple life-preserving treatment—externally made insulin.

Thus diabetes became a chronic malady instead of a quick killer. As University of Chicago diabetologist Arthur H. Rubenstein notes, insulin let diabetics survive long enough to suffer blindness, gangrene, kidney failure, neuropathy, and cardiovascular disease.

Far from claiming his virus is the main cause of insulin-dependent diabetes, Dr. Notkins points out that half the population has antibodies showing previous infection with Coxsackie B4. Fewer than 0.1 per cent develop the disease, and not all who do show signs of prior viral infection. He adds, however, that serum samples from most newly diagnosed insulin-dependent patients do contain an autoantibody—presumably inherited—to islet cells. Dr. Notkins believes immunological, genetic, and virological discoveries will show that diabetes has as many causes as the common cold.

MANAGING DIABETES IN THE 80'S

Meanwhile, after half a century of frustration, many developments are making diabetes easier to diagnose, manage, monitor, and talk about:

• Nomenclature: Newly adopted multinational terminology is intended to deconfuse the misleading classification of diabetes mellitus as "juvenile" or "adult."
• Monitoring: Sensitive, reproducible tests for blood sugar and beta-cell function are making their way into practice.
• Insulin control: Some patients are now wearing portable infusion pumps that regulate blood glucose far better than once- or twice-daily shots of insulin.

The islets of Langerhans in the pancreas are the sites of insulin production in the body. The discovery of virus-destroyed islet cells in a boy who died of diabetic ketoacidosis led Dr. Abner Notkins to report the first-ever evidence of virus-caused diabetes.

E. R. Degginger

NIH

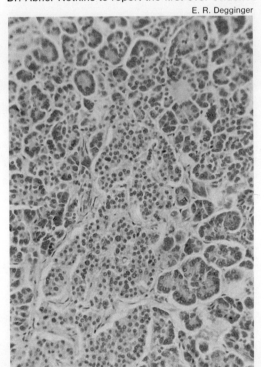

• Islet replacement: In 1979, for the first time, islets of Langerhans were transplanted from one outbred animal to another—and they "took."

• Insulin production: Gene-jugglers striving to make insulin by splicing recombined human DNA into obliging bacteria have succeeded—though not yet in useful volume.

• Etiology: New evidence about familial inheritance, gene associations, antibody formation, and autoimmune complexes is raising hopes for population screening, more effective treatment, prevention, and even prenatal diagnosis.

• Eye surgery: Best of all, these is now a way to prevent—and even arrest—diabetic retinopathy's threat to vision, and the National Eye Institute is inviting physicians to enroll patients in a national early-laser-therapy trial.

THIRD LEADING FATAL DISEASE

According to the National Commission on Diabetes, the disease with its complications now ranks as the third leading fatal disease in the United States. It is surpassed only by cardiovascular disease and cancer. And many deaths ascribed to other causes are diabetic in origin. Close to 5 per cent of all Americans have diabetes, and the number is going up 6 per cent a year.

"After 15 or 20 years, a high proportion of diabetics get complications affecting their eyes, kidneys, nerves, and large blood vessels. Is there something patient, family, and doctor could be doing during those years to prevent or minimize those disabilities? That's the main question," says Dr. Rubenstein, who heads the American Diabetes Association's scientific-program committee.

"The precise relationship, if any, between strict blood-sugar control and degenerative complications has never been completely established," declares ADA president Ronald A. Arky, chief of medicine at Mount Auburn Hospital in Cambridge, Mass. "We're still in the Dark Ages."

For more than half a century, diabetes was understood in terms of insulin. "The reason past studies are so unsatisfactory," explains Dr. Rubenstein, "is that our ability to control blood sugar has been either moderately bad or very bad. Now, for the very first time, methods are beginning to emerge that may normalize blood sugar, not just make it better or worse."

Two subtle new blood tests lie behind Dr. Rubenstein's optimism. The glycosylated hemoglobin (GH) test measures sugar buildup on hemoglobin. The Chicago C-peptide test measures beta-cell function by detecting an insulin-forerunner molecule.

"There's been an explosion of knowledge about how diabetes is inherited and transmitted," says the Bostonian GH test-developer, Dr. Kenneth H. Gabbay, who directs the cell-biology laboratory at Children's Hospital Medical Center. "In a few years," he adds, "we may be able to pick out people likely to get diabetes and explain the mechanism of beta-cell destruction in insulin-dependent diabetes. I even foresee the possibility of some prevention."

NEW PATIENT STUDIES

The National Institutes of Health has enrolled young insulin-dependent diabetics 10 to 12 years old who have lived with their disease up to 10 years but as yet have no major complications.

Another study compares patients who receive conventional treatment with those getting "vigorous, rigorous control," as Dr. Rubenstein puts it. "This is one advance that will certainly make a difference in treatment."

In Boston, Dr. Gabbay's group has a study in its fourth year, looking more directly at the relationship between control and complications. Their subjects are 140 insulin-dependent diabetics in the early teens. A needle biopsy first measured the subjects' muscle-cell basement-membrane thickness. Then the young people were monitored at two-month intervals—conventionally and with the new GH test that records accumulated blood glucose. Muscle biopsies, repeated after three years, are now being analyzed.

The Boston diabetologist points out that the tissues most destroyed in diabetic complications admit blood sugar across their cell membranes even without insulin. Thus during high blood sugar episodes they take in even more sugar.

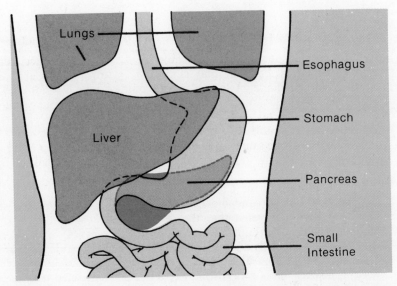

Insulin, produced in the pancreas, has widespread effects on metabolism. Its lack or reduced amount can cause serious—and even fatal—effects.

Lungs

Esophagus

Liver

Stomach

Pancreas

Small Intestine

KEEPING TRACK OF BLOOD SUGAR

Red blood cells continuously record blood sugar concentrations in plasma. Like other proteins, hemoglobin takes up circulating sugar molecules in a permanent chemical bond. Erythrocytes have a mean life span of 120 days. Their add-on glucose accumulation—glycosylation—thus builds a clear quantitative record of average blood-sugar levels over the preceding few months.

Normally hemoglobin A1—the fraction of the protein that takes on sugar molecules—accounts for 5 to 7 per cent of total hemoglobin. In uncontrolled diabetes, this percentage may be doubled or tripled.

"The GH test," says Dr. Rubenstein, "measures how the patient was controlled over several weeks or months. It's a number that correlates extremely well with every other test."

Thus if a GH result disagrees with a clinician's judgment of control, it's a signal to find out why. Unlike urinalysis, GH doesn't depend on a patient's cooperation or accuracy, or on time of day, meals, exercise, or emotional stress. However, the GH number is no help to a physician in choosing between short-term insulin manipulation and diet. It may alert him to the need for better control, but it won't tell him how much insulin to prescribe or when.

Yet the test can "help a physician in everyday management," the Chicago clinician urges. "GH is a distinct end point toward which treatment should be directed. Moreover, it unmasks a patient's noncompliance absolutely," he points out. "You can pick up in a minute the person who controlled himself a day or two before but has a high GH or who is embarrassed to come in with blood sugars. It also shows who hasn't kept written results but fears his doctor's chastisement and produces a book with made-up results."

If doctors had tested the GH of the boy who died in Washington, Dr. Gabbay points out, "this would have told us just how hyperglycemic he was, and for how long—with tremendous implications for the suspected viral cause of his diabetes."

The GH test is not yet ready for routine use. Its current methods are cumbersome, costly, unreliable, and unstandardized. Gabbay expects to perfect a simplified, accurate, cheaper version soon, making GH much more helpful to practitioners.

Some clinicians say a GH reading is no better than a blood-sugar test. In this criticism Dr. Rubenstein finds "truth and untruth, right and wrong." For a stable patient, he grants its truth. Otherwise, "a single blood sugar is not a good monitor. The hemoglobin sugar is invaluable."

THE PEPTIDE CONNECTION

The second new clinical indicator, developed by Dr. Rubenstein, may enable insulin-dependent diabetics to rely partly on their own beta cells and not entirely on injections. The C-peptide test detects an apparently inactive molecule that is secreted into the blood at the same time and from the same place as insulin—and in proportional amounts.

A decade ago at the University of Chicago, endocrinologist and biochemist Donald F. Steiner discovered that the double-chain molecule of insulin, as assembled in the beta cell, is actually a longer single chain. He named this "proinsulin." The extra connecting peptide splits away from the active insulin segments but accompanies them into the bloodstream. There the C-peptide (C for connecting) can be detected as an independent test of beta-cell function.

Until the present, by the time a juvenile-onset diabetic was diagnosed, his pancreas was ruined and its beta cells gone. This assumption became self-fulfilling. As soon as insulin injections began, "it was no longer possible to measure beta-cell function." Laboratory tests cannot tell human hormone from the pig or cow forms.

Yet clinicians know that in the weeks or months after treatment begins, most insulin-dependent patients go through a "honeymoon phase" of sharply lowered insulin need. There is apparent recovery of beta-cell function.

Many physicians believe tight control in the prehoneymoon period right after diagnosis may help prolong this remission and maintain some measure—say, even 20 per cent—of in-body insulin secretion. "This calls for far better blood-sugar control than most physicians can achieve by injections," observes Dr. Rubenstein. He suggests a weekend in the hospital "with a small open-loop insulin-infusion pump to keep blood sugar normal for two or three days."

This procedure is recommended to find out whether early tight control can salvage or restore some beta-cell function and make a major difference later on in the course of the disease.

THE PORTABLE PANCREAS

In Connecticut and Ontario such miniature pumps are already normalizing blood sugar for diabetics who can't maintain control without wide fluctuations or who become hypoglycemic (their blood sugar becomes very low). In 1979, Yale endocrinologists Philip Felig and William V. Tamborlane unveiled the belt-mounted device. It injects insulin under the skin round the clock on a preset schedule—with extra-large doses before meals and snacks. About a third of a day's insulin is delivered in small pulses every 4, 8, or 32 minutes round the clock. The rest is injected in four larger dollops 30 minutes before mealtimes and a regularly scheduled bedtime snack.

After initial trials with ambulatory inpatients, the Yale team has tried out its portable insulin pump on outpatients at home, work, school, and play. Eight had been studied 4 to 26 weeks when Dr. Felig reported on them in late 1979 at the International Diabetes Congress in Vienna. "Within three to four weeks," he says, "we can lower their glycosylated hemoglobin to normal. Their urine is free of glucose and remains so."

Yale's belt-worn quasi-pancreas is easily manufactured from off-the-shelf hardware—a 500-gram battery-driven infusion pump with timer. It accepts an ordinary disposable syringe and a 27-gauge subcutaneous needle. Miniaturizing this assembly will be mechanically simple, says Dr. Felig. But he emphasizes that the external pump approach to diabetes control "is by no means the final answer."

LASER THERAPY NOW

To diabetologists like Dr. Rubenstein, the issue "is how to stop complications from diabetes from happening right now and how to alleviate their destructive effects. Surgery to prevent diabetic destruction of the retina, or retinopathy, is the most dramatic example so far of available intervention," he says. However, many physicians are still unaware of the favorable results achieved in the eight-year nationwide clinical trial of laser therapy for diabetic retinopathy.

One major revelation has been that the

laser reduced by more than half the proportion of eyes with severe visual loss that progressed to total blindness in four years. Only about 13 per cent of those treated with a laser ray went blind, against about 30 per cent of controls.

Twenty U.S. eye clinics are enrolling up to 3,600 diabetics with early retinopathy for a seven-year study to answer the main question left open by the first trial: would laser treatment be even more successful if done early rather than late?

Dr. Lloyd M. Aiello, national chairman of the new Early-Treatment Diabetic-Retinopathy Study, heads the eye unit at the Joslin Diabetes Foundation in Boston, where laser treatment got its start in the United States. He expects relatively few patients to be nominated for the sight-saving study by ophthalmologists.

Primary physicians should be the main source of these patients, Dr. Aiello believes. "These will be people who still have good vision—good enough that they may not have been sent to an ophthalmologist yet." He adds fervently, "We'll need these physicians

as partners to get this trial done." Dr. Aiello will refer physicians who call to participating clinics near them.

At least 80 per cent of all diabetics progress toward blindness, he notes. After 15 years, 63 per cent of juvenile-onset diabetics have retinopathy. The Retinopathy Study offers patients whose sight has not yet begun to fail "a one-half to two-thirds chance of retaining good vision" in exchange for a seven to eight per cent risk of side effects from the laser—mild loss of central vision or visual acuity. "It only means accepting the risk a little sooner," says Dr. Aiello.

ANOTHER EYE OPERATION

Sometimes a diabetic goes blind almost overnight when a curtain of blood comes down across his vitreous chamber. Such ocular catastrophes now lead to an operation on the vitreous body within the eye (a vitrectomy). When vitrectomy works, the curtain lifts and sight returns—though perhaps just central vision and some peripheral vision. But its side effects can be horrendous and frequent.

Dr. Lloyd Aiello is placing a special contact lens on a patient's eye in preparation for laser therapy.

Robert Cavicchi, Joslin Diabetes Foundation

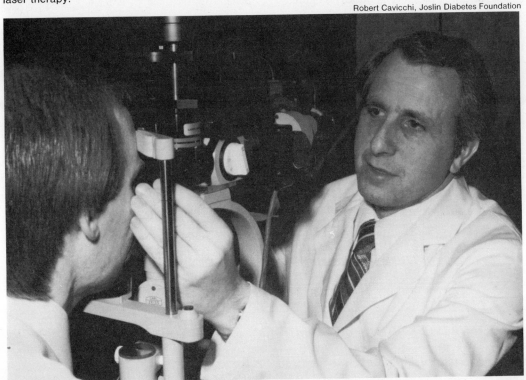

Vitrectomy works like a mini-vacuum cleaner, sucking blood and clots out of the vitreous and replacing their volume with clear saline. This scavenging restores optical clarity and prevents new retinal deformation.

Its risk of major intra- and postoperative complications is fully 25 per cent. However, 40 per cent of fresh hemorrhages progress to total loss of useful vision within a year. Earlier experience at six centers practicing vitrectomy showed more than 41 per cent of 5/200 (technically blind) eyes achieving 20/200 vision or better four to nine months after the operation, versus only 8 per cent that recovered such sight spontaneously.

CATARACTS—A CLUE AND A HOPE

Comparatively, cataracts are a minor manifestation of diabetes. But to biochemist Jin H. Kinoshita they are "a window on a larger world," the new world of aldose-reductase inhibitors and the sorbitol pathway.

After glucose's chemical coupling to hemoglobin was discovered, scientists speculated that diabetic patients' excess sugar might be forming troublesome bonds with other proteins. This could happen especially in various organs' basement membranes. These thicken slowly as diabetes advances.

One tissue that swells rapidly as glucose enters is the lens. There a widespread enzyme, aldose reductase, converts sugar to sorbitol. Sorbitol is a relatively dead-end metabolite that can't break down further or leave the lens rapidly. Its accumulation eventually causes clouding and cataracts.

But no other tissue comes within hailing distance of a diabetic patient's lens in its buildup of sorbitol-pathway intermediates. Thus cataracts are a ready-made model for attempts to answer the unanswerable: What causes the complications of diabetes?

Better yet, at least in theory: since aldose reductase underlies the process, a drug that inhibits this enzyme should block the pathway and prevent the disease. For the past five years, says Dr. Kinoshita, a handful of pharmaceutical firms have been developing such inhibitors. These have, indeed, delayed or prevented cataracts in diabetic animals. Several commercial aldose-reductase inhibitors are being prepared for testing □

 SELECTED READINGS

"Diabetes: more theories offered" by D. Schultz. *Science Digest,* June 1979.

"Diabetes: the outlook is bright" by R. Luft. *World Health,* May 1979.

"Virus isolated from juvenile diabetic" by T. Maugh. *Science,* June 15, 1979.

This is what the ophthalmologist sees through an operating microscope during the final stages of vitrectromy surgery. A vitreous infusion suction cutter, shown here inside the eye, removes blood and clots from the vitreous of the eye.

Johns Hopkins University Wilmer Ophthalmological Institute

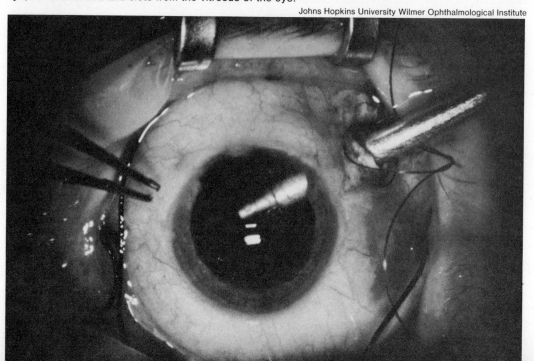

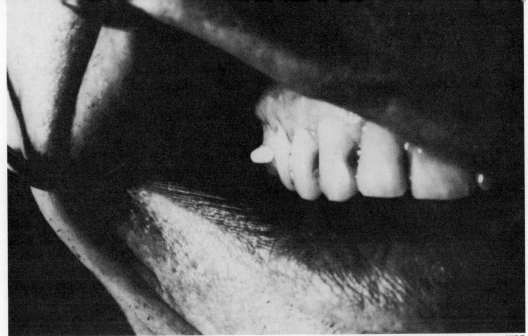

A timed-release fluoride pellet attached to a back tooth is being tested as one way to help decrease caries in certain persons.

PROTECTING YOUR TEETH

by Julie Ann Miller

WE all play host to a collection of microorganisms that frequent the human skin, gut, and mouth. Among the most destructive long-term guests are the bacteria that cause tooth decay. They glue themselves to a tooth, consume the host's food, and churn out acid that demineralizes the tooth. Having adapted to withstand the cleansing flow of more than a liter of saliva a day, these bacteria hold their ground tenaciously. Evicting them from the mouth's cozy niche has proved to be a formidable task.

A variety of research forces, however, are bearing down on the harmful bacteria. In addition to progress with antiseptics and vaccines, one novel approach involves replacing destructive bacteria with a laboratory-devised, non-virulent bacterial strain.

THE CULPRIT BACTERIA

Since 1924 bacteria have been known to cause tooth decay. Rats raised under germ-free conditions, for instance, do not develop dental caries, or cavities. When the same rats are allowed to consort with normal, germ-infested animals, they quickly pick up the harmful bacteria and become subject to tooth decay.

The prime biological culprit in human tooth decay is a bacterium called *Streptococcus mutans*. Although other microorganisms in the mouth produce acid, none causes cavities at the same rate or to the same extent as does *S. mutans*, says William Bowen of the U.S. National Institute of Dental Research (NIDR).

Bowen suggests that much of the bacterium's virulence comes from its ability to attach and colonize the tooth surface. Once microorganisms adhere to the tooth, they form a coherent layer of transparent or white material called plaque. The plaque then traps other species of bacteria. In samples of plaque, *S. mutans* makes up only 0.1 to 20 per cent of the microorganism population. Plaque also contains food particles, dead bacteria, and other debris. The electrical charge distribution of plaque further allows sucrose from food to diffuse into the plaque to nourish the densely packed bacteria but prevents outward diffusion of the vast quantities of acid produced. "It amounts to a sponge of acid being supplied to the tooth surface," Bowen says.

PROTECTIVE BUGS

Limiting that acid is one approach to avoiding dental caries. Besides being champion at sticking to teeth, *S. mutans* characteristically produce a huge amount of acid from sugar metabolism, says Jeffrey D. Hillman of the Forsyth Dental Center in Boston. Several years ago Hillman isolated a mutant strain of *S. mutans* that makes much less acid than the parent strain. Hillman suspected that the mutant bacteria could provide a dental service by occupying the same niche as more harmful bacteria, but doing less damage there.

Animal tests and further analysis of the mutant strain now support that possibility. The mutant is deficient in the enzyme that forms lactic acid, so its metabolism of sugars leads to different end products, some of which are neutral instead of acidic.

When Hillman and his colleagues introduced the mutant bacteria into the mouths of germ-free rats and then fed the rats a high sugar diet, virtually no decay resulted. In contrast, rats exposed to the parent *S. mutans* strain suffered rampant caries. Although successful in animals, the method is still only in the experimental phase, Hillman cautions. Rats are generally good models for tooth decay, but rats and humans have significantly different oral practices.

The idea of replacing harmful bacteria with more benign strains is not new in medicine. However, "this [*S. mutans*] is the first time a laboratory-derived strain has been used for replacement therapy," Hillman says.

Seven slightly different strains of *S. mutans* have been identified in human mouths. Yet in almost every case, a person hosts only a single strain. A child, after acquiring a tooth or two, probably is infected with an *S. mutans* strain from a parent. If many persons become infected with the harmless strain, the protective bacteria should, it is hoped, spread naturally to future generations.

Once ensconced in a mouth, the protective bacteria should provide their host lifelong protection. "It is hard to displace a strain that occupies colonization sites," Hillman says. "Competing strains have no place to go." So getting rid of a person's endogenous *S. mutans* infection is a major problem if the mouth is to be colonized with the less virulent mutant. However, Hillman says, a potent mouthwash has been developed in Sweden, and clinical tests with the mutant bacteria have begun there.

VACCINE

A more traditional goal of dental researchers has been a vaccine against the caries-causing bacteria. Can a simple injection, or more likely a swallow, of bacterial material produce long-lasting protection against dental decay? In medical practice successful vaccines against bacteria, rather than against their toxins, are rare. And creation of a vaccine against *S. mutans* involves special problems. The harmful bacteria are present in the mouths of almost all individuals and the "disease" can last as long as a person has teeth. The tissue at risk is a hard surface, instead of soft tissue, as in most disease. Finally, scientists know much less about the immune system present in saliva than about the immune system of the blood, which fights most other diseases.

The principal protein of the secretory immune system, found in breast milk and tears as well as in saliva, is called immunoglobulin A. "It is uniquely suited to the mucosal environment," says Martin Taubman of the Forsyth Dental Center. It seems to interact directly with bacteria, instead of calling in secondary fighters as do the antibodies of the blood immune system.

"Immunization does seem to be protective," Taubman says. In laboratory experiments, antibodies against *S. mutans* have already protected rodents and primates from dental caries. Young, bacteria-free animals injected with killed *S. mutans* showed significantly less disease than did control animals when each group received a high-sugar diet and was exposed to virulent bacteria.

The best way to administer such a vaccine will probably be oral. Progress on an injectable vaccine was set back when scientists discovered that some of the antibodies to *S. mutans* appear to bind to heart muscle.

Germ-free rats fed killed *S. mutans* produced saliva and milk antibodies to the bacteria and were protected from infection. An experimental vaccine has been administered to humans in preliminary tests, and there is evidence of antibodies to *S. mutans* in their saliva, although no data yet link the immunization to decreased tooth decay.

GTF

Another approach to a safe vaccine involves selecting a single component of the bacteria and stimulating production of antibody to it. The choice is important, because the component selected must be essential to the bacteria's harmful effect. Antibody bound to a bacterium doesn't kill it, but it may interfere with its functioning. Components that have been extensively studied as potential vaccine material are the glucosyltransferase enzymes (GTF) crucial to a bacterium's ability to accumulate on the tooth surface. Glucosyltransferase enzymes are responsible for converting sugar from food to the sticky material by which bacteria adhere to teeth and form plaque.

Antibodies to GTF impair the ability of *S. mutans* to stick to a hard surface. When rats and hamsters were injected with GTF they produced the appropriate antibodies, and the number of caries formed was less than that in control animals. Experiments with GTF from several of the seven strains of *S. mutans* indicate that GTF from one type may elicit a protective immune response against infection with many or possibly all the strains, thus simplifying the immunization problem. However, the rat and hamster injections include materials to enhance the immune response that are not suitable for human use.

"Oral immunization studies are necessary to get a form acceptable for human use," says Daniel J. Smith of the Forsyth Dental Center. Working with Taubman, he finds that feeding animals GTF, instead of killed bacteria, produces a good immune response. It also prevents much bacterial colonization of tooth surfaces and reduces the decay. Smith and Taubman hope to soon begin limited clinical trials on GTF oral immunization.

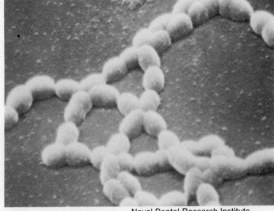

Naval Dental Research Institute

The bacterium *Streptococcus mutans* is the main culprit in human tooth decay.

ANTISEPTICS

Another traditional approach to cavity control is administration of an antiseptic to limit the number of microorganisms in the mouth. "The big problem with any anti-microbial agent for use in the mouth is that it must be present for sufficient duration to exercise its maximum potential," Bowen says. Many mouthwashes are cleared by saliva within minutes of the rinse, so they never get to do their job.

If an antiseptic does not linger long enough in the mouth, controlled release may be the answer. A small device that can be attached to a back tooth and that releases fluoride, is undergoing preclinical tests at NIDR. (Fluoride acts to kill bacteria, as well as to increase a tooth's resistance to decay.) Bowen says that the device has already been tested in dogs and monkeys and the results are "extremely promising." Still, he does not expect it ever to play a general, public health role. Instead it is intended for special cases: persons unusually susceptible to caries and those unable to clean their teeth adequately.

Several possibilities are under consideration for the slow release of other antiseptics, possibly for more general use. Tiny capsules containing antiseptics could bind to the tooth surface and gradually leak their contents. Or an anti-microbial agent might stick to teeth more effectively if it were sprayed on under pressure.

SALIVA FACTORS

Saliva contains a complex mixture of proteins beyond its antibodies. Although the natural functions of most of the saliva components are obscure, saliva is known to retard tooth decay. People with impaired saliva flow are unusually susceptible to caries.

Sialin is currently one of the most promising saliva factors. This small molecule, made up of just four amino acids, was isolated in 1972 by Israel Kleinberg, who is now at State University of New York at Stony Brook. Sialin appears to be taken up by bacteria and converted to compounds that neutralize the acid bacteria produce. Kleinberg recently contracted with a pharmaceutical company to do further studies toward using Sialin in mouthwash and toothpaste and in soft drinks and candy to offset the effects of sugar.

Other researchers have focused on different compounds among the more than 50 proteins found in saliva, as well as on the natural buffers in saliva, agents that affect saliva flow, and a large peptide called statherin, which controls calcium and phosphate incorporation into tooth and plaque material.

FINDING FOOD CULPRITS

The prospect of antiseptics, vaccines, and additives limiting dental caries should not be taken as an alternative to water fluoridation programs, nor should it be considered license for unrestricted consumption of sugars, Bowen says. "There is overwhelming evidence that sugars form an essential part of the pathogenicity of dental caries," he warns. "There is no doubt that people who curb their sugar intake have better dental health than those who do not."

Ways to sweeten the task of cutting back on sugars are being examined at NIDR. In collaboration with industry, the scientists there are trying to identify sweeteners that don't promote tooth decay. Among the promising candidates are derivatives of citrus peel (dihydrochalcones), the depeptide aspartame, a component of leaves of an African plant (thaumatin), and three other naturally occurring compounds: trichlorosucrose, stevioside, and monellin.

Identification of the most tooth-damaging snacks on the market is another task of NIDR investigators. In a new procedure being used, no food other than the snack being assessed touches the animal's teeth. A rat is fed an essential liquid diet through a tube to its stomach. The test foods are then offered by a computer-programmed feeder, so that a food is available only at a specific time and all the rats are fed identically. "All lesions [caries] can then be ascribed only to the test food," Bowen says.

Another evaluative technique uses a partial denture fitted with electrodes connected to a pH meter. A person wearing the appliance chews the test food while the researcher observes how much acid is produced. Bowen warns, however, that instantaneous acid production is only one aspect of the caries problem. Eating patterns are also important since each time a person eats a food containing sugar, the bacteria in plaque begin churning out acid.

ATTACK ON ALL FRONTS

Avoiding sweet snacks, promoting oral cleanliness, and expanding fluoridation—the current methods for prevention of dental caries—can substantially decrease tooth problems. But, says the staff of the Forsyth Dental Center in a background paper for *Healthy People, The Surgeon General's Report on Health Promotion and Disease Prevention:*

"... until far more effective preventive methods become available, oral diseases will remain a costly public health problem for the nation. The pandemic nature of the major oral disease suggests that simultaneous implementation of many different preventive techniques may be needed before total eradication of the major oral disease can be achieved."

Perhaps it will take the equivalent of bouncers, watchdogs, noxious chemicals, and crowds of more welcome guests to dislodge the undesirable, uninvited freeloaders from the human mouth □

 SELECTED READINGS

"Case of the decaying teeth: filling in the gaps" by L. A. Phillips. *Technology Review,* March 1979.

"Nutrition and dental health" by H. G. Day. *Chemistry,* March 1979.

"Sugar and spice ... and cavities." *Family Health,* June 1978.

UPI

Do these long-lived men of Soviet Georgia know the secret of aging?

GROWING OLD

by Carol Kahn

WE are growing older. The United States as a nation is growing older. In July 1972, 10 per cent of the U.S. population was over age 65. By the year 2025, it is estimated that one out of every five persons will be 65 or older. This change is bound to have enormous social, political, and economic consequences. Suddenly we have an imperative to know what happens—and how and why it happens—when we grow old.

TESTING CLICHÉS

To answer these questions, we now have a discipline called gerontology: the scientific study of the aging process. Medical research that was once directed solely at understanding disease and disability has begun to concern itself with the normal effects of time's passage on the body and mind. Startling questions are being asked: Is aging inevitable, or can the process be controlled, retarded, or even reversed? Is the human life-span genetically fixed, or can it be extended far beyond the 110 years or so that now appears to be the upper limit?

Questions like these are being explored at the U.S. National Institute of Aging (NIA), through its grant programs and at its own Gerontology Research Center (GRC) in Baltimore. As Richard Greulich, director of the GRC and scientific director of the NIA, sees it, the institute has four objectives: "The first is to understand enough about aging so

that people can live to a modest approximation of a normal life-span in reasonably good health. The second is to advance our understanding enough so that we may be able to enjoy extended middle age right into what we now consider old age. The third is to try and restore some functional capacities to people who are already old. The fourth, and to my mind the distinctly last order of business, is to extend the life-span itself."

Most of us make a number of assumptions about growing old. Among the commonest are these: that advanced age and senility—physical and mental infirmity—go hand in hand; that "obese" people do not live as long as thinner people; that exercising actively is sure to add life to your years and years to your life; and that an old dog can't learn new tricks. Some startling facts are now emerging to contradict every one of these clichés.

IS SENILITY NECESSARY?

We know that senility is not the result of normal aging, but of disease. According to Robert Terry, chief of pathology at Albert Einstein College of Medicine in New York City, 85 per cent of people over age 65 go through "relatively mild changes," which include a slowing down of reaction time, diminished quickness in learning, greater unwillingness to take risks and, in many cases, some impairment of short-term memory.

Probably only about 15 per cent of the elderly are affected by any degree of senile dementia—that is, severe memory loss, disorientation in time and place, failure to recognize friends and relatives, or even losing track of who they are.

"Senile dementia" is an umbrella term for a number of different diseases involving deteriorated mental faculties. About 50 per cent of the senile population suffers specifically from SDAT (senile dementia of the Alzheimer Type, named for a German neurologist). Another 20 per cent deteriorate as a

Paul Conklin/Monkmeyer

Loneliness and lack of stimulation are thought by many to be important factors in aging.

result of cerebral arteriosclerosis, while an additional 12 per cent have both conditions simultaneously. This leaves about 18 per cent whose changed behavior is the result of other diseases or as yet undetermined causes.

Researchers have found that people suffering from SDAT are missing up to 90 per cent of an enzyme responsible for the synthesis of acetylcholine. Acetylcholine is a chemical in the brain that, among other things, is believed to be involved in memory function.

Scientists are searching for either a substitute chemical or a means of stimulating the brain's remaining acetylcholine to work harder.

They are using choline, a common food substance found in eggs, meat, and fish, and known to be involved in acetylcholine production to stimulate production of acetylcholine—with modest success in a small number of patients at the beginning stages of senile dementia.

EXCESS WEIGHT

At the Gerontology Research Center, the main source of clues to many mysteries of aging is a group of 650 healthy, highly educated, upper-middle class, executive-type men ranging in age from early 20's to late 90's, who comprise the Baltimore Longitudinal Study. Since 1960 these men (and since 1978, women as well) have periodically been given batteries of exhaustive mental and physical tests. Every scrap of data—from the DNA in their cells to the kinds of daydreams they enjoy—is studied. The Baltimore study and reports dealing with totally different populations around the world—including longshoremen in San Francisco, elderly people on welfare in Chicago, and whole communities in Massachusetts, England, and Australia—provide the basis for one of the most surprising conclusions to be reached about aging.

It was arrived at by NIA's clinical director, Rubin Andres, MD, after he had pored over every available report containing information on obesity and mortality rates. When he finished, he concluded that "the ideal weights as given on the commonly available height-weight tables are unrealistically below the levels desired—if what you are interested in is total mortality." People who were 20 to 30 per cent over the chart weights did not in fact die any younger than those of normal weight. A few studies even showed that the moderately obese lived longer.

Dr. Andres finds this exceedingly interesting. After all, obesity is a known risk factor in such killing diseases as hypertension and coronary-artery disease. "Therefore," he says, "you would expect the total mortality to be higher for heavier people. But it isn't."

A healthy volunteer is being tested to measure age-related changes in the speed of nerve impulse conduction at a GRC facility.

EXERCISE AND PERSONALITY

The case for exercise also has not been nailed down. The difficulty with studies involving physical activity and longevity is isolating the role of exercise from all the other factors at work. So far none of the studies on the role of exercise—or on other life-style factors, for that matter—fully resolves the question: do some people in any given study live longer because they exercise more, or are healthier people more likely to exercise?

Another cliché biting the dust is that functional capacities, once lost, cannot be restored. At the GRC-affiliated Baltimore City Hospital, biofeedback techniques are helping old people with fecal incontinence regain control of their bodies. The problem of bowel control has many ramifications for the aged, points out gastroenterologist Marvin Shuster. "These are people who are afraid to go out," he explains. "And because they withdraw from society, they are cut off from constant intellectual stimulation and regress in many ways. After treatment, patients tell us it's like beginning life over again."

The ways in which mental factors—particularly the ability to resist stress—affect longevity are also being studied. Says NIA's Greulich, "Intuitively, I am convinced that having a reason for living is probably the most important concomitant of successful aging." As a case in point, Greulich describes a trip he made to the Soviet Union, where he met some of the long-lived people from the Republic of Georgia. "We asked one man who was one hundred sixteen—give or take thirty-five years—to what he owed his longevity. He owed it to his family, he said, because by virtue of being the eldest in his clan he was looked up to as the wise man. And he said one other thing that struck me: "I live each day for its own sake." The implication was that each day was a new experience to be welcomed and dealt with. I thought these were not bad words to live by, even if you only live to be eighty!"

Shirali Mislihov, reportedly 167 years old and the oldest man on earth. This healthy, agile resident of the southern Soviet village of Barzavu says, "Work is what makes my blood run fast."

WHY DO WE GROW OLD?

Why do we grow old? There are a number of theories. According to Leonard Hayflick, a senior researcher at the Children's Hospital Medical Center in Oakland, California, and a pioneer in the study of aging, there are several popular theories. One holds that age changes are programmed into the body's genes before birth on a kind of time-clock schedule. Another theory suggests that changes occur whenever the genes simply run out of new genetic program material the way tape runs out at the end of a reel. Others believe that aging is due to an accumulation

Famed cellist-composer Pablo Casals performed almost to the end of his life at age 96.

of errors that creep into the cells' repair machinery as a result of the wear and tear of living, or that some combination or variation of all of these processes is responsible.

GENETIC STOPWATCH

Hayflick's own work points strongly to a genetic stopwatch set at birth and timed to run out at a fixed point. In the mid-1960's, he discovered that human embryo cells grown in culture would not live indefinitely, as had been supposed, but went through about 50 doublings and then died out. The older the donor of the cell, the fewer the number of doublings before death—a finding that seemed to indicate an association between age and the cell's ability to divide.

Some recent experiments have cast doubt on the idea that a built-in aging program exists. David Harrison, an immunologist at the Jackson Laboratory in Bar Harbor, Maine, took bone-marrow cells from both young and old mice and transplanted them into other mice. He found that "old and young cells functioned equally well after transplantation, suggesting that whatever changes occur with age, they are not intrinsic to the cell itself, nor are they irreversible."

AGING HORMONE

Some gerontologists think that hormones from the hypothalamus-pituitary system in the brain control the rate at which we slow down. In a series of experiments, Donner Denckla, a visiting scientist at the National Institute of Alcohol Research, removed the pituitary glands from rats' brains and replaced the pituitary hormones necessary for life by adding them to the rats' water supply. By doing this, he so rejuvenated the rats that doddering 80-year-olds (or the rodent equivalent) were scampering around like gay young blades. In almost all tests that Denckla applied, youthful function had indeed been restored. The animals even looked young.

The reason for this astounding restoration, he believes, is that taking out the pituitary removes a mysterious, not yet isolated substance he has christened DECO, for Decreasing Oxygen Consumption. His evidence indicates that as the body ages, the pituitary

Lew Merrim/Monkmeyer

Each of these women is probably aging at a different rate and has different age-related problems, but one thing they have in common helps: they keep busy.

gland manufactures more and more DECO, which blocks the ability of peripheral cells to respond to several important hormones, including thyroid hormones, necessary for metabolism and growth, repair, and general support of the body.

Denckla is now looking for a substance that could serve as a selective blocker, shutting off the effects of the hormone. Even if he finds it, there is no guarantee that the discovery will increase longevity, since interestingly, Denckla's rejuvenated rats didn't live much longer than their untreated counterparts. The finding would, Denckla says cheerfully, make the life-span more satisfactory, however.

DIET TO EXTEND LIFE

Even if scientists don't yet know why we age, the fact is that they have some interesting evidence on how to extend life. In 1935, a famous experiment showed that rats who were started early in life on a diet that was extremely low in calories but included all the essential nutrients outlived rats on a normal diet by about 50 per cent.

Over the years, these experiments have been repeated on a wide variety of species—from one-celled animals to thousand-celled guppies—all with the same results. In general, the restricted diet appears to retard all aspects of aging. The animals grow at a slower rate, and take a much longer-than-usual time to reach sexual maturity and to get age-associated diseases.

Researchers have also found that cutting down only on dietary protein will increase life-span, and that it may not be necessary to start the restricted diet very early in life. Diet restriction must be done carefully, however. The diet must still be nutritionally balanced and contain essential vitamins and minerals.

FIGHTING FREE RADICALS

A rigid regimen of dieting is not, however, the average person's notion of the fountain of youth. What we all crave is the magic pill, that one-a-day wonder that keeps both the doctor and the undertaker away. To this end, a number of researchers are experimenting with various foods, vitamins, and chemicals.

Since the mid-1950's, Denton Harman, professor of medicine and biochemistry at the University of Nebraska, has been studying substances that block the effect of "free radicals." Free radicals are highly reactive molecule fragments that bump against other molecules, particularly those containing oxygen. These incessant "accidents" cause reactions that, Dr. Harman believes, are primarily responsible for age changes and age-related diseases such as cancer.

Gerontologist Ronald Hart found that DNA repair efficiency is a "longevity-assurance system."

One way to combat free radicals is to tie them up with antioxidant agents to keep them from causing mischief. Among the most potent antioxidant agents is BHT, the controversial food preservative often used to extend packaged cereals' shelf life. Using it on live rats extended their lives by 44 per cent. Another promising compound is centrophenoxine, a drug sold over the counter in Europe to relieve symptoms of senility. The drug is not available in the United States, but one U.S. study using mice showed that it improved mental and physical functioning and lengthened average lifespan by about 20 per cent.

IMMUNE RESPONSES

Many gerontologists are also looking at ways to shore up the immune system—the body's adaptive mechanism for dealing with environmental assaults such as carcinogens, or cancer-producing agents, viruses, and bacteria. William Adler, GRC chief of immunology, and other investigators have shown

that an important component of the immune system primarily responsible for meeting new threats to the organism declines with age. This decline is associated with the rapid shrinkage of the thymus gland around the time of puberty.

A second age-related phenomenon is a rise in the level of autoimmune antibodies. These antibodies turn against the body's own tissues as if they were foreign transplants to be rejected. Through the Baltimore Longitudinal Study, Dr. Adler has already turned up one fascinating fact: of people aged 85 and over, those who are still going strong have levels of immune function similar to those of much younger people.

Gaining control of immune mechanism is a prime goal of many scientists. Harman recently discovered that the same antioxidant compounds that extend life in rats also enhance their immune response. The compounds include santoquin, a preservative used in animal food; levamisol, an anti-cancer drug; and vitamin E. Researchers are also testing sulfur compounds and a recently isolated thymic hormone.

DOWN TO BASICS

In recent years a number of scientists have begun to piece together evidence uniting the often conflicting theories about aging and to address themselves to a basic question. How does one account for the vast multiplicity of changes that take place in every cell, every tissue, every organ of the body, as time goes by?

Much of this work is being done by molecular biologists, delving into the mysteries of the DNA molecule, the genetic blueprint for life hidden in the nucleus of every cell. A central figure in this research is Ronald Hart, a gerontologist who is also a professor of radiology and pharmacology at The Ohio State University College of Medicine. Hart believes that aging, like cancer, is a degenerative disease, and that all such disease may be associated with damage to DNA. Although many things inside and outside the body can produce DNA damage, nature has evolved a number of mechanisms to repair this damage or to prevent some of it from occurring.

If, however, this repair is not carried out

correctly, errors (or mutations) occur in the genetic information. These errors are then passed on when the cell replicates itself. In Hart's view, the accumulation of damage in the cells either from lack of repair or misrepair interferes with the proper working of the body and eventually leads to such effects as the runaway growth called cancer and the deterioration called aging.

Around 1975 Hart and molecular biologist Richard Setlow noticed in the course of a cancer experiment that normal cells cultured from mice sometimes spontaneously changed to a state of uncontrolled growth, whereas this almost never occurred in cells from human beings, who live much longer than mice. This intrigued Hart. He suspected that a species whose cells were likely to undergo runaway cancerous growth might have less ability to repair DNA damage than a less vulnerable species. This difference might, in turn, be related to a general difference in life-span.

They collected cell cultures from nine different mammal species and found that there was indeed a large variation in repair capacity. Then, after obtaining accurate data on animal life spans, they found "there was a tremendous correlation between the life span achievable for a particular species and the capacity of its cells to repair genetic damage." In other words, the length of time a species lives is related to how efficiently its cells are able to repair at least one form of damage inflicted on its genetic information.

REPAIR ABILITY

Other researchers began to confirm a strong correlation between what Hart calls "longevity-assurance systems" and life span. It remained, however, for one more experiment to deliver the payoff.

The project, originally suggested by Hart to gerontologist Joan Smith-Sonneborn, examined the effects of ultraviolet light, an agent known to produce DNA damage, on the life span of paramecia. These one-celled animals carry out numerous functions—including DNA repair—similar to those of human body cells. As expected, the ultraviolet rays damaged the paramecia's DNA and cut their life span by about half.

Gerontologist Joan Smith-Sonneborn showed that stimulating a DNA-repair mechanism in paramecia increased their life span.

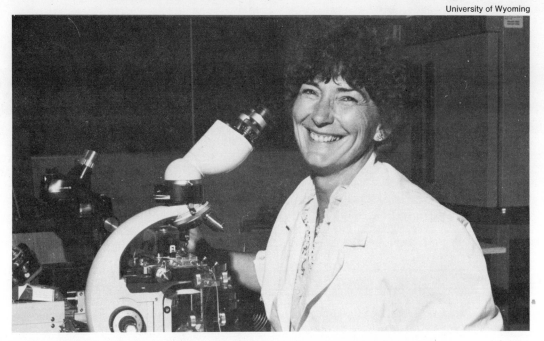

But then something quite unforeseen occurred. When Smith-Sonneborn took steps to repair the damage by stimulating a specific repair mechanism in the tiny animals, the treated paramecia actually lived slightly longer than the controls. Even more surprising, when she repeated the procedure on the same tiny organisms, she reported that the twice-treated paramecia showed a "dramatic increase in life span, up to 50 per cent."

Smith-Sonneborn, now professor of zoology and physiology at the University of Wyoming, believes that the experiments liberated an unknown repair mechanism in the paramecia that was able to prevent or clean up some of the damage that accumulates with age.

She is trying to identify the mysterious repair mechanism. If she succeeds, the implications will be staggering.

Hart is impressed. To him, this study has the "ring of direct proof" that a particular form of DNA damage can shorten the life span and that repairing the damage can reverse the process. Using a newly developed technique for taking accurate measurements

This woman feels—and is—needed. Will she live longer?

Dorothy Reed/Monkmeyer

of genetic damage in living animals, Hart and co-workers are now measuring the rate of DNA damage in different body tissues. They hope to answer such questions as: How do diet, exercise, and stress affect the speed of aging, as measured by the rate of genetic-damage accumulation? What environmental chemicals damage the DNA? Are some systems of the body, such as the immune system, especially susceptible?

"The ultimate experiment," says Hart, "would be to . . . see if by manipulating all the known repair systems of the body, we can modify the amount of genetic damage. If we do modify the genetic damage, do we change the maximum achievable life span?"

HELPING EVOLUTION

One thing is known: longevity-assurance systems are under the control of the genes, and just how well these systems function is probably the result of hundreds of millions of years of evolution. The hope is that soon we may be able to give evolution a helping hand. One way to accomplish this may be to trick cells into thinking they are older than they really are, thus stimulating repair. Or maybe repair genes from bacteria can be spliced into the cells of higher animals.

All that, of course, is in the future. Says Hart, "While I do not believe that the problems of degenerative disease or aging will be solved tomorrow, I do believe that science is making significant progress in these areas. If this progress continues, I think that 25 or 35 years from now—perhaps sooner—we will solve these problems. And for the first time we will be faced with the tremendous responsibility of controlling life span by manipulating the information in the genetic material."

That responsibility may prove onerous as well as exciting □

 SELECTED READINGS

Aging magazine.
"Exposing the myth of senility" by R. M. Henig. *New York Times Magazine,* December 3, 1978.
"Old age: what is normal?" by J. Greenberg. *Science News,* April 28, 1979.
"Time clock in your genes: is the life cycle preset?" by K. Cassill. *Science Digest,* October 1979.

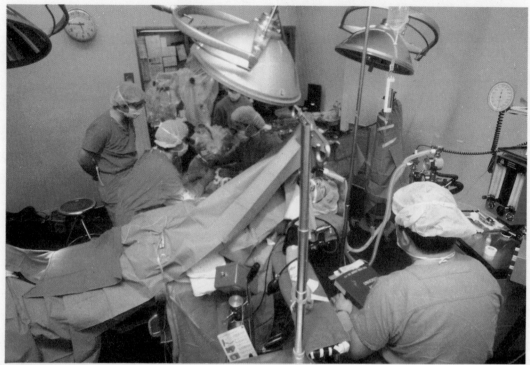

Jim Pozarik, Liaison

Microsurgeons at work using powerful lights, zoom-lens microscopes, and fine-tipped scalpels.

MICROSURGERY

by Gurney Williams III

A 35-year-old businessman was walking down the hall of his office when the floor seemed to slide away under him. He staggered and fell as the walls appeared to swirl. The nauseating dizziness continued even after fellow workers helped him back to his desk. He found he didn't have enough sense of balance to sit upright in his chair.

The terrifying 20-minute episode, as doctors later analyzed it, was the first sign of a stroke—an arterial obstruction partially damming off blood flow to the brain. Dr. Jack Fein of New York, to whom the case was referred, said the man was in extraordinary danger. If this had happened in 1975, he probably would have died.

But it happened in 1979, and today the businessman is alive and healthy. He is one of thousands of beneficiaries of surgery performed under the lenses of microscopes, with scalpels and other tools whose tips are so small they can hardly be seen by the naked eye.

ZOOM-LENS MICROSCOPES

Using microscopes with foot-controlled zoom-systems, surgeons across the United States have since the mid-1970's reattached severed limbs and restored sight to eyes that are clouded by hemorrhaging. They have reversed vasectomies with a better-than-even chance of success, removed tumors, and redirected blood flow in the brain to save lives. In the course of their work, many have become accustomed to watching life processes on a Lilliputian level. They've cheered at the

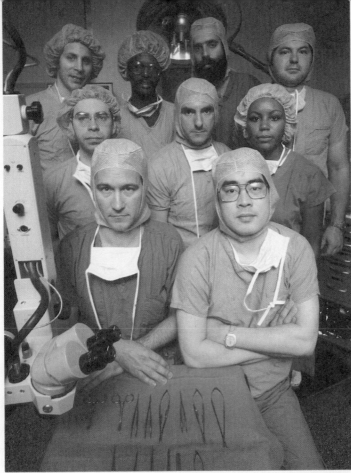

Microsurgery is a team effort. Vascular surgeons, neurosurgeons, orthopedists, anaesthesiologists, specially trained nurses, and others often participate. At left: the microsurgery team at Bellevue Hospital in New York City where some dramatic reimplantations have taken place.

Bob Adleman

pulsing of tiny pink vessels. They have also tracked nerves like a pilot following road patterns.

Almost all microsurgery operations are dramatic. Fein's work often draws small audiences of medical students and others who come to watch the procedure on a closed-circuit color television system which also records operations on videotape. There were about ten observers, he said, on the day of the businessman's operation.

Much of the equipment Fein used to work on the surface of his patient's brain was delicate and sophisticated. Forceps are so delicate, for instance, that dropping them from a height of one or two centimeters could throw them out of adjustment. The principle behind the operation was simple, however. It involved finding an artery on the outside of the man's scalp, cutting a silver-dollar-sized hole through the scalp, and splicing the outside artery into a vessel supplying blood to the brain. The connection, located higher than the blockage, would allow an adequate supply of blood to the brain without having to open up the clogged vessel.

NEEDLE THINNER THAN HAIR

The operation takes about four hours. The hardest work is stitching the open end of the outside vessel down over an oval-shaped hole cut in the cerebral artery. Fein attaches the two vessels with 30 stitches, or sutures, using a splinter-sized curved needle, and thread one-fifth the thickness of human hair. The site of the stitching, magnified 40 times by the microscope, is bloodless. Clamps on either side of the hole in the whitish vessel squeeze down just enough to stop blood flow.

The critical moment comes when these clamps are released and blood is allowed to flow through the new junction for the first time.

What happened in the case of the businessman was typical. As soon as the clips were opened and removed, the vessels began pulsing rhythmically. They turned from white to pink. There were no leaks. Within seconds of watching the throbbing arteries, everyone knew the man who would have died young without the operation now had a good chance to lead a normal life. The operating room crowd applauded.

That kind of scene has become more common in recent years as equipment has improved and success rates for microsurgery have risen. At Albert Einstein College Hospital, where Fein practices and teaches, he has performed the operation about 60 times since 1975, 30 times in 1979. Only one patient died and the death, Fein said, might have been unrelated to the operation. Fein anticipates doubling the number of such operations each year for the immediate future.

THE MEDITATION STANCE

Other surgeons across the United States confirm that more and more microscopes are appearing in the operating rooms of large hospitals. The trend means some retraining for doctors who are unaccustomed to working with the equipment and techniques. Microsurgery calls for ascetic discipline and a tremor-free touch. A slight twitch of a wrist during an operation on the brain can cause life-threatening damage to a blood vessel.

To keep hands rock solid during microsurgery, surgeons adopt a posture that makes them look as though they're meditating. Their hands rest side by side on a flat surface to control any trembling from wrist or arm. They sit straight-backed. A prism system in the microscope bends images through 90° so surgeons don't have to lean forward. Prior to surgery, they avoid strenuous lifting work which can produce slight quivering for hours after the work is done. Many cannot drink coffee before an operation.

Apart from the fear of trembling on the job, microsurgeons need to adjust to what one called the "unreal feeling" of performing major surgical procedures in an area often no bigger than a fingernail.

LIKE AN AERIAL PHOTO

"All doctors looked at slides under a microscope in medical school," said Dr. William Shaw, chief of plastic surgery at Bellevue Hospital in New York City. "But it takes

A triumph for microsurgery: Renee Katz after operation that reattached her hand severed by a subway train.

a lot of retraining to learn what you can do to change the scene under the microscope. At first, you think you're moving a millimeter, and you wind up moving a kilometer."

At a research laboratory at New York University, Dr. D. L. Ballantyne Jr. invited me to have a look through a Zeiss operating microscope to get a feel for what microsurgeons see. The view was startling. It looked like an aerial photo of a silvery pipe floating on a brilliant blue lake. The pipe was cut in the middle. As I watched, a curved needle held in the jaws of what looked like a giant pair of tweezers was driven into the pipe's wall on one side. Pulling black cable behind it, the needle arched across the gap and plunged decisively through the wall of the pipe on the other side of the lake.

Then the view changed suddenly. With a whirring sound, the microscope zoomed up and away to a higher perspective, revealing what looked like pink land bordering the lake. In a few seconds, other instruments had worked the cable into a loop, and pulled a free end through the loop to make half a square knot. The two ends of the pipe came together over the blue lake as instruments pulled the cable taut.

INVISIBLE THREAD BECOMES CABLE

I backed away from the eyepiece and looked down at the brightly lit table. There was a small white rat lying there, its nose breathing ether and air from a test tube, its legs held fast to a dissecting board with rubber bands. I had been watching the reconnection of the rat's femoral artery, a sliver of a vessel carrying blood to the rat's left leg. The site of the reconnection, performed by technician Alice D. Harper, was less than 7 square centimeters.

The blue lake was a patch of blue rubber used as a backdrop to make the vessel—the broken pipe—stand out. Without the microscope, the needle was barely visible. And I couldn't find the thread—the "black cable" seen under the lens—at all.

The procedure I had watched, the reconnection of severed vessels, is the first skill microsurgeons learn—the critical technique that enables them to reattach severed hands and fingers. The procedure was still in experimental stages in the mid-1960's. In 1977, the latest year for which figures are available, U.S. doctors performed 1,300 such operations, according to government estimates. Success rates on reattachments are im-

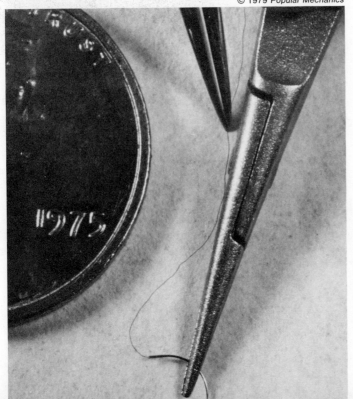

The thread used for suturing in microsurgical work is extremely fine—one fifth the thickness of human hair. To help illustrate the thread's thinness, some thread is shown next to a penny in the photo at left.

Time is a crucial factor in reimplantation surgery. Here Linda Fitzsimmons is shown with the police officers whose quick action in getting her and her severed arm to the hospital made the successful surgery possible.

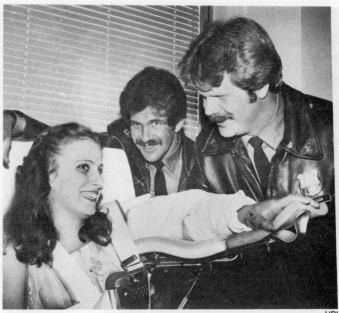

UPI

pressive. Dr. Laurence LeWinn of New York Hospital says that about nine out of ten of his operations result in fingers that function more or less normally.

MAKING TOES INTO THUMBS

One of LeWinn's first patients was a cook in a New York restaurant who cut his right index finger off while chopping chocolate for a soufflé. In his haste to get to the hospital, he forgot his finger on the kitchen block. The maitre d' found it, wrapped it in linen, and packed it in ice in a silver wine bucket for delivery. Within an hour, LeWinn was at work fastening bones back together with a small pin, reattaching arteries, veins, and nerves. The chilled finger regained its color and warmth. Shortly after the operation, it was moving again.

LeWinn said doctors today have learned to be more discriminating about when to reattach fingers. It isn't always a good idea, he said. "We've discovered that people who lose index fingers quickly learn to compensate with middle fingers. And sometimes the operation results in stiff and only partially functioning finger. So to put a patient through surgery and recovery sometimes seems to be a waste."

LeWinn will almost always try reattachment when several digits are cut off, or when children lose any finger, or whenever anyone loses a thumb. "The thumb is your most important finger," he said. "We'll try to reimplant that in almost everyone." The thumb is so important, in fact, that surgeons have come up with a microsurgical technique that works in cases where the thumb is too badly mangled to reattach. They amputate a toe and move it to the thumb's position. This restores the hand's power to grasp.

HOPE FOR BLIND DIABETICS

Other surgeons are using the lenses and small-tipped tools of microsurgery to restore sight to patients blinded by diabetes. Doctors aren't sure what leads to the condition, but about one half of the more than 10,000,000 victims of diabetes in the United States notice some deterioration in vision. In a small percentage of these cases, new and abnormal blood vessels grow on the retina at the back of the eye. They push out into the clear jelly-like vitreous which fills the interior of the eye. Often, these spurious vessels develop small leaks, clouding the vitreous with blood.

A new operation now offers some hope for these patients. Working under a microscope, doctors insert an instrument into the side of the eye. It cuts into the opaque vitreous, draws it out, and replaces it simultaneously with a clear solution. Many of the once hopelessly blind patients who have undergone the operation—called a vitrectomy—now see well enough to get around by themselves. A few can read.

The procedure is, however, still fairly new. It doesn't always help. And it does entail risk. Some patients develop infection, cataract, or other problems after surgery. But many are willing to face the odds for the chance to see.

REVERSING VASECTOMIES

Microsurgery has also improved the odds for men who wish to reverse vasectomy.

At times in history, vasectomy—the cutting and closing off of the thick-walled tubes that carry sperm out of the testes—has been touted as a cure-all for afflictions including leprosy, alcoholism, tuberculosis, poverty, and even the urge to steal chickens. Today, approximately 500,000 men each year undergo vasectomies as a convenient form of birth control. Operations take little time and often cost less than $200.

In the past, the disadvantage has been that the process has been difficult to reverse. In 1950, chances were only about one in four that a surgeon could re-establish fertility if a man changed his mind after vasectomy. Today, microsurgery has turned the odds around. Chances are now better than even, and some doctors report that four out of five of their patients are able to produce sperm.

The typical patient, reports Dr. Larry Lipshultz in Houston, Texas, is a 30-year-old man in his second marriage. "He's had two children," Lipshultz said, "then gotten a divorce. After two years of remarriage, he wants another child.

"I tell him if the vasectomy was performed within 10 years, the chances are 60 per cent for pregnancy. And if during the surgery I see sperm coming from the testicular side of the vasa, then chances are even better."

During the three-hour operation, Lipshultz removes the severed ends of the vasa, establishes fresh ends, and sews them together, doing most of the work under a microscope. Lipshultz currently performs more than 25 such operations annually.

AND IN THE FUTURE

A return of fertility, sight to the blind, and use of a severed limb—microsurgery has made possible all of these achievements. In years ahead it might help doctors in even more spectacular ways.

Dr. Shaw suggested one possibility. "A 13-year-old boy, let's say, suffers a painful elbow for a few weeks," Shaw said. "On an X-ray, doctors find a tumor on the bone, and it turns out to be malignant. Now, if you operate on the tumor, you risk spreading it. That's why doctors frequently amputate the arm in such cases."

But theoretically—and currently this is just theory, years away from trials that would prove whether it worked—microsurgery could provide a way to save the arm without risking the boy's life.

During a half-hour operation, a microsurgeon would amputate the arm, carefully placing small clamps on each vessel. Then the arm would be moved to a laboratory where a surgeon and a pathologist would work together to cut out all the tumor. Then, Shaw continued, "You would ensure that there's no tumor spread within the arm by feeding arteries with a high concentration of chemotherapy, in doses that would harm the patient if the arm were attached." Blood would then be given to wash the tumor-killing agent out of the vessels. Finally, after two or three days of treatment and tests, the arm would be reattached, under a high-powered microscope, giving the youth a chance for a normal life □

📖 SELECTED READINGS

"Delicate art of microsurgery: hand reimplantation" by M. Clark and S. Shapiro. *Newsweek*, June 25, 1979.

"Medical technology: a new revolution" by Laurence Cherry. *New York Times Magazine*, August 5, 1979.

"Microsurgery" by J. Arehart-Treichel. *Science News.* April 7, 1979.

"Microvascular surgery for stroke" by J. Fein. *Scientific American*, April 1979.

Dr. Frank Lilly, Chairman of the Department of Genetics at Albert Einstein College of Medicine, is a leading investigator of genetic markers. His work on genetic markers for leukemia in mice has greatly advanced work on an entire group—the HLA antigens—of chemically related markers in humans.

Albert Einstein College of Medicine

USING GENES
TO PREDICT DISEASES

by Zsolt Harsanyi and Richard Hutton

FOR centuries, schoolteachers on the Mediterranean island of Sardinia have witnessed a curious phenomenon. Every February, as spring arrives, some of their students suddenly become listless. For the next three months, they feel dizzy and nauseous; they fall asleep at their desks; their schoolwork suffers. Then, just as suddenly, their energy returns. They remain healthy and active until the next February rolls around.

In some countries, such incidents would be ascribed to boredom, spring fever, or a massive, collaborative effort to disrupt the learning process. But the Sardinian teachers know that adults can suffer from similar symptoms and that, in fact, some can die after urinating quantities of blood. At times, as many as 35 per cent of the islanders have suffered from the disease.

MISSING ENZYME

Dr. Marcello Siniscalco of Memorial Sloan-Kettering Cancer Center in New York City and Dr. Arno G. Motulsky of the University of Washington came across the disease in 1959 while studying patterns of heredity. They determined that the Sardinians were afflicted with hemolytic anemia, a hereditary disease that causes the red-blood cells to explode in the blood vessels. Its victims urinate blood because the kidneys filter out and excrete the cell's wasted hemoglobin. If the amount of destruction is minimal, the result is lethargy; if it is severe, death.

Hemolytic anemia can have many origins. But in Sardinia, tests indicated that almost everyone with the disease was lacking a single enzyme, called glucose-6-phosphate dehydrogenase, or G-6-PD. This enzyme forms a crucial link in the chain of energy production for the red-blood cells. With the chain cut, the cells become more fragile, and internal pressure tears the weakened cell walls.

But why did the Sardinians become ill only during the spring? This fact indicated

FPG

The identification of specific genetic disease markers may help this Irish boy avoid disease-triggering environmental conditions—an opportunity his grandfather didn't have.

danger—that is, those lacking the G-6-PD enzyme—and warned them to avoid fava beans during the flowering season. As a result, the incidence of hemolytic anemia—and lackadaisical schoolchildren—declined.

DISEASE MARKERS

The use of genetic markers to predict the Sardinians' reaction to fava beans in the late 1950's was one of the first times genetic markers were used in that way. It was the beginning of a development that may change the face of modern medicine.

Genetic markers may now predict the possible onset of other sicknesses, and, as with hemolytic anemia, may help doctors prevent the attacks entirely in many instances. The markers are being linked to a variety of diseases. Red hair, especially among the Irish, has been tied to high rates of skin cancer. Blood Type A leaves a woman five times as susceptible to blood clots if she takes oral contraceptives, as a woman with a different blood type. People with elevated levels of the enzyme persinogen I in their blood are five times as likely as others to develop a peptic ulcer. Other genetic markers have been discovered for everything from diabetes and lung cancer to emphysema, malaria, and hepatitis.

While many markers are still locked in the laboratory, it will not be long—perhaps by the year 2000—before a person can head down to the local clinic, have a blood sample drawn, and be tested for susceptibility to 50 or more common diseases. The results would appear in the form of a computer printout. It would include the genetic markers found, the diseases they prophesy, and the amount of risk involved. It would also include a list of environmental factors, from smoking to vacations in tropical climates, that might in some way affect the diseases associated with the genetic markers.

NATURE AND NURTURE

Like most medical breakthroughs, genetic prophecy is not occurring in a vacuum. It has been accelerated by two other important medical developments—one experimental, the other theoretical.

Experimentally, the biological revolu-

that something in the environment had to be taking advantage of the enzyme deficiency. A genetic defect resulting in the lack of the enzyme may have been the gun, but an environmental factor was pulling the trigger.

"Among the plants that flower during the Sardinian springtime is the Italian broad, or fava, bean," Dr. Siniscalco noted. "It has had a bad reputation ever since 500 B.C., when the Greek philosopher and religious reformer Pythagoras barred his followers from eating it, or even from walking through fields in which it was growing." Now, it became clear why: only those people who both carried the defective gene and ate raw or partly cooked fava beans (or breathed the pollen from a flowering plant) were having trouble. Everyone else was resistant.

Within two years, Dr. Motulsky developed a simple blood test to measure the presence or absence of G-6-PD. Armed with G-6-PD as a genetic marker for hemolytic anemia, geneticists then began to screen the island's population. They located those in tion since 1950 has revealed the impact of the gene on human life. Within each cell there are genes. These are housed in long threads of DNA (deoxyribonucleic acid). They contain a record of a body's heredity and act as a blueprint for the body's actual physical structure. Painstaking research is revealing why each gene exists and how genes are tied to one another. A theory of life, where genes and the environment work together, is emerging.

The genes determine the range of potential possibilities, and the environment selects among them. Thus, for example, genes may dictate that someone grows to a height between 170 and 180 centimeters but diet, hygiene, stress, and general health will determine the precise point at which growth stops.

The same holds for disease. Both genetic predisposition and appropriate environmental factors must be present for many diseases to occur. This became clear as researchers investigated the question of why some individuals were more susceptible than others to such diseases as tuberculosis, diphtheria, and bacterial pneumonia.

PREVENTIVE MEDICINE

The second development central to genetic prophecy is the increased emphasis on preventive medicine—the strengthening of the belief that it is simpler, cheaper, and more effective to prevent disease from occurring, than to have to combat it once it breaks out. Originating in medical circles, this belief has been buttressed by a general movement toward medical responsibility on the part of the public.

As improvements in treatment, diet, and hygiene have greatly diminished the threat of acute infectious diseases, the proportion of chronic, debilitating diseases—like heart disease, arthritis, and diabetes—has increased. To fight these chronic diseases, the character of medicine has had to change—from trying to build a better mousetrap for disease to trying to create a more congenial mouse.

Because of the recent explosion of genetic knowledge, researchers are increasingly able to make predictions about an individual's medical fate. First, the triad of elements for a particular problem—disease, genetic marker, and environmental triggering factor—must be identified. Then whole populations of perfectly healthy people can be screened, not for the nascent symptoms of a disease, but for a disease's genetic marker alone. Such a screening would indicate that the disease could someday appear in the individual. The list of triads already discovered is awesome. We shall discuss a few of the more significant.

Some of these smokers may suffer from emphysema, lung cancer, or other diseases connected with smoking; others may not. Genetic markers can help identify those most in danger.

Bill Anderson/Monkmeyer

LUNG CANCER AND SMOKING

Ever since the first cigarette was lighted, there have been two sides to every argument about the health hazards of smoking. Non-smokers dredge up lurid tales of blackened lungs, wheezing coughs, and slow, painful deaths while smokers always seem to have an Uncle Harry who smoked 10 packs a day, dying at the age of 85 only when he lost control of his Maserati during a highspeed chase.

Both sides ignore the simple fact that there are scores of different compounds in cigarette smoke. Someone who is resistant to their toxicity is safe; someone who is not is at risk.

Now two genetic markers have been discovered that can identify those in danger from two of the more hazardous effects of smoking: lung cancer and emphysema.

The first, aryl hydrocarbon hydroxylase (AHH), is an enzyme system that can be detected in the white blood cells. It works to transform insoluble compounds like drugs, insecticides, and tobacco smoke into soluble compounds that the body can excrete.

While ridding the body of unwanted chemicals, however, AHH sometimes becomes an unwitting accomplice in still another process: producing intermediate compounds that happen to be carcinogenic, or cancer-producing. One set of the compounds so transformed is known as polycyclic hydrocarbons. They are found in coal tars, pesticides, and tobacco smoke.

The potential levels of AHH in humans are genetically determined. Some people produce high amounts, some produce low amounts. In at least one study, conducted by Dr. Gottfried Kellermann, now at the Department of Human Oncology at the University of Wisconsin, high levels of AHH activity were found in 9 per cent of the normal population and low levels in 47 per cent. But the distribution of AHH activity among 50 lung-cancer patients was shockingly different. Only 4 per cent had low levels, while 30 per cent had high levels. When Dr. Kellermann calculated the relative risks for his groups, he found that someone with a high level of AHH activity was 36 times as likely to contract cancer as someone with low levels.

The implication is clear. Those with low AHH levels can be less concerned with the danger of developing lung cancer. Those with high levels must be more concerned and should make a greater effort to avoid environmental triggers. They, in particular, should not smoke.

Dr. Kellermann's findings are controversial, and some investigators have been unable to duplicate his results. But recent animal studies confirm his conclusions that a high level of AHH is associated with increased risk of developing cancer when an individual is exposed to polycyclic hydrocarbons.

At present, the determination of AHH levels is made by a complicated blood test, and mass screening is not yet available. Still, according to Dr. Kellermann, a more promising approach is now being developed. It measures the body's ability to break down certain specific drugs. This is a breakdown that reveals, by comparison, the amount of AHH in the body. That test may turn out to be more reliable than screening for AHH itself.

EMPHYSEMA AND SMOKING

The second genetic marker linked with one of the hazardous effects of smoking is alpha-1-antitrypsin (AAT). AAT is a protein that has been linked since the mid-1960's with pulmonary emphysema. It has been found in much lower concentrations than is normal in individuals with two so-called Z genes. Approximately 70 per cent of ZZ-type individuals eventually develop emphysema.

Surveys indicate that smokers with the ZZ genes develop the symptoms of emphysema on the average of nine years earlier than nonsmokers. Furthermore, ZZ individuals are more susceptible to a whole range of respiratory irritants found in industry. Research on individuals who are carrying only one Z gene is incomplete.

MALARIA

Resistance to infection by the parasite *Plasmodium vivax,* one of the two most common agents of malaria, is found in nearly 100 per cent of West Africans and about 65 per cent of American blacks. Their protection

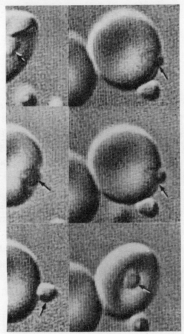

Dr. Louis Miller has found that only Duffy-positive individuals—that is, those whose red blood cells are equipped with appropriate receptor sites—contract malaria. The malaria parasite attaches to the red-blood cell, causes distortion of the cell, and invades it as shown in this sequence of microscopic slides, running from top left to lower right.

Both photos: National Institutes of Health

has been traced to a genetic marker, a blood group characteristic known as "Duffy negative."

Plasmodium vivax seems to infect its victims by attaching itself to complex molecules that exist on the outsides of red blood cells. These so-called "receptor molecules" enable the parasites to hitch a ride on the cells and enter them to begin their replication cycle. The red blood cells of Duffy-negative individuals are not equipped with receptor molecules.

Investigators at the U.S. National Institutes of Health, led by Dr. Louis Miller, have found that when groups of individuals were infected with *Plasmodium vivax,* all of the Duffy-positive individuals—and none of the Duffy-negative individuals—contracted malaria. As a result, Dr. Miller points out, "We can tell who will get vivax malaria and who will not simply on the basis of their Duffy blood type."

INFLUENZA

Immunoglobulins are the proteins that help the body fight infections and exposure to foreign substances. One of them, known as immunoglobulin A, or IgA, is normally found in saliva, tears, the gastrointestinal tract, and lung fluids. People who totally lack IgA constitute slightly more than 1 in 500. In the United States, there are thus more than 500,000 people who are deficient in IgA.

IgA-deficient individuals are more prone to recurrent gastrointestinal infections and respiratory diseases than the normal population. Evidence indicates that they are also far more susceptible to influenza infections. A simple laboratory procedure exists to screen for those lacking IgA. These people thus can be advised specifically of the need for vaccinations during flu epidemics.

HLA AND ANKYLOSING SPONDYLITIS

Dr. Frank Lilly of the Albert Einstein College of Medicine in New York has discovered that certain strains of mice are more likely than others to be infected by viruses that cause leukemia. He experimented with certain mouse antigens. (Antigens are body molecules that cause the production of proteins that fight off disease or foreign agents.) Lilly discovered that the mouse antigens could be used as genetic markers for susceptibility to leukemia in the animals. These mouse antigens are similar to the histocompatibility antigens, or HLA antigens, in humans.

HLA antigens in humans are found on the surface of practically all cells. They are the structures that determine, say, whether or not a new kidney or heart will be accepted by the body after transplantation surgery. They come in a variety of shapes and sizes—a total of 69 of them, divided into five major groups.

Since the early 1970's research in the

HLA field has run riot, with promising results. Perhaps the clearest connection yet discovered between the HLA system and a disease exists between the antigen B27 and ankylosing spondylitis, an arthritic condition of the spine also known as "bamboo spine." The frequency of B27 in the normal population is about 8 per cent. In people afflicted with ankylosing spondylitis, however, it rises to an astounding 95 per cent. Some studies have calculated that a person who carries the B27 antigen has 175 times more chance of developing ankylosing spondylitis than someone without it. This fact helps explain the rarity of ankylosing spondylitis in African blacks: they have been found to lack B27 antigens.

OTHER DISEASES

Virtually hundreds of other projects are currently establishing links between disease susceptibility and HLA types. Several dozen have already succeeded.

Dermatologists have established that one common form of psoriasis is found about five times more frequently in people carrying HLA antigen Cw6. American Indians, who as a population do not have the gene for Cw6, do not suffer from psoriasis.

Gastroenterologists have found that people with HLA type B8 are three times as susceptible to chronic active hepatitis as people without it. They also have a nine-fold risk of developing sensitivity to wheat gluten, a protein which can cause severe intestinal disturbances.

Some researchers contend that people carrying a combination of A1-B8 or A2-B12 are more sensitive to ragweed pollen. Those with A1-B8 are also more prone to asthma.

Myasthenia gravis can be predicted by double genetic markers: both HLA antigens and the sex chromosomes play a role in defining predisposition to the disease. Female Caucasians with B8 carry a twelvefold risk of developing the disease; males with B8 have not been shown to have a greater risk than the general population.

HLA typing has also proved useful in determining whether certain diseases will be distributed within families. In a recent study, Dr. Pablo Rubinstein and his colleagues at the New York Blood Center found that, in families where one child had juvenile diabetes mellitus, the other children varied according to their HLA type.

If both parents were healthy, the best estimate that could be derived without HLA typing was that a brother or sister would have about a 1-in-8 chance of developing the disease. With HLA typing, however, the risk could be pinpointed far more accurately. Depending upon the antigen involved, a second child could be targeted as having approximately one chance in 1,000, one chance in 50, or one chance in two of becoming diabetic.

USING THE PROPHESIES

HLA typing and other genetic markers will have achieved their full potential in genetic prophecy only when the knowledge can actually be used to avoid disease. With Dr. Rubinstein's study, early complications of diabetes might be avoided if the parents were forewarned. A child with a one in two chance of developing the disease would certainly be more closely watched than one whose chances were one in a thousand.

The concept of medical screening is not at all new. Centuries ago, private physicians tested their wealthier patients for diabetes by tasting their urine to evaluate its sugar content. And today, everyone who applies for a marriage license is screened for syphilis; many women undergo yearly PAP smears for signs of cervical cancer; and newborn infants are routinely tested for a variety of problems, including phenylketonuria, a genetic disease that can cause mental retardation if it is not kept under control by careful dieting. Nevertheless, screening's uses have generally been limited to the recognition of the early stages of disease and to some prenatal testing. Screening for genetic markers may destroy those limitations.

While it foreshadows profound changes in general medical practice, genetic prophecy will also figure in the particular health problems of industry. Screening for genetic markers can pinpoint factory workers predisposed to specific diseases, and can protect them from exposure to chemicals that might trigger cancer, emphysema, or other problems.

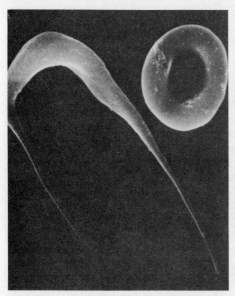
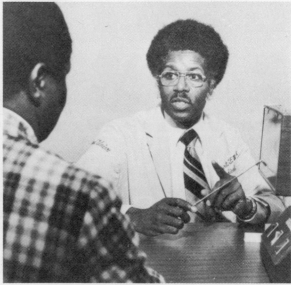

Both photos: National Heart, Lung, and Blood Institute, NIH

A black receives counseling during sickle-cell screening. In sickle-cell anemia—a disease that affects blacks and certain Mediterranean peoples almost exclusively—red-blood cells are sickle-shaped instead of circular and have impaired ability to transport oxygen.

POWERFUL—AND DANGEROUS—TOOL

The potential benefits of such screening programs are obvious. They can relieve needless suffering and save perhaps huge amounts of money in health care. Nevertheless, the practice of extensive genetic screening also raises some disturbing moral, ethical, and legal questions that will have to be answered before it is put into operation.

First, practical guidelines will have to be set for deciding which diseases should be screened, and which should not. In addition, the factors of cost per screen, reliability of the testing process, the number of people who are susceptible, and the usefulness of the knowledge gained will have to be considered.

More important, however, are the larger questions of how genetic screening will affect society. The cast of characters that might be pitted against each other comes in every conceivable combination. The knowledge to be had is a powerful tool, and individual, employer, government, and insurance company will all vie to reap its rewards. The questions concern obligations as well as rights.

• What constitutional issues arise from the screening of particular ethnic or racial groups? This problem is still unanswered after the controversy surrounding screening for sickle-cell anemia, a disease found almost exclusively among blacks and certain Mediterranean peoples.

• What constitutional barriers exist to deter states from compelling participation in screening programs?
• To what extent must the results of the screening be disclosed to the person screened?
• To what extent may the results be disclosed to others, without the individual's consent?
• Should society pay the health insurance of those who do not heed the warnings of genetic prophecy?
• Can parents be accused of child abuse if they fail to provide their child with an environment that might inhibit the development of a disease 50 years in the future?

The list can go on. But the problems will arise. Genetic prophecy is still at the tail of medicine's whip but it is moving inexorably toward the handle □

SELECTED READINGS

"Genetics and medicine: an evolving relationship" by C. Scriver and others. *Science,* March 26, 1978.

"Heredity insurance: screening" by M. Pines. *The New York Times Magazine,* April 30, 1978.

"New power to predict—and prevent—disease" by G. Bylinsky. *Fortune,* September 25, 1978.

"Why you should know your family medical history" by L. Galton. *50-Plus,* June 1979.

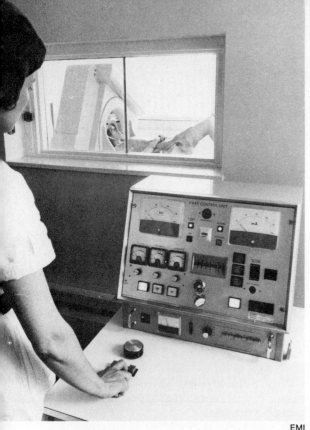

A radiographer is at the control unit while a patient undergoes a brain scan using EMI-scanner computerized axial tomography.

EPILEPSY

by Robert Geballe

At the age of fifteen, Randy Lee, sitting in a high-school classroom, noticed a strange tingling sensation in his right arm. It seemed to travel up and down and then subsided after several minutes. This odd event recurred several times during the year, once while Randy was reading his psychology textbook. Though he tried to deny it, he recognized a pattern—he realized that his strange sensations matched the description of epilepsy in his textbook.

Six years later Randy had a major seizure. He remembers it. "My right arm just started to rise to my shoulder, then over my head. The next thing I knew, I awoke in the hospital." He stayed in the hospital for a week while his doctor ran tests, adjusted medications, and tried to ease the shock of the event. Since then Randy's life has been a seesaw of frustration and hope, a seesaw he shares with epileptics all over the world.

RANDY is one of about 2,000,000 epileptics in the United States—one of the approximately one per cent of the population that has epilepsy. The causes of epilepsy are numerous and common, its occurrence more frequent in recent years. As researchers all over the world gradually untangle the incredibly complex web of chemical reactions, interrelated functions, and complicated structure that makes up the human brain, the mysteries of illnesses like epilepsy slowly unfold. Today, with the introduction of sophisticated diagnostic devices, new drugs and surgical techniques, and a higher level of public understanding, people like Randy can lead lives fuller than ever before.

ELECTRICAL STORM

Epilepsy comes from the Greek word *epilepsia,* which means "to attack or to seize." Epilepsy has been described as an "electrical storm of the brain." The millions of nerve cells that make up the brain communicate with one another by means of tiny electric currents. In epilepsy, for reasons not yet understood, groups of these nerve cells occasionally initiate a rapid, rhythmic type of electric activity. This can produce the tinglings which Randy first felt, or if the abnormal electrical activity spreads to the whole brain, the powerful whole-body convulsions of his major seizure.

Physicians divide epileptic seizures into two major categories: generalized and partial. Generalized seizures have no specific focus, or site, in the brain, whereas partial seizures originate in one or several discrete brain locations. A pattern of partial seizures sometimes evolves into generalized seizures, as happened to Randy.

There are two common forms of generalized seizures: grand mal and petit mal. Grand-mal seizures are the violent convulsions we usually associate with epilepsy, while petit mal often involves just a brief loss of awareness and can be mistaken for daydreaming. Grand mal can appear at any age, but petit mal tends to occur in children and often ceases at puberty.

A third common type of seizure is partial and is called psychomotor. It is characterized by a combination of psychological and motor aspects, such as tantrums or repetitive and inappropriate movements.

MANY TRIGGERS

The precise abnormalities that exist in an epileptic nerve cell are unknown. However, neuroscientists do have an understanding of many of the factors that precipitate the onset of epilepsy. Head injury is one of these factors. Ironically, the increasing incidence of epilepsy may result from modern medical techniques that allow many critically injured people to survive, some of whom suffer brain damage that later manifests itself as epilepsy.

Difficulties at birth, high fevers, stroke, and drug or alcohol abuse can also trigger the onset of seizures. Stress may play a role in the frequency of seizures in some sensitive people, as may lack of sleep.

Researchers are also gathering evidence that suggests a genetic component in petit-mal epilepsy. Studies have revealed that close relatives of petit-mal epileptics have a greater incidence of abnormal brain activity than the population at large. This finding, plus the occurrence of an unusual array of amino acids in the excretions of these people, suggests a genetic basis for the disease.

DRUG TREATMENT

The development and use of drugs to control seizures has greatly benefited victims of epilepsy in the 20th century. About 70 per cent of all epileptics can be helped with drugs. The seizure-controlling abilities of the traditionally used drugs—phenobarbital and Dilantin—are, however, sometimes offset by the sedation and lack of coordination these drugs produce. Closely related to anesthetics, these compounds affect properties of all nerve cells—not just epileptic nerve cells—and produce widespread and often uncomfortable side effects. This leaves some patients in a double bind: take the prescribed amount of medication and live with the loss of alertness or be undermedicated and alert but run the risk of having seizures.

Hope for many lies in drugs more specific in their actions. One of these is carbamazepine (Tegretol), usually substituted for Dilantin. In a study conducted at the University of Washington, neurologists found that

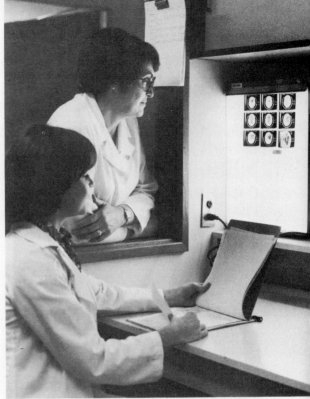

Epilepsy Center

Analysis of the brain scans of an epileptic patient can reveal the site of epileptic foci and may provide a way of treating the disease surgically.

the two substances were equally effective in controlling partial seizures and detailed psychological tests confirmed patients' reports that they were "more alert, brighter, and less drugged" with carbamazepine.

Valproic acid has given physicians a potent weapon against petit-mal seizures. This drug, pioneered in Europe, was approved by the U.S. Food and Drug Administration only in 1978. Researchers think that valproic acid's effects result from the increase in the brain substance GABA that follows its administration. GABA, an amino acid, is known to have an inhibitory effect on some brain cells.

Researchers are also now taking a hard look at several commonly prescribed tranquilizers for their effectiveness in seizure control. One of the most promising is chlorazepate, a close relative of the tranquilizer Valium. Dr. Allan Troupin of the University of Pennsylvania and several of his colleagues reported in 1979 that patients receive the same seizure control from chlorazepate as from Dilantin and suffer no side effects. Unfortunately chlorazepate is metabolized rapidly by the body so that it must be taken more frequently than other anti-seizure compounds.

SURGERY

For the nearly 30 per cent of all epileptics that are not significantly helped by drugs, new and precise techniques of brain surgery hold hope. Dr. George Ojemann, a neurosurgeon at the Epilepsy Center in Seattle, Washington, says that post-surgery improvement figures for some types of epilepsy "are so impressive that it is surprising that more surgery for intractable seizures isn't done." He and two other neurosurgeons report that surgery resulted in either complete cessation or substantial improvement in seizures in 76 per cent of their patients.

Epilepsy surgery involves removing the focus of epileptic activity—that is, the site of abnormal electric activity in the brain. The focus is often a small section of the brain in the temporal lobe of the cortex. This region is the seat of several major brain systems controlling functions such as memory, speech, and movement. The surgery is performed under local anesthesia whenever possible. The surgeon then stimulates various temporal lobe cells to determine, with the help and responses of the conscious patient, which cells play vital roles. The surgeon then attempts to leave these cells undisturbed and to remove only cells in a "silent" area.

ZEROING IN

Much of the current optimism about surgery stems from the recent development of improved techniques for precisely locating the sites of abnormal activity in the brain. Improved electroencephalographs (EEG's) —recordings of brain-wave patterns—now enable neurologists to locate the sites of epileptic activity to within two centimeters. Computerized axial tomography (CAT) scans create a three-dimensional image of the brain by taking a series of X-ray "slices" of the head. These scans are particularly helpful in identifying anatomical abnormalities such as tumors, scar tissue, or blood-vessel malformations that may contribute to epileptic seizures.

Another diagnostic tool, called the WADA test, helps determine which side of the brain is dominant. This is important in cases where epileptic foci are present as mirror images on both sides of the brain. The surgeon will then remove the focus on the non-dominant side, thus reducing the frequency of seizures without endangering important functions, such as speech, controlled by the dominant side.

Surgery is especially rewarding when used to help children suffering from severe partial seizures. In early life the brain has a great capacity to compensate for injury, and children recover more rapidly and completely than adults do.

Acupuncture, meditation, and various nutritional regimens have also been proposed as means of controlling epilepsy. Though a few patients gain a measure of control over their seizures by one of these techniques, the results are very difficult for scientists to substantiate.

MANY-FACETED PROBLEM

A person with epilepsy faces problems that are not just medical. An epileptic who is honest about his or her condition may have difficulty in finding work, often due to the heritage of misunderstanding that surrounds the disorder. Partly in recognition of this, the U.S. government has established five regional epilepsy centers to provide vocational training and job counseling as well as public education and clinical research.

Epilepsy has been a constant, if unwelcome, companion of many for many thousands of years. Its unusual aspects have historically given it a special place in our attempts to understand the relationship between the body and the mind. It is in our increasing capacity to fathom this relationship and in our humanity and compassion that people like Randy find hope □

 SELECTED READINGS

The Epilepsy Fact Book by Harry Sands and Frances Minters. Scribner, 1979.

Understanding Epilepsy by George Burden and Peter Schurr. Beekman, 1976.

NITRITES IN YOUR BODY

by Steven R. Tannenbaum

IN our cancer-conscious society, nitrites, nitrates, and nitrosamines (one group of N-nitroso compounds) have assumed an ominous and highly publicized position on the list of possible carcinogenic, or cancer-causing, agents in the environment. Nitrites and nitrates are thought to pose a health hazard by combining with organic compounds called amines to form nitroso-carcinogens, such as nitrosamines, in many foods.

IN MANY FOODS

Both nitrites and nitrates are currently added to many food products, including meat, cheese, and poultry, as food preservatives to deter spoilage and botulism. They are also used as flavoring and coloring agents, to keep meat and poultry looking fresh. Nitrates also occur naturally in many vegetables, including spinach, lettuce, and celery.

These nitrates are easily converted into nitrites, which, in turn, can be converted into nitroso-organic compounds. N-nitroso compounds themselves exist in many substances: rust-protected metals, cigarette smoke, cosmetics, weed killers, Scotch whiskey, and beer.

The argument has been made that discontinuing the use of nitrites and nitrates as food preservatives would reduce or eliminate the nitroso-carcinogenic risk. So would limiting the amount of nitrosamines allowed in cooked foods and distilled beverages.

Efforts have been made towards this end. For example, the nitrite content of meat products such as bacon and sausage has been reduced from 200 to 120 parts per million. It may ultimately be reduced to 40 parts per million. The nitrosamine content of beer may soon be less than 5 parts per billion.

Reducing the rate of nitrate and nitrite exposure to decrease the risk of cancer is an

This array of sausages looks good—but is it good for us?

Ulf Sjostedt, FPG

The nitrosamine content of the beer in these kegs may soon be limited to five parts per billion.

admirable goal. This goal, however, is attainable only if we also understand certain endogenous, or natural, body processes involving nitrates and nitrites. There is increasing evidence that nitrites other than those ingested from the air, water, and food make large contributions to the total amount the body is exposed to.

These additional sources of nitrite are located within the normal healthy body itself—in saliva, the stomach, and the intestines. It is therefore essential to look at the dietary and environmental sources of nitrite and nitrate in conjunction with the healthy body's natural production of nitrite and nitrate. Then one must look at the following internal synthesis of these products into nitroso-carcinogenic substances.

NITRITE PRODUCTION IN THE BODY

Since 1975 my research group has studied the various endogenous processes in human beings which lead to the formation of nitrites and determine their eventual fate. We have done this in collaboration with other research groups headed by Drs. Pelayo Correa and Carlos Cuello in Colombia, South America, and Dr. W. R. Bruce in Toronto, Canada.

It is difficult to make accurate estimates of the total amount of nitrites the body is exposed to each day from its own natural processes, but estimates are feasible for the stomach and intestines. About ten times more nitrite enters the stomach each day from the reduction of naturally produced nitrate in saliva than from the ingestion of nitrite in cured meats. Probably thousands of times more nitrite is formed in the intestine than is contributed to the intestine from preformed nitrite in the diet.

Considering present and proposed U.S. Department of Agriculture regulations concerning nitrite uses in food, the risk that arises from such nitrite use may be minuscule compared to the risk resulting from the body's natural processes. Further research on animals and humans consuming cured meat products may establish this fact.

Nitrite formation occurs extensively throughout the digestive tract, beginning in the mouth and terminating in the colon. In estimating the body's total exposure, we must deal separately with nitrite that is introduced into or formed in the mouth and then enters the stomach, and with nitrite that is formed directly in the intestine. The latter nitrite is converted to nitrate in blood, and ultimately contributes to the amount of nitrite formed in saliva. In the stomach, we must balance the preformed nitrite entering in food against the nitrite that is formed in saliva as a result of normal body processes.

IN SALIVA

The existence of nitrite in saliva has been known for about 100 years, but this fact escaped all the early reviews on N-nitroso compound formation. Saliva entering the mouth through the salivary glands contains nitrate but not nitrite. Bacteria that inhabit the oral cavities of all normal, healthy individuals reduce the nitrate to nitrite. The amount of nitrite formed is related to the amount of nitrate in the mouth. This, in turn, depends upon the exposure of the individual to nitrate—either directly from food or indirectly from synthesis in the intestines.

Nitrate ingested in food is cleared from the body through the kidney in 24 to 48 hours, depending upon dose. The maximum nitrate concentration in saliva occurs approximately three hours following a meal. The concentration may reach hundreds of parts per million for an individual consuming large amounts of nitrate in the form of, for example, vegetable juices.

At the present time, I believe that a conservative estimate of the amount of exposure of an individual to salivary nitrite would be on the order of 10 to 20 milligrams per day. For some individuals, the total intake might be as low as 5 milligrams per day. For others who consume large amounts of nitrate-containing vegetables, the amount could be on the order of 100 milligrams per day.

IN THE STOMACH

Nitrite is generally found in the normal human stomach at concentrations of less than one part per million. Part of this comes from saliva. There are, however, several conditions in which the stomach has nitrite concentrations of tens or even hundreds of parts per million. This occurs when the stomach—which is normally quite acid—becomes so acid that it allows the growth of certain bacteria that can reduce nitrate to nitrite.

Under these conditions, the stomach environment becomes similar to that of the

MIT

Steven Tannenbaum is studying how the body produces nitrites and what becomes of them.

mouth and even contains similar types of bacteria. Several conditions that lead to the growth of these bacteria appear to be associated with greater than ordinary risk of gastric cancer. These are all serious pathological conditions and should not be considered in the overall determination of sources of nitrite exposure to the normal, healthy individual.

IN THE INTESTINES

The human body can excrete more nitrate than that which is consumed in the diet. This excess nitrate may arise through processes that lead to the formation of nitrite in the intestinal tract. The nitrite formed in the intestines may also make a major contribution to or even exceed the other sources of nitrite to which the body is exposed.

Nitrite is formed in the small intestine and either is absorbed into the blood or reacts farther down the intestinal tract. A study has been made of fecal samples both from healthy individuals and from individuals who had part of the intestine removed. It was discovered that microorganisms in the gut are capable of synthesizing nitrite from compounds like ammonia. This nitrite may react in the gut to form N-nitroso compounds. It may be converted by bacteria

Courtesy, Gardenway Associates

Nitrates occur naturally in many vegetables.

to nitrate, which then appears in feces, or it may enter the blood. Nitrite is very unstable in the blood. It reacts with oxygen-laden hemoglobin to form methemoglobin, and is then rapidly converted to nitrate. Thus, most of the nitrite that is synthesized in the intestine ultimately winds up in the blood as nitrate.

This nitrate is indistinguishable from nitrate that has been absorbed from food. Experimentally, one could attempt to distinguish between these two sources by the use of nitrogen isotopes, and this research is planned for the near future in our laboratory.

The nitrate that is in the blood plasma is concentrated by the salivary glands and secreted into the saliva, where it continues the cycle and is converted to nitrite. Information from other researchers supports the results of our controlled metabolic studies. It suggests that gastrointestinal nitrite synthesis may be general in the human population. The stability of nitrite and its propensity to yield N-nitroso compounds is governed by a series of

complex factors. These include the physiological condition and diet of the host.

ROLE OF DIET

The effect of diet on the metabolic activities of the gastrointestinal system is far from well understood. Nitrite may be found throughout the oral cavity and gastrointestinal tract. Its formation and reactivity are related to the chemical environment at each site. The influences of such dietary variables as vitamins C and E, fiber, fat, and protein on this chemical environment and thus on possible endogenous formation of N-nitroso compounds should now be investigated.

The source of nitrites or nitrates may be either food itself or a series of reactions that begin in the intestines. However, the overall balance of relative exposure is strongly dependent on diet. Thus, individuals eating large amounts of vegetables would most probably be exposed to large amounts of nitrites. Individuals who eat small amounts of vegetables and uncured meat products would show low nitrite exposure in the upper gastrointestinal tract.

For the individual who eats a relatively balanced diet, consuming both vegetables and cured and uncured meat products, the major source of nitrite—probably by quite a large factor—is nitrate conversion in saliva. The conditions under which the nitrite reacts in the stomach must also be considered.

BLOCKING AGENTS

Dilution and competing reactions lessen the quantity of N-nitroso compounds which can be formed. Food is mixed and diluted with saliva in the mouth and further diluted with gastric juice in the stomach. Therefore, both salivary nitrite and nitrite preformed in food might be at only 25 per cent or less of their original concentration at the time they react in the stomach. Nitrites entering the stomach from consumption of cured meats are accompanied by large amounts of proteins, amino acids, and blocking agents such as vitamin C and vitamin E. These blocking agents may effectively prevent the formation of N-nitroso compounds in the stomach, just as they block the same or similar reactions in the stored product.

The nitrite which enters the stomach from saliva during a meal is subject to the restrictions described above. These considerations, however, do not apply to the condition following extensive stomach emptying. The highest measurable nitrite concentrations are found in the fasting stomach. At that time, blocking agents—usually obtained in food—may be absent from the reaction environment, and there is correspondingly less dilution. The greatest risk from nitrites may arise from the presence of certain drugs or chemicals with high nitrogen contents in the absence of food or a suitable blocking agent.

OPTIMAL DIET?

We are all exposed to carcinogens in our environment, some of them manufactured and others of natural origin. To this already significant burden, we must now add those carcinogens formed by endogenous synthesis of nitrites and nitrates into nitroso-carcinogenic compounds. There is also residual-food-additive nitrite. However, one must

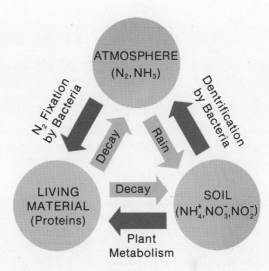

Nitrogen compounds are widespread in the environment—in the air, in the soil, in many of the foods we eat.

conclude that the relative risk of nitrite from cured meats—which, remember, also contain a blocking agent—is much less than the relative risk from nitrite produced within the body.

Does this mean we cannot alter or control the endogenous processes which could potentially lead to formation of carcinogens? On the contrary, the available evidence suggests that the endogenous nitrite-forming processes can be blocked or minimized through diet. The consumption of quantities of vitamins C and E in excess of the normal dietary intake inhibits the nitrite-forming process. How much of these substances should we take and in what form? Is there an optimal diet to minimize nitrite and nitrosamine formation? These are questions that can be answered only by further research □

SELECTED READINGS

"Bringing home the nitrite-less bacon" by N. Glick. *FDA Consumer*, May 1979.

"Sodium nitrite in the stew" by S. Neustadtl. *Technology Review*, February 1979.

"Use of nitrite in meat" by R. Cassens and others. *BioScience*, October 1978.

WINNING THE BATTLE AGAINST HEART DISEASE

by Anne K. Shelly

TAKE heart! Heart disease, the number-one killer in the United States, is on the decline. Together the U.S. public, acting on information gleaned from years of research, and physicians, armed with better methods of diagnosis and treatment, have turned the tide against this killer.

Coronary heart disease is the most deadly type of heart disease. It results from the clogging and narrowing of the large arteries that supply the heart with oxygen-bearing blood. The process can be gradual, with the heart slowly starving from lack of oxygen, or it can be sudden, with a clot forming and cutting off the blood supply abruptly. Atherosclerosis, a disease in which deposits of cholesterol and other fatty materials build up on the walls of the arteries, and spasm, or constriction of the artery wall, are two major factors responsible for coronary heart disease. Although coronary heart disease still claims some 600,000 lives each year in the United States, the death rate is down—23 per cent since 1968.

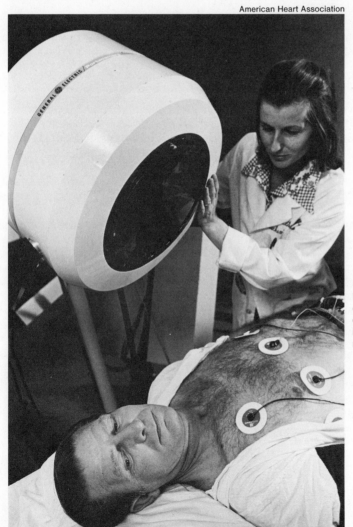

Improvements in diagnosis are helping to lower the heart disease death rate. Here a myocardial scintigram will provide an image of the heart muscle and reveal if there is tissue damage.

CHANGES IN BEHAVIOR

"The decline in the death rate is due to many factors—changes in the way potential heart attack victims are acting, better diagnostic techniques, improved hospital care, better and more ingenious types of surgery, faster ambulance service, and new drugs," says Dr. Kanu Chatterjee, associate chairman of cardiology at the University of California at San Francisco. "By applying information from research now in progress on atherosclerosis and other coronary problems, such as spasm, we can expect an even greater decline in the death rate over the next ten years," he continues.

Men between the ages of 45 and 54 are most susceptible to coronary heart disease. The average U.S. male has one chance in three of having a heart attack or other major cardiac problem before he reaches 60. Women are far better off statistically.

According to the National Heart Association, people who have a high risk of heart attack are those who have a family history of heart disease, are diabetic, have high blood pressure, have a high level of cholesterol in the blood, are heavy smokers, are obese, have chest pains, or have had a previous heart attack. These potential victims have been warned to smoke less, keep their weight under control, keep their blood pressure levels normal, minimize stress, get more exercise, and maintain a diet low in fats. Although there is considerable doubt about whether or not exercise decreases a person's chances of having a heart attack, many physicians continue to recommend it as a way of contributing to overall good health.

"Potential heart attack victims are listening to what cardiologists have been telling them," says Chatterjee. "Not only is the public health-conscious, it is coronary-conscious. People are practicing good nutrition, having their blood pressure checked regularly, and going to get medical treatment when they recognize early warning signals."

One of the most promising changes in behavior that has been adopted by a large segment of the public is in diet. There has been a shift away from food high in cholesterol—eggs, red meat, butter, and other dairy products—and toward low-cholesterol

American Heart Association
Pacemakers are just one of the ways heart attack victims are being helped to lead productive lives.

foods—fruits, vegetables, fish, and poultry.

There does, however, remain room for improvement. To cite just one example: women are smoking more.

EARLY DETECTION

The development of new detection methods is also helping to lower the heart disease death rate. Early detection is particularly important in fighting heart disease. Of those who die of a heart attack before reaching the hospital, roughly one half did not recognize early symptoms or simply ignored them.

One new diagnostic technique is myocardial profusion imaging. Radioactive substances are used to label drugs that are then injected into the patient's bloodstream. A special scanning device then tracks and measures the flow of blood through the heart—while the patient is exercising on a treadmill and also while the patient is resting. If the scan shows that the blood is circulating properly while the patient is at rest but improperly while he or she is exercising, then narrowing or blockage of an artery is suspected. The test is particularly important because it provides examination of the heart under stress—in this case, exercise—when heart attacks often strike. Because of the extreme sensitivity of the scanning instruments and sophistication of the radioactive labels, the patient is exposed to less radiation than he or she would be during one standard X ray.

Echocardiology is also helping to detect heart disease early. Ultrahigh-frequency sound waves—sound waves beyond the hearing range of humans—are used to create an image of the heart and coronary arteries that can show if abnormal changes are taking place.

Both new techniques are relatively simple and painless—much more so than angiography, the traditional method of viewing the arteries and heart that involved the insertion of a catheter into an artery.

CONTINUING RESEARCH

"To continue with the successful fight against heart disease, we need a better understanding of atherosclerosis and other conditions that contribute to heart disease such as spasm," says Chatterjee. One study to determine if heart attacks can be prevented by lowering cholesterol intake is being carried out at the Universities of Southern California, Minnesota, and Arkansas. It will involve more than 1,000 patients. One half of them will have their cholesterol intake lowered through diet restrictions and drugs. The other half will undergo a bypass—but not removal—of the segment of the small intestine that absorbs cholesterol from food. This bypass will decrease the amount of cholesterol that is released into the blood. University of Southern California researchers David Blankenhorn and Albert Yellin will then try to determine the effectiveness of the two techniques. With the aid of a computer process known as image processing that enhances X rays, they will measure changes in the build-up of fatty tissues on the blood-vessel walls. The computer can analyze the edges and roughness of vessels and determine the degree of blockage more accurately than can a person subjectively estimating changes with the naked eye.

Researchers are also investigating the phenomenon of spasm—constriction of the artery wall inhibiting blood flow to the heart. People can have both atherosclerosis and spasm at the same time. In fact, a spasm may occur at the point where the artery is most clogged and narrowed. Researchers believe that spasm is produced by a complicated interplay of factors in the blood and inner walls of the arteries and a breakdown in the sympathetic nervous system responsible for controlling the contractions and dilations of blood vessels.

As of yet there is no defined treatment for spasm. Angina pectoris—chest pain caused by coronary-artery spasm—is treated with nitroglycerin and prevented by long-acting nitrates such as Isordil or NiroBid. There is new interest in drugs known as "calcium antagonists" that control the amount of energy in a cell and thereby control the cell's ability to contract.

FEWER HEART ATTACKS?

"Besides basic research on heart disease and atherosclerosis, we need to determine if, with the decline in the death rate, there has been a decline in heart attacks," says Dr. Richard Havlick, medical officer at the National Heart, Lung and Blood Institute.

"The decline in the death rate indicates that both the American public and researchers are doing many things right," says Havlick. "At least people are not dying from heart attacks. But are we stopping people from having heart attacks?"

"If we are not, then good nutrition, reducing smoking, and maintaining a diet low in cholesterol is not stopping people from having heart attacks. If we find that people are having the same number of heart attacks, it would indicate that medical technology is helping them to survive. If, on the other hand, there has been a corresponding drop in the number of heart attacks, then the many sacrifices made by the public have been worthwhile in the fight against heart disease" □

 SELECTED READINGS

Proceedings of the Conference on the Decline in Coronary Heart Disease Mortality, National Institutes of Health, 1979.

"Good news from the house on Lincoln Street" by Walter McQuade. *Fortune,* January 14, 1980.

"Big squeeze: coronary spasms as a cause of heart attacks." *Time,* November 26, 1979.

"Aspirin: an Rx for heart attacks?" by P. Bonventre and D. Shapiro. *Newsweek,* October 22, 1979.

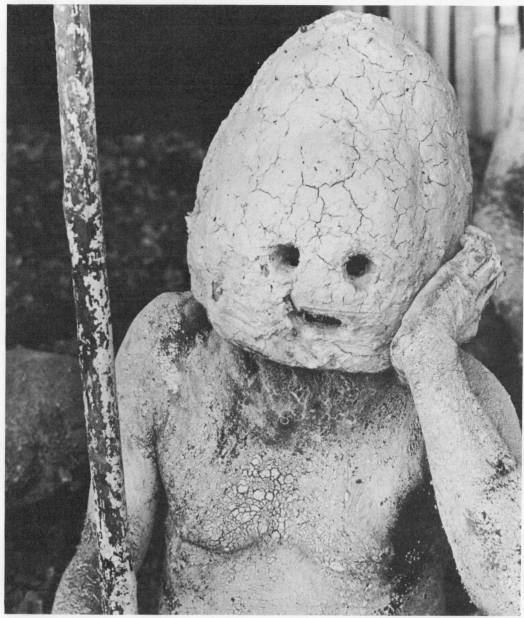

Barbara Kirk/Peter Arnold

The Asaro Valley people of New Guinea make mud masks and cover their bodies with mud for a ritual dance, whose origins are romantic but uncertain.

MAN & HIS WORLD

CP Photo

President Arturo Tanco addresses the opening session of the World Food Council meeting in Ottawa. The Council agreed on concrete approaches to the world food problem.

University of Paris researcher Bernard Vandermeersch believes that Cro-Magnon man may have evolved at least partially in the Middle East and then migrated to Europe where remains of his culture are found.

John H. Douglas, *Science News*

Food and Population. World grain production was moderately higher—1,538,000,000 tons—in 1979 than in 1978, and the world population growth rate dropped 0.1 per cent, to about 1.8. There was, however, no evidence of a significant worldwide decline in the birth rate, and available grain was still not equitably distributed among the peoples of the world.

In July 1979 the United Nations sponsored a World Conference on Agrarian Reform and Rural Development (WCARRD). Representatives of 140 countries, two dozen U.N. agencies, and scores of non-governmental organizations and institutes met in Rome and, after more than one week of debate, unanimously adopted a draft Declaration of Principles and Program of Action. They stated unambiguously that a more equitable distribution of land—agrarian reform—is a prerequisite for rural development and that the latter requires a fundamental redistribution of political and economic power as well.

WCARRD took place five months after the two-year-long international wheat negotiations, aimed at setting up an international grain reserve system, had adjourned in Geneva without positive results. Importing and exporting countries, rich and poor, were unable to reach agreement on the size of grain reserve, the rules for its operation, or the price at which wheat should be released from the reserve.

In September 1979 the World Food Council, set up by the Rome Food Conference of 1974, met in Ottawa, Canada, and approved two concrete approaches to the world food problem—*a*, an emphasis on long-range strategies to relieve hunger and its causes and *b*, an exploration of food entitlement schemes, such as rationing programs, subsidized purchases, and food stamps, to meet the immediate needs of hungry people. The Council's program for 1980 is focusing on these two items. ■ The International Fund for Agricultural Development, the other major entity created by the 1974 Food Conference, continued in its work—lending money to spur agricultural development. It has now lent a total of $493,000,000 of its initial $1,000,000,000 fund, and expects to make additional commitments of $400,000,000 in 1980. The fund will then need replenishment.

In the United States the Presidential Commission on World Hunger delivered a preliminary report to President Carter in December 1979. The report noted that hunger is still widespread, that it is caused by poverty, and that any remedy must attack the cause—that is, must concentrate on increasing food production and improving food and income distribution in food-deficient developing countries. The emphasis, the Commission said, must be on the small farmer and the poor.

Martin McLaughlin

Anthropology and Archaeology. During 1979 and early 1980 there were new discoveries about human ancestry, some exciting archeological finds, and continuing work on primate behavior.

Scientists have long been seeking clues to the early ancestors of both apes and humans. Elwyn Simons, head of Duke University's Center for the Study of Primate Biology and History, and his colleagues have reported about just such an ancestor. After analyzing a dozen jaw fossils found since 1977 in Egypt's Fayum Depression, they describe a tree-dwelling, vegetarian, and day-active ape about the size of the house cat as the common ancestor of both apes and humans. Named *Aegyptopithecus,* this creature is some 30,000,000 years back on the road to human evolution.

Reports published in 1978 about creatures much farther along the evolutionary line to humans continued to be the subject of study and controversy. Researchers wonder if the 3,500,000-year-old footprints of a walking bipedal hominid found by Dr. Mary Leakey in Tanzania and the remains of a 3,000,000-to-4,000,000-year-old population of hominids with both ape and human characteristics found by Dr. D. Johanson in the Afar region of Ethiopia represent the same species and how these finds are related to each other and to other hominid species.

Meanwhile the oldest footprints of a creature much closer to modern man, one classified in the same genus—*Homo*—as modern man, were reported discovered. A team headed by Leo F. LaPorte and Anna K. Behrensmeyer of the University of California at Santa Cruz found seven footprints in 1,500,000-year-old volcanic rock along Lake Turkana in northern Kenya. The prints, 26 to 27 centimeters long and thought to belong to a creature about 1.5 meters tall and weighing about 55 kilograms, were found with fossils of hippopotamuses and large birds. Sharp-edged tools characteristic of *Homo erectus* sites elsewhere were found nearby.

Closer still to modern humans, scientists continued seeking clues to the origin of Cro-Magnon man, a direct ancestor of modern man that appeared rather suddenly in Europe about 35,000 years ago as Neanderthal man seemed to disappear. Excavations of 50,000-to-70,000-year-old skeletons at Qafzeh cave near Nazareth, Israel, have led University of Paris researcher Bernard Vandermeersch to propose that Cro-Magnon man may have evolved at least partially in the Middle East and then migrated to Europe.

The search for America's first inhabitants has become one of the most exciting—and controversial—fields of archaeology. The oldest widely accepted finds tell of a Clovis culture some 11,500 to 12,000 years ago. Some researchers believe that there were no inhabitants in America before that, while others, citing evidence from several disputed finds, believe that there were pre-Clovis peoples. If there were earlier peoples— what were they like? where did they come from? Continuing digs and improved dating techniques will, it is hoped, provide some answers. ■
More recent North American history was revealed when University of South Carolina archaeologists unearthed the remains of a 16th-century Spanish fort and part of the town of Santa Elena, founded in 1566, on Parris Island, South Carolina.

Anthropologists continued primate studies during the year. Baby orangutans have been found to be strikingly similar in development to human infants for the first two years. Like human infants, baby orangs progress through stages of reflex behavior, self-awareness, reaching out and grasping, experimentation, and simple problem solving. The rate of development is, however, different, as is vocal behavior. Orangutans do not progress from crying through babbling to speaking words.

Barbara Tchabovsky

San Francisco Zoo

Cute as babies—and like them, too, in development. For the first two years baby orangs progress through developmental stages strikingly similar to those of human infants.

This 1,500,000-year-old footprint found in Kenya is thought to belong to a close relative of modern man— probably *Homo erectus.*

Leo F. LaPorte

Stewart M. Green

The Fajada butte, site of the Anasazi sun dagger.

THE ANASAZI SUN DAGGER

by Kendrick Frazier

ON the morning of June 29, 1977, a group of amateur archaeologists fanned out through Chaco Canyon National Monument in northwestern New Mexico to work on cataloging ancient Indian rock art. One of them, a Washington, D.C., artist, Anna Sofaer, climbed Fajada, a 130-meter-high sandstone butte that stands like a sentinel at the entrance of the canyon. She climbed a steep, narrow rock chimney on the north side of the butte, avoiding the still-sluggish rattlesnakes lying in the morning sun near the summit. Then she worked her way cautiously along a ledge to the southeast face. All the while she scanned the walls for petroglyphs, rock carvings etched long ago by the Anasazi—the "Ancient Ones"—former inhabitants of this remote, arid canyon country.

Up ahead she recognized the vertical stack of sandstone slabs, three of them, leaning against a cliff face. She had seen them before and knew that two petroglyphs were cut into the cliff wall behind the slabs. One of the petroglyphs is a large nine-ring spiral, and the other a smaller, three-ring spiral with a tail. It was close to 11 A.M. Her timing, it

later became clear, proved amazingly lucky. For as she gazed behind the slabs, she saw in that shaded recess not only the two petroglyphs but this time also a bright, vertical, dagger-shaped shaft of sunlight moving slowly down the larger petroglyph.

"It moved as though alive," she recalls. She watched, fascinated, as the dagger of light passed just a short distance to the right of the spiral's center. In about 12 minutes, the dagger traversed completely down the spiral and disappeared.

A UNIQUE SUN CALENDAR

Sofaer was witnessing the working of a unique sun calendar constructed by the Anasazi sometime before their decline around A.D. 1200. Indeed, Sofaer and others later concluded that the astronomical system she stumbled across that June morning—a little more than a week after summer solstice—was extraordinary. It was at least equal in precision to any other ancient device yet found in the New World or the Old.

Most ancient devices use architectural features for alignment and take their orientation from points on the horizon where the sun rises and sets. However, Fajada, in contrast, uses sunlight itself as an indicator. It is oriented to the changing height of the midday sun through the year. Moreover, Fajada not only marks the solstices and equinoxes with specific images, it appears to be able to predict lunar eclipses as well. Subtly constructed despite its haphazard appearance, the site reveals that the Anasazi achieved a stunningly high level of geometrical and astronomical sophistication. The "Ancient Ones," therefore, might also be called the "Cosmological Ones."

SOLSTICE MARKER

It took Sofaer and two colleagues almost two years to unravel the exact workings of the site. In precision, accuracy, and functional versatility, Fajada ranks high among ancient astronomical structures such as Stonehenge and those of Babylon.

That first day, Sofaer, who had recently studied the numerous ways ancient Indians of the Southwest kept track of the seasons, suspected at once she had found some kind of midday solstice marker. To prove it she would have to return on the day of the summer solstice and see whether the shaft of light descended exactly down the petroglyph's center. Accordingly, a year later she came back to Fajada, this time with two colleagues: Volker Zinser, an architect, and Rolf M. Sinclair, a physicist with the National Science Foundation. The team brought with it a battery of cameras.

On the morning of June 21, 1978—the day of the summer solstice—they focused the cameras on the petroglyphs. To their jubilation, the dagger of light appeared and descended vertically precisely through the center of the larger spiral petroglyph. The hypothesis that Fajada worked as a midday solstitial calendar had been dramatically proved. Yet there must be more to the system than that, reasoned the researchers. What happens during the rest of the year?

A SEASONAL CALENDAR

Sofaer and her colleagues decided to find out. As a result, they climbed the butte to observe events at the solstices and equinoxes. In addition, they arranged for regular, detailed photographic records. On the twenty-first of each month from June through December, a photographer made the difficult climb with ropes to ascend through the rock chimney. He amassed an invaluable photographic record of the moving patterns of light at 30-second intervals on each one of those days.

These sequential photographs provide visual evidence that this seemingly simple assemblage of slabs and petroglyphs marks the seasons. It is a calendar. It divides the year into four quarters, with a unique pattern marking the beginning of each. And it can also be used to give a rough idea of the number of days elapsed between these four times.

"The singling out of the equinoxes and solstices by special markings is achieved by the entire system acting as a whole—slabs, petroglyphs, and sun," says Sofaer and her colleagues. "Intermediate dates could be found by recalling the exact patterns formed in previous years or by counting days after a better-marked quarter point."

From a chance sighting of this "light dagger," archaeologists learned that the Anasazi were sophisticated astronomers.

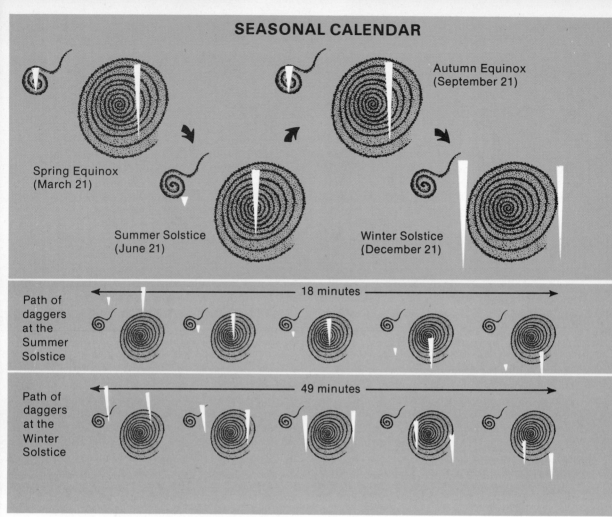

Art by Mary Challinor

The movement of a shaft of light across a stone slab marks time on the Anasazi calendar.

The patterns and movements of light on the spiral at these four key times of the year are striking. At summer solstice as the light dagger passes halfway through the spiral, the beam is centered exactly both left to right and top to bottom within it.

At midday on the equinoxes, September 21 and March 21, the light beam descends through the point between the fourth and fifth of the nine turns of the spiral outward from the center toward the right edge. "Thus at these mid-points between summer and winter solstices," says Sofaer, "the light bisects the nine turns on the spiral's right side."

THE SMALL SPIRAL

Something else also comes into play at these times: a more specific marker of the equinoxes. To the upper left of the large spi-

ral sits the smaller one. At equinox, a second light beam, this one wider, shorter, and wedge-shaped, is created by sunlight passing through an opening between the center slab and the left-hand slab. (The longer shaft of light that shines on the large spiral comes through a narrow opening between the center and right-hand slab.) At equinox, this new wedge of light descends exactly through the center of the smaller spiral.

At winter solstice, December 22, still a third kind of phenomenon occurs, perhaps the most striking of all. Throughout the fall, the descending long light shaft appears slightly more to the right of the spiral each day. At winter solstice it has moved far enough to the right that it just touches the right edge of the spiral. Concurrently the smaller wedge of light increases in length and moves to the right. At winter solstice, it is exactly tangent to the left edge of the large spiral.

At all other times of the year some light passes through the large spiral. But at winter solstice, the shortest day of the year, two bands of light frame the spiral.

From December to June the light beams move leftward again. Since the sun is retracing its path, the effects are reversed.

AN 18-MINUTE SUN DAGGER

Clearly the Fajada calendar could not have been easy to design or construct. The cliff face on which the spiral petroglyphs are carved faces southeast. The three sandstone slabs range in height from two to three meters and in thickness from 20 to 45 centimeters. They weigh about two metric tons each. The slabs are only roughly parallel. They are just far enough apart that for 18 minutes late in the morning at summer solstice a small amount of sunlight passes through the gap between the center and right-hand slab. The sunlight illuminates the cliff where the large petroglyph is carved.

The downward movement of the light beam at this time is remarkable. The sun is moving horizontally in the sky during those 18 minutes, yet the light beam progresses vertically.

The vertical movement of the light dagger is possible only because of the details of the double-curved surfaces of the slabs. As the sun moves across the sky different surfaces of the slabs' upper edges come into play to keep the light beam's motion vertical.

When the two daggerlike shafts of light frame the large spiral (shadowed area), it's winter solstice—December 22. The beams are created by sunlight passing through openings between sandstone slabs. Their movement is kept vertical by reflections off the edges and curved surfaces of the slabs.

No chance occurrence here. The three stone slabs, each about two metric tons, were taken by the Anasazi from the cliff wall and intentionally erected, leaning against the cliff face.

Karl Kernberger, © The Anasazi Project Inc.
The three slabs viewed from the cliff side. They are roughly parallel.

Sofaer and her colleagues built clay models and used a flashlight to duplicate the effect. After considerable work, they succeeded.

BY CHANCE OR DESIGN?

Theoretically, it could all be coincidence. Theoretically. The coincidence hypothesis requires that the three slabs fell naturally into their present vertical position. Then some Anasazi carved a spiral on the cliff face to make use of the light dagger.

This hypothesis was shattered in April 1979 by a geological solution to the puzzling question of where the three rock slabs came from. As long as there was a chance that the slabs had fallen from the cliff face just above them, the coincidence theory lived.

It was put to rest when a geologist found the original location of the slabs on the cliff wall. They had been too low and too far to the left to have fallen naturally into the present position. They had to have been intentionally erected.

CHACO CANYON

Fajada is in Chaco Canyon, a shallow, 32-kilometer-long depression in the center of the San Juan Basin of northwestern New Mexico. The basin extends between the San Juan river and the Continental Divide. It's a timeless land of wide vistas unimpeded by trees. Its soft, dry soil supports a meager retinue of hardy plants like greasewood and rabbit brush. The few carved washes are devoid of water except after the occasional rains that bring the area's limited rainfall. It is hot in the summer and cold in the winter. The main wildlife consists of an occasional rabbit, gopher, or rattlesnake.

This basin does not have an environment that appears particularly promising for the emergence of a socially complex, technologically adept civilization. Yet the Anasazi (the modern Navajo name) prospered in this setting from about A.D. 800 to 1250. Indeed, not only did they prosper, they produced just such an advanced civilization, focused to a large degree on Chaco Canyon. It is these Anasazi who are believed to have constructed the butte-top solar calendar.

THE ANASAZI INDIANS

Harsh it may seem, yet the basin has been occupied with some degree of success for several thousand years. First it was inhabited by hunter-gatherers, then by the first permanent Anasazi Indian dwellers beginning around A.D. 600 and continuing till gradual abandonment about 650 years later. A sparse population of Navajo Indians is now scattered through the area, although none live in Chaco Canyon itself.

Anasazi life and culture throughout the Four Corners region of Arizona, Utah, Colorado, and New Mexico has been reasonably well delineated. The men were about 163 centimeters tall, the women about 152 centimeters. They lived in houses or apartments (pueblos) with walls made of flat stones. The inside walls were often smoothly plastered. Heavy wood beams supported roofs and ceilings made of smaller wood strips and branches.

The people were expert farmers, adept at eking out crops on, at best, semiarid land. Using wooden digging sticks and a hoe-shovel combination, they planted and grew crops of corn, beans, and squash. Their diets also included rabbit and occasional larger game. They used bows and arrows, pottery and baskets, and carrying sacks and sleeping pads made of yucca fiber. They wore breechcloths and sandals made of yucca.

This description generally fits all the Anasazi. In and around Chaco Canyon, an unusual flowering of their culture seems to have taken place.

THE CHACO BUILDERS

The size of the rooms in the pueblos increased. The architecture and masonry in the buildings became more refined. In scope, massiveness, complexity, and refinement, the houses built in the canyon were unlike any others in the Southwest. One building, the 800-room, multistory Pueblo Bonito was the largest building in North America until 1882. (Then, a larger building was erected in New York City.)

The Chacoans built irrigation systems with canals and small dams to collect and channel the small runoff. They constructed a remarkable system of about 2,000 kilometers of roadways. The full extent of the network of roads is only now being charted.

These roadways have clearly demonstrated the ability of the Chacoans to engineer sophisticated projects. They have also provided some of the strongest evidence that Chaco formed an essential part of a highly interactive society of people in the San Juan basin.

Several features of the roads are unusual. Many of them are ten meters wide. For people who traveled exclusively on foot, this seems an extraordinary width. They are well surveyed and engineered. Great quantities of topsoil were scraped from the surface and mounded along their edges. In some places stone masonry curbs were erected. The roads are perfectly straight for kilometers at a stretch with a frequent and somewhat puzzling disregard of topographic obstacles. Causeways were built over low spots. When the roads had to ascend or descend a mesa wall, broad stairways were cut into the sandstone. Many of them are still clearly visible (and climbable) along the sides of Chaco Canyon.

Most of these roads are today invisible or barely seen from the ground. Where the soil was cut especially deep or where the stone curbing was especially high, sections of the roads can be seen. But there are many clues to their existence. These are best discovered through sophisticated analysis of aerial photographs, followed by documentation from the ground.

The roadway networks connect 30 to 40 population centers throughout the San Juan basin. Roads also lead to resource areas around the perimeter of the basin where trees were plentiful, where the soil was better for agriculture, or where there were deposits of chert, for chipping stone tools, or trachyte, for tempering pottery. It is now assumed that the tens of thousands of ponderosa pines used for beams in the multiroom pueblos of Chaco Canyon were carried along the roadways from mountain forests 30 to 50 kilometers away.

The Anasazi were accomplished builders. Excavations have revealed complex buildings, roadways, irrigation systems, and dams.

Stewart M. Green

Stewart M. Green

Unexcavated ruins in Chaco Canyon, the site of the most sophisticated building.

These kinds of evidence indicate a highly organized society, involved in engineering works and the trade and transportation of goods. W. James Judge, director of the Chaco Center, believes the canyon may have been a region-wide trade-redistribution center, with full-time administrative specialists running the operation. Here food and goods would have been stored and rerouted as necessary. Chaco Canyon appears to have been a means of efficiently managing the exchange of the region's limited resources. "The whole system," says Chaco Center staff archaeologist Thomas Windes, "staggers the imagination."

COMING TRADE-OFFS

The passage of time has changed and destroyed many of the remains of this system. Now there are added dangers. More and more scientists and curious visitors are poking around. What if one of the sandstone slabs becomes just a little dislodged? A priceless reminder of the skill of the Anasazi would be lost. The greatest danger, however, may lie in man's quest for energy sources. The San Juan basin is thought to contain one-sixth of the world's uranium and one-fourth of the strippable coal in the United States.

There is little doubt that the San Juan basin is going to be exploited. Of course, exploitation of resources is prohibited within national monument boundaries. But numerous archaeological remains are on private land, which will be mined or stripped.

The ancient network of roads will certainly be disrupted, and blasting will take its toll on standing structures. The sun calendar seems safe in the center of the national monument, but only time can tell in the coming trade-offs between energy needs and cultural preservation □

 SELECTED READINGS

"The archaeological wonders of Chaco Canyon" by M. Gardner. *Sierra,* November/December 1979.

"Solstice-watchers of Chaco" by K. Frazier. *Science News,* August 26, 1978.

"A unique solar marking construct" by A. Sofaer, V. Zinser, and R. Sinclair. *Science,* October 18, 1979.

The works of Edgar Rice Burroughs, shown here with his son John, illustrator of some of his father's works, introduced Carl Sagan and many others to science fiction.

GROWING UP WITH SCIENCE FICTION

by Carl Sagan

BY the time I was 10 I had decided—in almost total ignorance of the difficulty of the problem—that the universe was full up. There were too many places for this to be the only inhabited planet. And, from the variety of life on earth (trees looked pretty different from most of my friends), I figured life elsewhere would seem very strange. I tried hard to imagine what that life would be like. But despite my best efforts I always produced a kind of terrestrial chimaera, a blend of existing plants or animals.

About this time a friend introduced me to the Mars novels of Edgar Rice Burroughs. I had not thought much about Mars before,

but here, presented before me in the adventures of John Carter, was another inhabited world, breathtakingly fleshed out: ancient sea bottoms, great canal pumping stations, and a variety of beings, some of them exotic. There were, for example, the eight-legged beasts of burden, the thoats.

These novels were exhilarating to read—at first. But slowly, doubts began to gnaw. The plot surprise in the first John Carter novel I read hinged on his forgetting that the year is longer on Mars than on earth. But it seemed to me that if you go to another planet, one of the first things you check out is the length of the day and the year.

Popular Cultural Library

The short stories in *Astounding Science Fiction* got many young people hooked—and thinking.

BURROUGHS MADE US THINK

Then there were incidental remarks, which at first seemed stunning, but on sober reflection proved disappointing. For example, Burroughs casually comments that on Mars there are two more primary colors than on earth. Many long minutes did I spend with my eyes closed, fiercely contemplating a new primary color. But it would always be something familiar, like a murky brown or plum. How could there be another primary

color on Mars, much less two? What was a primary color? Was it something to do with physics or something to do with physiology? I decided that Burroughs might not have known what he was talking about, but he certainly made his readers think.

The following summer, by sheerest accident, I stumbled upon a magazine called *Astounding Science Fiction* in a neighborhood candy store. A glance at the cover and a quick riffle through the interior showed me it was what I had been looking for. With some effort I managed to scrape together the purchase price, opened the magazine at random, sat down on a bench just in front of the store, and read my first modern science-fiction short story, "Pete Can Fix It" by Raymond F. Jones, a gentle account of time travel into a postnuclear-war holocaust. I had known about the atom bomb—I remember an excited friend explaining to me that it was made of atoms—but this was the first I had seen about the social implications of nuclear weapons. It got me thinking.

I found I was hooked. Each month I eagerly awaited the arrival of *Astounding*. I read Verne and Wells, read, cover-to-cover, the first two science-fiction anthologies that I was able to find, devised scorecards, similar to those I was fond of making for baseball, on the quality of the stories I read. Many ranked high in asking interesting questions but low in answering them.

There is still a part of me that is 10 years old. But by and large I'm older. My critical faculties, and perhaps even my literary tastes, have improved. I can no longer manage credulous acceptance as well as I used to. The plot of Larry Niven's "Neutron Star" hinges on the astonishing tidal forces exerted by a strong gravitational field. But we are asked to believe that hundreds or thousands of years from now, at a time of casual interstellar space flight, such tidal forces have been forgotten. We are asked to believe that the first probe of a neutron star is a manned rather than an unmanned spacecraft. We are asked too much. In a novel of ideas the ideas have to work.

In Douglas Trumbull's technically proficient science-fiction film "Silent Running," the trees are dying in vast, spaceborne, closed ecological systems on the way to Saturn. After weeks of painstaking study and agonizing searches through botany texts, the solution is found: Plants, it turns out, need sunlight. Trumbull's characters are able to build interplanetary cities but have forgotten the inverse-square law. I was willing to overlook the portrayal of the rings of Saturn as pastel-colored gases, but not this.

UNBELIEVABLE STAR TREK

I have the same trouble with "Star Trek," which I know has a wide following and which some thoughtful friends tell me I should view allegorically and not literally. But when astronauts from earth set down on some far distant planet and find human beings there in the midst of a conflict between two nuclear superpowers—which call themselves the Yangs and Coms, or their phonetic equivalents—the suspension of disbelief crumbles. In a global terrestrial society centuries in the future, the ship's officers are embarrassingly Anglo-American. In fact, only 2 of 12 or 14 interstellar vessels are given non-English names, Kongo and Potemkin.

The idea of a successful cross between a Vulcan and an earthling simply ignores what we know of molecular biology and Darwinian evolution. (As I have remarked elsewhere, such a cross is about as likely as the successful mating of a man and a petunia.) I have similar problems with films in which spiders 10 meters tall are menacing the cities of earth: Since insects and arachnids breathe by diffusion, such marauders would asphyxiated before they could savage their first metropolis.

I believe that the same thirst for wonder is inside me that was there when I was 10. But I have since learned a little bit about how the world is really put together. I find that science fiction has led me to science. I find science more subtle, more intricate, and more awesome than much of science fiction. It also has the additional virtue of being true.

NEW FINDINGS

Think of some of the scientific findings of the last few decades:

• There are particles that pass effortlessly through the solid earth so that we detect as many of them coming up through our feet as down from the sky.

• The continents are moving on a vast con-

The late-19th-century works of Jules Verne (left)—*Twenty Thousand Leagues Under the Sea* and *Journey to the Center of the Earth*, for example—and of H.G. Wells—*The Time Machine*—have remained popular among science fiction buffs and the general public.

veyer belt with the Himalayas produced by a collision of India with Asia.

• Mars is covered with ancient dry river valleys.

• Chimpanzees can learn languages of many hundreds of words, understand abstract concepts, and construct new grammatical usages.

• All life on earth runs off one particular molecule that contains all the hereditary information and is able to make identical copies of itself.

• In the constellation Cygnus there is a double star, one of whose components has such a high gravity that light cannot escape from it (it may be blazing with visible radiation on the inside but it is invisible from the outside).

In the face of all this (and there is much more, equally fascinating), many of the standard ideas of science fiction seem to me pale by comparison. I see the relative absence of these findings in science fiction, and the distortions of scientific thinking often encountered in science fiction as terrible wasted opportunities. Real science is as amenable to exciting and engrossing fiction as fake science. I think it is important to exploit every opportunity to convey scientific ideas in a civilization based upon science but somehow unable to communicate what science is about.

THE BEST SCIENCE FICTION IS EXCELLENT

However, the best of science fiction remains very good indeed. There are stories that are tautly constructed. They are so rich in the accommodating details of an unfamiliar society that they sweep me along before I have even a chance to be critical. Such works include Robert Heinlein's "The Door into Summer"; Alfred Bester's "The Stars My Destination" and his "The Demolished Man"; Jack Finney's "Time and Again"; Frank Herbert's "Dune"; and Walter M. Miller's "A Canticle for Leibowitz." You can ruminate over the ideas in these books.

Heinlein's asides on the feasibility and social utility of household robots wear exceedingly well over the intervening years. The insights into terrestrial ecology that are provided by hypothetical extraterrestrial ecologies, as in "Dune," perform, I think, an important social service. "He Who Shrank," by Henry Hasse, presents an entrancing cosmological speculation that is being seriously revived today, the idea of an infinite regress of universes. In other words, each of our elementary particles is a universe, one level down from the previous one, and we are an elementary particle in the next universe up.

A rare few science-fiction novels combine a standard science-fiction theme with a

Jan Kay Klein

Science fiction can convey bits and pieces of knowledge. For example, in "And He Built a Crooked House," Robert Heinlein provided an easy-to-understand introduction to four-dimensional geometry.

deep human sensitivity. I am thinking, for example, of Algis Budrys's "Rogue Moon," Ray Bradbury's "The Martian Chronicles," and many of the works of Theodore Sturgeon—including "To Here and the Easel," a stunning portrait of personality dissociation as perceived from the inside. Isaac Asimov's story "Breeds There a Man" provided a poignant insight into the emotional stress and sense of isolation of many of the best theoretical scientists. Arthur Clarke's "The Nine Billion Names of God" introduced many Western readers to an intriguing speculation

Science-fiction ideas are widely dispersed, and found today in somewhat different guises. For one, we have science-fiction writers such as Asimov and Clarke providing, in nonfictional form, cogent and sometimes brilliant summaries of many aspects of science and society. Some contemporary scientists are introduced to a vaster public by science fiction. For example, in the thoughtful novel "The Listeners" by James Gunn, we find those directing a major radio search for extraterrestrial intelligence 50 years from now comparing their progress with the ideas

NASA

Older science fiction writers dreamed up a canal-covered Martian surface. What will future writers say about the rock-strewn plains found by Viking spacecraft?

in Oriental religions.

One of the great benefits of science fiction is that it can convey bits and pieces, hints and phrases of knowledge unknown or inaccessible to the reader. Heinlein's "And He Built a Crooked House" was, for many readers, the first introduction to four-dimensional geometry that held any promise of comprehensibility. One science-fiction work offers as a ditty the mathematics of Einstein's last attempt at a unified field theory. Another presents an important equation in population genetics.

of my colleague Frank Drake: "Drake! What did he know?" A great deal, it turns out.

THE ANCIENT ASTRONAUTS AND UFO's

We also find straight science fiction changed into a vast proliferation of writings, belief systems, and organizations. One science-fiction writer, L. Ron Hubbard, has founded a successful cult called Scientology. Classic science-fiction ideas are now institutionalized in pseudoscientific UFO and ancient-astronaut belief systems—although Stanley Weinbaum (in "The Valley of

Dreams") did it better as well as earlier than Erich Von Däniken (author of "Chariots of the Gods?"). In "Wine of the Dreamers" by John D. MacDonald (a science-fiction writer now transformed into one of the most interesting contemporary authors of detective fiction), we find the sentence "And there are traces, in Earth mythology, . . . of great ships and chariots that crossed the sky."

R. De Witt Miller in his story "Within the Pyramid" manages to anticipate both Von Däniken and Immanuel Velikovsky, and to provide a more coherent hypothesis on the supposed extraterrestrial origin of pyramids than can be found in all the writings on ancient astronauts and pyramidology.

GUESSING REALITY

The interweaving of science and science fiction sometimes produces curious results. It is not always clear whether life imitates art or vice versa. For example, in Kurt Vonnegut Jr.'s superb epistemological novel "The Sirens of Titan," a not-altogether-inclement environment is postulated on Saturn's largest moon.

When in the last few years some planetary scientists, myself among them, presented evidence that Titan has a dense atmosphere and perhaps higher temperatures than expected, many people commented to me on the prescience of Kurt Vonnegut. He was a physics major at Cornell University and naturally knowledgeable about the latest findings in astronomy. In 1944, an atmosphere of methane was discovered on Titan, the first satellite in the solar system known to have an atmosphere. In this, as in many similar cases, art imitates life. (Many of the best science-fiction writers have science or engineering backgrounds; for example, Poul Anderson, Isaac Asimov, Arthur Clarke, and Robert Heinlein.)

In fact, our understanding of the other planets has often changed faster than their representations in science fiction. A clement twilight zone on a synchronously rotating Mercury, a swamp-and-jungle Venus, and a canal-infested Mars, while all classic science-fiction devices, are all, in fact, based upon earlier misapprehensions by planetary scientists. But as our knowledge of the planets has changed, the environments in the corresponding science-fiction stories have also changed.

Erich von Däniken

Some science fiction ideas have given birth to cults and belief systems. Followers of Erich von Däniken, author of *Chariots of the Gods,* for example, believe in ancient astronauts that helped early earthlings.

Star Wars' Darth Vader used extrasensory powers to get what he wanted. A foreshadowing of the future? Or just plain fiction?

It is satisfyingly rare to find a science-fiction story written today that posits algae farms on the surface of Venus. (Incidentally, the UFO-contact mythologizers are slower to change, and we can still find accounts of flying saucers from a Venus that is populated by beautiful human beings in long, white robes inhabiting a kind of Cytherean Garden of Eden. The 500°-Celsius temperatures of Venus give us one way of checking such stories.) Likewise, the idea of a "space warp" is a hoary science-fiction standby, but it did not arise in science fiction. It arose from Einstein's General Theory of Relativity.

SCIENCE FICTION IN EDUCATION

The great interest of youngsters in science fiction is reflected in a demand for science-fiction courses in high schools and colleges. My experience is that such courses can be fine educational experiences or disasters, depending on how they are taught. Properly planned science-fiction courses, in which real science or real politics is an integral component, would seem to have a long and useful life in school curriculums.

The greatest human significance of science fiction may be as thought experiments. Or they may be conceived as attempts to minimize future shock or as contemplations of alternative destinies. This is part of the reason that science fiction has so wide an appeal among young people. It is they who will live in the future. No society on earth today is well-adapted to the earth of 100 or 200 years from now—if we are wise enough or lucky enough to survive that long.

ALTERNATIVE FUTURES

We desperately need an exploration of alternative futures, both experimental and conceptual. The stories of Eric Frank Russell were very much to this point. We were able to see conceivable alternative economic systems, or the great efficiency of a unified passive resistance to an occupying power. In modern science fiction one can also find useful suggestions for making a revolution in an oppressive computerized society, as in Heinlein's "The Moon Is a Harsh Mistress" □

 SELECTED READINGS

"Science spawned from fact and fantasy" by M. Rothman. *SciQuest,* November 1979.

"Science fiction" by B. Bova. *Writer,* May, 1979.

"Science fiction: is it really only a couple of steps ahead of the real science?" by R. Wolkomir. *Science Digest,* April 1979.

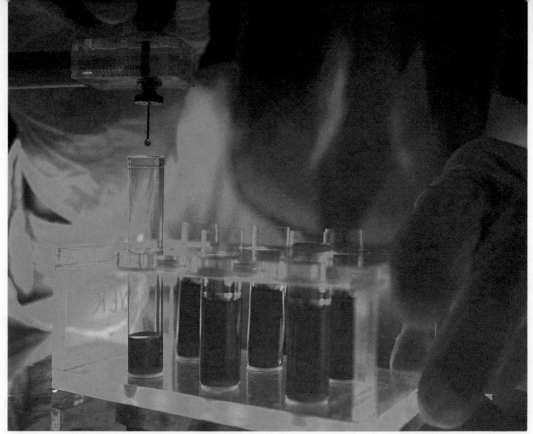

Genetic engineering will be in the forefront in the 1980's. Here, a scientist injects genes into bacterial culture to produce a new drug for humans.

THE 1980's

by Isaac Asimov

PREDICTION has its limitations. One can't be expected to predict breakthroughs with any hope of success, other than by pure chance, since the essence of a breakthrough is that it is unexpected. Were it predictable, it would not be a breakthrough.

Nor does scientific advance, or any other aspect of the human story, exist in a vacuum. It all hangs together, and what we may expect as far as future technology is concerned depends a great deal on what the political, economic, and psychological climate of earth might be.

Would the nuclear bomb have been developed in 1945 if it had not been for World War II? Would the United States have landed on the moon in 1969 if there had been no cold war?

What we must do, then, is to suppose that there will be no unexpected ricochets in the 1980's; that the world in general will proceed in the pattern that is now shaping up; that there will be no great war, no planetary economic collapse, no irresistible upwelling of cultist pseudo-science. If that is so, we can assume that scientific and technological advance will follow the lines of greatest push.

For instance, since about 1950, computers have been growing steadily smaller, and yet more versatile. In the very teeth of a world-wide inflation, they have been growing cheaper. The 1980's could very well be the decade in which the microcomputer enters the home and the small office in a massive way.

INCREASING COMPUTERIZATION

The 1980's could see the computerization of society as the 1920's saw its automobilization and the 1950's its televisionization.

It is entirely possible that by the end of the 1980's, almost every office will be filled with electronic devices for the receiving, transmitting, and printing of information. The clack of ordinary typewriters will have gone the way of the scratching pen.

In the home there will be an increasing use of computerized telephones and kitchen equipment. It will become more common to possess computer terminals through which instant information on weather, on supermarket bargains, on news headlines can be obtained.

In an allied direction, communication by laser is bound to increase during the 1980's. The use of optical fibers in place of copper wiring for transmitting messages will increase rapidly. It is also likely that communications satellites that are capable of receiving and emitting modulated laser beams will come into use.

Everything points to a new era of rapid and personalized communication. This will have its light-hearted aspects as well. The use of computer games, with or without a television screen, is almost certain to be the fun of the 1980's. Nor will it be confined to two or more heads bent over the same device or viewing the same screen.

It is quite likely that anyone will be able to play chess, bridge, or any of myriad newer games with anyone else in any part of the world. Or play those games with a computer. The ability to learn chess or bridge by playing with a computer that is endlessly patient and entirely at your call will alert the public to the possibility of general education by computer.

The 1980's will see the birth of a new generation of teaching machines. They will be sufficiently versatile and sufficiently connected to information sources, to be able to teach reading, arithmetic, the simple data of history and geography, and so on. It is likely that these devices will be used to supplement ordinary schoolwork and to meet the individual needs of schoolchildren for whom the general flow of the curriculum is too rapid or too slow. Such teaching machines would be of particular use in those parts of the world where educational facilities are still few and where qualified teachers are hard to come by.

ENERGY BOOSTS

The advance in communications is a logical prediction because we happen to be moving in that direction. However, much more on the minds of people, right now, is the problem of energy. Each year of the 1980's is going to make the nations of the world more aware of the oil crisis and of the necessity of finding a way out.

It is therefore very likely that significant

The 1980's may see the ''Three R's'' taught by computer.

Courtesy of Borg-Warner

advances will be made in a dozen different directions designed to make more practical and more available the energy from wind, from water, from vegetation, and so on. It seems to me, though, that the two most important such advances that will take place in the 1980's will involve nuclear fusion and improved photovoltaic cells.

First, the 1980's will see, somewhere in the world, the first self-sustaining nuclear-fusion operation on a laboratory scale. This is not to say that an electric-power station using fusion energy will at once be set up. In passing from the laboratory demonstration to a large-scale station, enormous engineering difficulties will have to be overcome. Fusion power as a substantial contribution to the world's energy needs may not be with us till the beginnings of the 21st century.

I suspect, however, that before the 1980's are over, the problem that has stalled fusion research for so long—namely, maintaining the tremendously high temperature needed for a fusion reaction—will be solved. With this solution will come not only controlled fusion reactions, but also the ability—with the extremely high temperatures—to break down any material to a mixture of its elementary components. When

Elaborate insulation and coils of very cold helium gas make this tiny cable exceptionally efficient.

these cool, they will form simple compounds. This will represent the ultimate recycling device and will point the way toward making the garbage dumps and the slag heaps of the world a new source of raw materials. This would greatly alleviate the pollution problem.

A second great energy advance will be the development of cheaper, sturdier, and more efficient photovoltaic cells capable of turning sunlight directly into electricity. Such cells will finally hold promise of producing sun-powered electricity produced by hydroelectric or fuel-burning plants.

With appropriate photovoltaic cells, we can look foward to the coating of substantial areas of the world's deserts with solar collectors and related equipment. These will produce needed electricity in a totally nonpolluting way. Indeed, in order to increase greatly the efficiency with which solar energy can be harnessed and converted into electricity, solar-collecting equipment may be set in orbit around the earth. It would be set in a geosynchronous orbit, always poised over the same spot on earth and thus exposed to solar energy continuously.

It isn't likely that the 1980's will see substantial amounts of sun-powered electricity from earth's surface and certainly not from space, but progress will surely be made in both directions.

ASTRONOMY THEORIES TO BE CONFIRMED

In space, the U.S. space shuttle will be the great advance of the 1980's. This will make possible the contribution of a space station larger, more versatile, and more long-lived than the ill-fated Skylab—and more maneuverable, too, so that orbital decay need never be a problem.

There is an outside chance that such a space station will be constructed with the collaboration of other nations. If so, that would not only spread the costs, but it would be an example of international cooperation that, we can hope, would be contagious and would spread to other areas.

There are a number of projects in space toward which the world will be heading in the 1980's. The amount of progress they

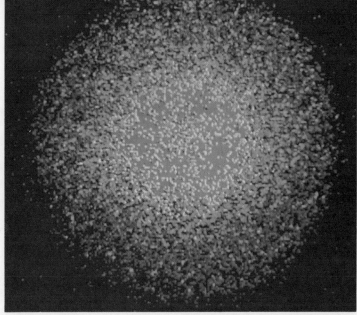

A microscopically small glass pellet of hydrogen fuel is made even smaller by implosion when it is hit by laser beams traveling at the speed of light. The outer blue ring represents the original size of the pellet; the red area its size when imploded. It all happens in one six-hundredth of a billionth of a second.

University of Rochester, Laser Energetics Lab

make will depend, in part, on the extent to which nations are willing to spend money on space and survival. One of the projects that the 1980's will see will be the construction of a large telescope in space. This telescope will be tended, when necessary, by rotating teams of astronomers brought to the telescope and taken home again by a space shuttle.

If the space telescope is successfully deployed, it should be capable of answering some questions about the overall fate of the universe. I have two guesses I would like to make in this connection concerning information gathered by the end of the 1980's—if the space telescope is in operation by the mid-1980's.

First, I suspect that continuing studies of quasars, those starlike objects in the heavens that emit so very much energy, will establish beyond doubt a cutoff for universe studies somewhere this side of 15,000,000,000 light years. (A light year, a measure of distance used in astronomy, is the distance light travels in one year. One light year is equal to approximately 9,500,000,000,000 kilometers.) Beyond the cutoff we will be probing so far back in time that only the high-energy haze that existed immediately after the universe's origin in a giant explosion would be visible. This would be a final confirmation that the universe did, indeed, originate in a giant explosion—and a final confirmation of the big-bang theory of the universe.

Second, a detailed study of the space between stars and of clusters of galaxies will make it clear that the masses of major astronomical objects have been seriously underestimated. Future studies will show that, in general, interstellar gases and intergalactic stars represent a large fraction of the mass of the universe. In short, we will be on the way toward discovering the mass long thought missing—and needed—if the universe were closed. We will then be on the way to deciding that the universe is closed after all; that it will someday begin to contract again; and that the big-bang that set us all going was only one of an endless series stretching back to the indefinite past and forward to the indefinite future.

There could be probes to Halley's comet when it passes near earth in 1986. There could be a probe to the asteroid Icarus when it passes. In the latter case it might be useful to set up instruments that would then be carried by the asteroid closer to the sun than Mercury is at its nearest. That is, if systems can be devised that would survive the heat and radiation such a trip would involve.

Other projects in the planning stage, if sufficient money and interest are present, are a soft-landing of instruments on Mercury, and the landing on Mars of an automated vehicle that could move about the surface in search of interesting spots to examine. Probes might go to some of the larger asteroids, and, of course, probes will continue to the outer solar system.

Plans could be made to return to the moon in order to set up a mining station. I also see an outside chance that before the end of the 1980's, a visit would actually be made and a pilot mass-driver tested.

CLONES AND INDUSTRIAL BACTERIA

In biology, the various branches of genetics will continue to be in the forefront.

Methods for transplanting nuclei in mammalian cells will surely be carried through successfully. The cell nucleus is the home of the cell's hereditary material. The technical ability to transplant nuclei between mammalian cells will open new avenues of possible genetic manipulation and cloning. Before the 1980's are done, it is very likely that the news media will feature photographs or television shots of the first cloned rabbit.

This will mean that the cloning of humans will at once be possible. However, it is likely that ethical and psychological, rather than technological, problems will stand in the way.

Bacteria will continue to receive concentrated attention, and, as the 1980's progress, we will receive reports of example after example of bacteria with altered genes. These bacteria will be capable of this or that exotic ability, such as the production of some molecule of biologic importance to humans. Already they have been altered to produce insulin. It is possible that by the end of the 1980's, some of these abilities will be put to use on an industrial level, at least under pilot conditions.

Laser fusion, which may provide the energy of the next century, is being researched in the 1980's.
University of Rochester, Laser Energetics Lab

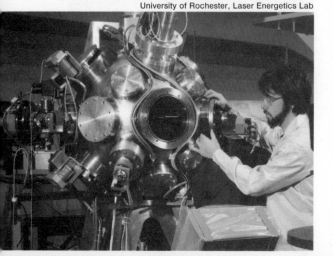

The mammalian brain—particularly the human brain—will continue to be an object of intensive study in the 1980's. It should begin to yield at least some of its secrets. I suspect that the probing of its organization, perhaps with the aid of computer simulations, might begin to present us with possibly tenable theories of memory and recall.

THE COSMIC EGG

In the field of theoretical physics, almost all progress is likely to come in unexpected directions. I will again make some guesses.

First, I believe that physicists will continue their search for a simple fundamental particle. Instead, they will find a seemingly endless array of particles. This will convince them that there is an indefinite series of particles at successively higher energy levels. The most energetic such particles would be, naturally, those which require all the energy of the universe to produce them.

I will anticipate the suggestion that the cosmic egg may have been just such a single universe-energetic particle (the cosmon?) formed at the end of a contracting-universe stage and immediately exploding again.

Second, I think that improved telescopes will detect sufficient solar subatomic particles called neutrinos. These would be at various energy levels, making it possible to explain the sunspot cycle and the periods during which the sun does not appear to have sunspots. Such findings may also reveal more details about stellar evolution.

Finally, I suspect that gravitational waves may be detected indisputably. Such a determination would offer still another method of probing the central cores of galaxies. Such a discovery would make it possible to learn more about the black holes that may exist there than we could possibly find out by any other means □

📖 SELECTED READINGS

"Challenges of the 80's." *U. S. News and World Report,* October 15, 1979.

"Dawn of the 80's" by T. Sanchez. *Feature,* February, 1979.

"Forecast 2000: brighter" by C. Warren and others. *Environment,* June 1979.

IN MEMORIAM

by Barbara Tchabovsky

SEVERAL people important in science and technology died in 1979 and early 1980. Among them were oceanographer-cinematographer Philippe Cousteau; John W. Mauchly, coinventor of the first electronic computer; astronomer Cecelia Payne-Gaposchkin; parapsychology researcher J. B. Rhine; Nobel-winning chemist William H. Stein; and theoretical astronomer Immanuel Velikovsky.

PHILIPPE COUSTEAU

Philippe Cousteau, the youngest son of famed oceanographer Jacques Cousteau, was born in Toulon, in 1940. He studied at the College de Normandie and at the Massachusetts Institute of Technology. As a youth he worked as a diver and photographer—he made his first Aqualung dive at the age of four—on his father's research ship, the *Calypso*. In 1965 he participated in and filmed an underwater experiment in which he and five other aquanauts lived 100 meters underwater for 28 days.

Philippe Cousteau filmed the Emmy-award-winning television series *The Undersea World of Jacques Cousteau* and coproduced with his father the television adventure series *The Cousteau Odyssey*. He and his father also coauthored *Sharks* (1969).

Philippe Cousteau died when a seaplane he was piloting capsized and sank off the coast of Portugal. He was a resident of Marina del Rey, California, and is survived by his wife and daughter.

JOHN W. MAUCHLY

John W. Mauchly, coinventor of the world's first electronic computer, was born in Cincinnati, Ohio, in 1907. He received a Ph.D. in physics from Johns Hopkins University and in 1941 joined the staff of the Moore School of Electrical Engineering at the University of Pennsylvania in Philadelphia.

In 1942 Mauchly wrote a proposal for a machine to apply electronic speed to the solution of mathematical tasks. Under a U.S.

Wide World

John Mauchly

Army contract, he and coinventor J. Presper Eckert, Jr. completed the machine by 1946. This first electronic computer was named ENIAC, or Electrical Numerical Integrator And Computer. It covered the entire floor (1,400 square meters) of the Moore School basement.

In 1949 the two men unveiled another computer, BINAC—one-tenth the size of ENIAC but with 25 times the memory capacity. In continuing work to perfect computers—adding functions and reducing size, they directed the development of UNIVAC 1, first used by the U.S. Census in 1951.

The company founded by the two inventors in 1947 was bought in 1950 by Remington Rand, which in 1955 merged with Sperry Corporation. Mauchly then remained with Sperry for ten years, directing UNIVAC research. In 1959 he established Mauchly Associates, and three years later introduced a

Cecelia Payne-Gaposchkin

Harvard University

computer designed for complicated scheduling problems. He also embarked on the development of a pocket-sized computer to replace his suitcase-sized one. In 1967 he founded the computer consulting firm of Dynatrend, and in 1973 returned to Sperry, serving as a consultant.

Despite his extremely important work Mauchly never became well known to the public. He did, however, receive numerous scientific awards. He died on January 9, 1980 while undergoing heart surgery at Abington Hospital near his home in Ambler, Pennsylvania.

CECELIA PAYNE-GAPOSCHKIN

Cecelia Payne-Gaposchkin, one of the foremost women astronomers, was born in Wendover, England on May 10, 1900. After studying at Cambridge University in England, she went to Harvard in 1923 to work for her doctorate. She investigated the significance of spectral lines in the light coming from various stars. Then, throughout the 1930's she and her husband Sergei I. Gaposchkin made millions of observations of variable stars, the results of which provided standard source material for researchers for many years. She also made detailed studies of novae and worked in many other fields of astronomy.

Cecelia Payne-Gaposchkin was the first woman to receive a tenured professorship at Harvard University and she headed the department of astronomy from 1956 to 1960. Once called "the greatest woman astronomer in history," Cecelia Payne-Gaposchkin died on December 7, 1979, at Auburn Hospital in Cambridge, Massachusetts.

J. B. RHINE

Joseph Banks Rhine, a psychologist who pioneered in the scientific investigation of extrasensory perception, was born on September 29, 1895, in Waterloo, Pennsylvania, a rural region where, according to Rhine, beliefs in unknown agencies were not uncommon. He developed an early interest in religion and philosophy. He received a B.S. degree from the University of Chicago in 1922 and a master's degree in 1923. After working as an industrial psychologist

at the Bryce Thompson Institute in Yonkers, New York, and serving as an instructor in botany at West Virginia University in Morgantown, he returned to the University of Chicago to earn his doctorate in psychology.

Interest in "psychic occurrences" led Rhine and his wife, the former Louisa Ella Weckesser, to accept an invitation from Professor William McDougall to join him at Duke University where he was establishing a Parapsychology Laboratory. Rhine then began detailed scientific investigations of clairvoyance, mental telepathy, and other "paranormal powers." His work led him to a theory of extrasensory perception which he presented in *ExtraSensory Perception* (1934), summarizing the results of more than 90,000 experiments using a wide variety of subjects. The book was met with skepticism by the scientific community. Then, three years later, scientists had to take a more serious look when Rhine presented an expanded version of his theory in *New Frontiers of the Mind* (1937). The book became a best seller, bringing Rhine's ideas to the public and making ESP—short for extrasensory perception—a household word.

In a technical report in 1940 Rhine and a few of his assistants concluded that "at least one person in five has had some experience where his mind received knowledge through supernormal channels."

In 1940 Rhine became director of the Parapsychology Laboratory at Duke University. He retired from Duke in 1956 and established his own research center—the Foundation for Research on the Nature of Man. Although the validity of extrasensory perception is still questioned by some, there appears to be growing acceptance of the idea among scientists. Dr. V. Ramakrishna Rao, director of the Foundation's Institute for Parapsychology, believes that "Dr. Rhine's work will come to be one of the most significant of this century."

Dr. Rhine died at his home in Hillsborough, North Carolina, on February 20, 1980.

WILLIAM H. STEIN

William H. Stein, Nobel-winning chemist for his work on the structure of a pancreatic enzyme, was born in New York City on June 25, 1911. He was educated at Phillips Exeter Academy and Harvard University, where he received his B.S. degree in 1933. Five years later he received a doctoral degree from Columbia University and joined the staff of the Rockefeller University as an assistant. He became a professor there in 1952.

Throughout his career Stein investigated the structure of proteins. With colleague Stanford Moore he deciphered the molecular structure of the enzyme ribonuclease and identified that part of the molecule that performs its vital role. The work raised hopes for using chemical means to "repair" defective enzymes. Stein and Moore shared the 1972 Nobel Prize in Chemistry with Christian B. Anfinsen for this work.

From 1968 until 1969 when he was stricken with a rare paralyzing disease, Stein was editor of the Journal of Biological Chemistry. After his illness, he maintained a continuing interest in research until his death in New York City on February 3, 1980.

IMMANUEL VELIKOVSKY

Immanuel Velikovsky, whose theories about colliding planets outraged the scientific community but mesmerized much of the public, was born in Vitebsk, Russia, on June 10, 1895. He studied history, economics, law, and languages in Moscow. Then, after studying botany and zoology at the University of Edinburgh, he pursued medical studies at the Charite and Kaiser Wilhelm Academy in Berlin.

Combining ideas taken from Freud's analysis of the mind of Moses with his own knowledge of the Bible and mythology, Velikovsky developed theories that shook the scientific world. In *Worlds in Collision* (1950) he proposed that a fragment of Jupiter had once careened through the heavens, hitting the earth about 1500 B.C., and then continuing on to become the planet we now know as Venus. This collision caused, according to Velikovsky, a series of catastrophes on earth: a disruption of the earth's rotation, the spilling of oceans, the flattening of some mountains and uprising of others. These catastrophes, said Velikovsky, were forgotten by mankind in a type of "collective amnesia."

Wide World

William H. Stein

Velikovsky further said that Venus left a trail of hydrocarbons in its wake—some represented by oil droplets on earth.

Velikovsky's theories were met with outright rejection or, at best, skepticism by scientists. In opposing his ideas, geologists, for example, pointed out that fossil tree rings showed an uninterrupted cycle in world history for at least 360,000,000 years. Opponents also showed that Velikovsky used discredited measurements and often took statements out of context to try to prove a specific point. Many of Velikovsky's critics were adamant, ridiculing him and even threatening to boycott the company that published his works. Others, however, criticized him more affectionately, sometimes calling him the "grand old man of the fringe." He did, too, have some supporters— reportedly among them Albert Einstein.

The enthusiastic, hard-working and feisty scientist-writer was not easily put down. He continued to present his unorthodox ideas in *Earth in Upheaval* (1955), *Ages in Chaos,* Volume I (1952), and other books as well as in countless articles and lectures.

Velikovsky lived in New York City from 1939 until 1952 when he moved to Princeton, New Jersey. He died there on November 17, 1979 □

SCIENCE BOOKS OF THE YEAR

by Lansing P. Wagner

Many books on science and technology are published every year. The titles below were selected for review by the editors because they seemed of particular significance, interest, or usefulness. The choice was not restricted to books appearing within the last year, since this does not affect the value of their contents. The titles that were chosen represent the range of subjects that is provided within the various sections of this annual.

The Cambridge Encyclopedia of Astronomy *edited by Simon Mitton. Crown Publishers, 1977, 500 pp., illus., $35.00.*

Light-sensitive telescopes brought the study of the heavens into the middle of the 20th century. Then the invention of radio-sensitive and X-ray-sensitive telescopes gave astronomers a new way of looking at the heavens. They gave them a new perspective, new interpretations, and brand new ideas. Giant rockets have sent explorers to the moon and exploratory probes throughout the solar system. These inventions, in this Golden Age of Astronomy, have produced such a rush of new data that many astronomers realized it was time to take stock of all the new discoveries by preparing a new reference book. Members of the Institute of Astronomy in Cambridge, England, have prepared this masterpiece in the great tradition of British documentation, such as NOVA. The writing is clear, imaginative, and at a level that is comprehensible to the uninitiated to astronomy. This reference book is more like a textbook than an encyclopedia, because its content does not consist of alphabetized items. Rather, astronomy is presented in cohesive themes. For example, there are five chapters on the solar system and four chapters on galaxies. The physical aspects of this book compel you to go further. The descriptive captions to the photographs and diagrams provide you with a base to explore the main text, even though that may not have been your intent. And you can compare the computerized star charts with the real thing on a clear night.

New Worlds: Discoveries from Our Solar System *by Wernher von Braun and Frederick I. Ordway. Doubleday, 1979, 284 pp., illus., $24.95.*

This informative and beautiful book was written by two of the most prominent members of the U.S. space team. They are not astronomers; they are space scientists. It is through their efforts in building giant rockets that astronauts have been able to walk on the moon and that unmanned rocket vehicles are now exploring the outer planets as well as the inner ones. We are now only at the beginning of the third decade of exploration of the inner solar system. Therefore, most of this book is about the inner planets—Mercury, Venus, Earth, Mars, and their moons. By the end of this century, the outer planets may also be explored as thoroughly as the inner ones. However, the distances are so vast to Jupiter, Saturn, Uranus, and Pluto that missions will consume large parts of a space scientist's career. The authors guide us through the solar system with poetic prose, photographs, and colorful NASA drawings of their hardware in

The Cambridge Encyclopædia of Astronomy

"Without the use of mathematics, the authors have succeeded in communicating the essential features of modern and classical astronomy. It is written in such a lucid and careful manner that readers with only a minimal technical background can benefit from it. Moreover, it is so thorough and covers so many topics that it can serve as a reference book for the professional astronomer who wants a quick exposition of some astronomical facts or theories."
LLOYD MOTZ, Department of Astronomy, Columbia University

space. Not only do we learn about the solar system, but also how the information was gained. New instruments were developed to link with new telescopes. New microcomputers were created to interpret the wealth of new observations. Space scientists and astronomers in their search for understanding of such remote worlds must be optimists and enthusiasts. They have met the challenge of the unknown and the ultra-difficult—but for what earthly good? Perhaps the authors feel that their endeavor is necessary for public support in this time of energy and political crisis.

The Eighth Day of Creation: The Makers of the Revolution in Biology *by Horace Freeland Judson. Simon and Schuster, 1979, 686 pp., illus., $15.95.*

With extreme skill and untiring patience Judson interviews the great scientists of molecular biology to give us an outline—or scenario—of the science. The reader is treated to fascinating and witty dialogues by these great scientists. These dialogues carry the story of molecular biology from the insights of Thomas Hunt Morgan, an early geneticist and embryologist, to the present understanding of the structure of DNA and its function in genetics and body regulation. Now that genes and viruses are understood, the problems that Morgan pondered can be considered again with some hope of solving them: "How does a wounded organism regenerate to exactly the same structure as before? How does the egg form the organism?" With the solution of the structure of DNA came an expansion of research in molecular biology, and the big question was: what is the meaning of the structure of DNA? Gradually it was learned how the DNA molecule unzips itself for replication. But how does it control the cell? How does it specify the creation of a protein molecule? The author leads the reader through the intellectual maze of breaking the genetic code—the discovery of the nucleic acid, messenger RNA. What Judson has done so remarkably throughout his book is to show the researchers having their theoretical insights and later doing the critical experiments that the insights inspired.

The illustrated encyclopedia of the **Mineral Kingdom**
Consultant editor
Dr Alan Woolley

The Illustrated Encyclopedia of the Mineral Kingdom *edited by Dr. Alan Wooley. Larousse and Co., 1978, 240 pp., illus., $19.95.*

There are only about 300 widespread and common minerals out of about 2,500—variation in life is immensely more. About one quarter of this beautifully illustrated book is devoted to the description of these 300 common minerals, which are divided into 9 families, such as native elements, sulfides, and silicates. Minerals are the principal components of rocks, which constitute the outer solid portion of the earth. For that reason the authors open the book with a discussion of the origin and evolution of the earth. This includes the formation and occurrence of its rocks. It also includes the theory of plate tectonics, which accounts for the location of volcanicity, earthquakes, and mountain building. The overview enables the mineral collector to know where a particular mineral is most likely to be found. However, this review of planet Earth does not offer a theory of the formation of elements, from which minerals were formed. Crystal growth is discussed followed by a classification based on shapes and chemical composition. The line drawings here are particularly educational. This leads into a well-done outline of the characteristic set of physical properties. Most of these properties, such as color, streak, cleavage, hardness, specific gravity, and optical properties, make mineral identification fairly easy. This book with its clear writing, large print, and many and large illustrations is just right for any stage of mineral collecting.

Running On Empty *by Lester R. Brown, Christopher Flavin, and Colin Norman. Norton, 1979, 116 pp., $7.95.*

This book is generally about transportation in a world when the supply of oil is running dry, and specifically it is about the future of the automobile. The reader will find many interesting statistics about autos and oil. For example: autos now consume about one-fifth of the oil produced in the world. American autos use one third of all oil consumed in the United States. Between 1950 and 1973 there was a fivefold increase in the world's oil output. Then OPEC quadrupled its price. By 1980, world oil production had almost leveled off. Now with increasing population and development of the Third World nations more essential demands for oil will leave less for the auto. These demands are for home heating, agriculture, industry, and mass transportation. There may be alternative fuels such as ethanol, methanol, synthetic oil, batteries, and hydrogen. None of these, however, will be economical (as we now know it) by the end of the century. The authors then turn to increasing the efficiency of autos—more miles per gallon. Shaving ten per cent of the weight off an auto saves seven per cent on fuel. Less than 15 per cent of the fuel's energy propels the auto. Too much energy is lost in the engine and the transmission. For that reason diesels and new forms of transmissions are being researched for future use. Light-weight materials must be used for better gas mileage. Autos will also have to be used more efficiently—slower driving, less acceleration, and more persons to the car.

Energy Future: Report of the Energy Project at the Harvard Business School *edited by Robert Stobaugh and Daniel Yergin. Random House, 1979, 353 pp., $12.95.*

If there ever was a topic concerning the mix of technology and economics that needed to be investigated it is energy. The authors of *Energy Future* consider the many facets of this topic in a nonpartisan and scholarly way. Wars, economic expansion, and general indifference to future energy needs brought on the crisis. The authors describe the technology, economics, and politics of the four conventional sources of energy and find each of them inadequate for the long run: We have come to the end of "easy oil"—domestic and foreign—and even new oil finds in Mexico and China will not make a substantial change in the world-oil balance. Natural gas, the "prince of hydrocarbons," cannot stop the rise in oil imports because its supply is also shrinking. In spite of the great coal reserves coal presents too many social, political, and environmental problems as well as technical ones. The problems of nuclear safety and nuclear-waste disposal are so far from being solved that America can expect no massive contribution to its energy needs from nuclear fission. (Nuclear fusion is not discussed.) What is left? Conservation of energy is the major alternative to imported oil—40 per cent worth seems possible to the authors. The other alternative is low-technology passive and active solar heating, which is here and now and requires no technological breakthrough.

Just So It's Healthy *by Lucy Barry Robe. CompCare Publications, 1977, 96 pp., $2.75.*

Have you wondered whether it is safe to have an alcoholic drink when you are pregnant? Have you ever wondered if such-and-such a medicine will affect your unborn child as well as yourself? The first section is about alcohol, and the second section is about other drugs, including comments about thalidomide—the terrible deformer of the early 1960's. In *Just So It's Healthy,* you will learn that the fetal-alcohol syndrome consists of small size, small head, mental retardation, slitlike eyes, fishlike mouth, caved-in nose, cleft palate, and many other deformations. "Minutes after taking your first sip, alcohol's irritant, chemically poisonous content enters your tiny, underdeveloped baby's body." One and one-half ounces of hard liquor, four ounces of wine, or 12 ounces of beer will work on the baby's body for one hour. Alcohol in the mother's body—and this also includes many medicines—when any organ of the fetus is taking shape, may adversely affect that organ. Therefore, alcohol and other drugs deform most during the first three months of pregnancy. Terrible damage can be done to a fetus even before a woman knows she is pregnant. In spite of evidence of this for hundreds of years, the medical profession has taken it seriously only recently. Alcohol does not fall under the jurisdiction of the Food and Drug Administration, so they have made little attempt to inform the public. Lucy Robe has done this for us.

Sleep Less, Live More *by Everett Mattlin. Lippincott, 1979, 176 pp., $8.95.*

This book is well researched and documented. It presents a program for sleeping less, while waking up better rested and more energetic. The book also contains a list of sleep-disorder clinics. Experimentation has shown that if a person is motivated to accomplish more, he or she can gradually reduce the amount of sleep time. Sleep clinics report that half the people who come to them are really sleeping well, but they need less sleep than they think they do and become anxious about not getting the magical eight-hour's worth. Mattlin describes the recent research on sleep and its four now-recognized stages. Everyone agrees that sleep seems to be important. But why do professional athletes and the bedridden both sleep about eight hours? How does sleep make us feel rested? What does sleep do to the brain? To the body muscles? No one yet knows. Whatever sleeplessness does to our ability to concentrate, it has little effect on the body for at least a week. There is no change of weight, heart rate, respiration, blood plasma, or the composition of blood and urine. And then there is the quality, or soundness, of sleep, as opposed to the quantity. Three hours of

New evidence that drinking and drugs can harm your unborn baby.

Just so it's healthy

by Lucy Barry Robe

foreword by
Stanley E. Gitlow, M.D.

CompCare
publications

sound sleep are better than eight hours of restless sleep. Sticking to a bedtime routine and getting enough exercise are ways of preparing for sleep efficiency, that is, falling to sleep quickly and having sound sleep.

Broca's Brain *by Carl Sagan. Random House, 1979, 347 pp., $12.95.*

Like Jacob Bronowski, Carl Sagan is an ardent scientist—questioning, fascinated by many fields of inquiry, joyous at finding how the world works, astounded at the bigness and smallness of things—as well as being an excellent writer. If you have read his *The Dragons of Eden: Speculations on the Evolution of Human Intelligence,* you will understand why Sagan named this collection of essays *Broca's Brain,* which is the first essay and a tone-setting theme for the book. First of all, Sagan is fascinated by the development and the computerlike qualities of the brain. Paul Broca was a French surgeon, neurologist, and anthropologist in the middle of the 19th century. At the Musée de l'Homme in Paris Sagan once wandered through back storage rooms and found an old collection of pickled brains. One of them was Paul Broca's. These 25 essays first appeared as addresses, lectures, magazine articles, and even sermons for the "general public." Not too general, for Sagan is pretty difficult to follow with all his intellectual allusions. He has sequenced the essays into five major topics, which he has labelled, "Science and Human Concern"; "The Paradoxers" (those who invent elaborate and undemonstrable explanations—like Velikovsky); "Our Neighborhood in Space"; "The Future"; and "Ultimate Questions." A number of themes weave through the topics. These are: science as a way of looking at the world; borderline, or pop, science, and its relationship to religious doctrine; the exploration of the planets; and the search for extraterrestrial life. Some science historians like to point out watersheds of science. The period of Kepler, Galileo, and Newton is one. Sagan feels that we are presently within or approaching another watershed whose farther slope will answer questions on origins and fates and as-yet unthought-of questions.

The Rocket Team by Frederick I. Ordway III and Mitchell R. Sharpe. Crowell, 1979, 462 pp., $14.95.

This account of a group of German rocketeers is like a brief and one-sided history of World War II in Europe. Ordway and Sharpe eventually worked with the members of the team in the United States after the war so they came to know them personally. The authors spent ten years planning, researching, interviewing, and writing this remarkable history. To catch the reader's interest, they open the book with members of the rocket team arranging a self-surrender to the American army, pleading "Take us to Ike." Then the account takes the reader back to the formation of an amateur rocket club in the 1920's. Wernher von Braun, in his early twenties, came to inspire and direct this group of scientists. Their efforts and his persuasion culminated in the building of Peenemünde, the German rocket-development center on the Baltic coast. There the "vengeance weapons" V-1 and V-2 were developed to destroy England. The reader learns what British intelligence did about growing reports of the secret weapons. After they were able to pinpoint Peenemünde as the center of this activity, the British bombed it. At the end of the war each of the allied nations grabbed as many of the rockets as they could. The reader learns how the team members adjusted to American life, and more specifically to El Paso, Texas, and finally to Huntsville, Alabama. Eventually they were to develop the enormous Saturn rocket, which was to fulfill the team's dream of sending people into space.

Simon and Schuster's Guide to Trees. Simon and Schuster, 1978, 200 pp., illus., $7.95.

Each of the 300 described trees has a four-color photo. On the facing page is a detailed black-and-white sketch of the characteristic shape of the tree, its leaves, and its fruit. On that page is a text about the tree, including the headings: family, etymology, habitat, description, conditions for growth. There is also a color code on the page, but the reader is not told what the colors mean. It may refer to the color coding for the worldwide zones of natural forest vegetation, on pages 12 and 13—however, it may not. And in some cases the color is missing. The book makes a weak plug for the North American market by including an annual-average-and-minimum temperature map for Canada and the United States. The introduction is well done. It includes sections on the history of trees, trees and ecosystems, wood, the leaf, flower, and seed. Perhaps it should have included an identification key—or at least a reference to a good one. North American publishers should know better than to market a book on plant or animal life that has been written and illustrated elsewhere than the target market. At least half the trees described are not found in North America. And worse than that, many well-known North American trees are missing □

Fred W. McDarrah

Fiber-optic devices may soon be used in television, transportation, and many other industries. Shown here:
Dr. Suzanne Nagel of Bell Laboratories, a pioneer in the use of fiber optics for communications.

PHYSICAL SCIENCES

PHYSICAL SCIENCES
REVIEW OF THE YEAR

General Atomic Company for DOE

There were continuing efforts to find practical ways to confine plasma so that fusion energy can become a reality. One of the newest advances—General Atomic Company's "Doublet III"—is the largest magnetic fusion research machine in the world.

Analysis of a "single" interplanetary dust particle by neutron activation methods revealed a composition similar to primitive solar system material.

Dr. R. Ganapathy

Physics. The growing importance of physics to the medical profession was symbolized by the awarding of the 1979 Nobel Prize in Physiology or Medicine to U.S. physicist Allan McLeod Cormack and British engineer Godfrey N. Hounsfield for their development of computerized axial tomography (CAT), a process through which thin "slices" of the body are photographed by X rays and computer-analyzed. (See "The 1979 Nobel Prize in Physiology or Medicine," starting on page 86.)

There were several other medical applications of the principles and equipment of physics during the year. The development of improved gamma-ray detectors and associated techniques is making safer and simpler the measurement of the blood "ejection factor," an important indicator of the heart's status as a pump, and at the same time making possible evaluation of heart-wall motion. ■ Magnetometers sufficiently sensitive to measure the very weak magnetic fields that accompany electric currents in the brain were developed. This now makes possible better measurements of brain function—even better than can be done with more traditional electric means. ■ And there was continued improvement in and increased use of ultrasound—high-frequency sound waves—to visualize body cavities.

There is also intensive research on the role of magnetic fields in animal orientation and migration. The discovery that magnetite in certain bacteria is linked to their spatial orientation and the finding of magnetic tissue in certain animals has greatly spurred this research. ■ Magnetic-resonance studies have been applied to solids permitting such diverse applications as the detection and mapping of abnormal sections in a living organism and the monitoring, through radioactive isotopes, of the rate that fertilizer is absorbed in a soybean leaf.

In particle physics, the search for elementary particles went on . . . and on. Based entirely on theory, three different quarks had originally been announced as the only basic particles—until more and more quarks were "discovered," including a "bare bottom" quark in 1979. There are now five separate types of quarks—with a property called "color" being ascribed to each. This quark hypothesis has, in turn, led to the hypothesis of another set of particles—gluons—which, being the "exchange particles" for quark interactions, supposedly hold quarks together by a so-called "color force." Direct experimental evidence for quarks remains nonexistent.

Einstein's theory of relativity was given support during the year through observations in astrophysics. The existence of gravitational waves has long been a prediction of this theory but such waves have never been experimentally detected. Now, orbit measurements, through radio-emission analyses, of a pulsar (pulsar PSR 1913+16) with a large companion have provided indirect evidence for such waves. ■ Observations of a double quasar—two closely associated quasars with essentially identical behavior—has been interpreted, but not conclusively, as the double image of a single quasar (quasar 0957+561). The double image is believed produced by the gravitational "lens" associated with a massive body in the line of sight—another direct result of the theory of relativity.

Hugh F. Henry

Chemistry. There were advances in many diverse fields of chemistry during 1979. Among some of the most significant was the discovery of a new means of isolating some rare isotopes, research into the mechanics of fast reactions, and continuing work on drugs and related chemicals. Rare isotopes of certain elements are used in medical diagnosis, in industrial research, and for nuclear fuel. The separation of these isotopes has generally been a long, energy-intensive, and costly procedure. During 1979 Columbia University chemists reported the development of techniques, based on the magnetic properties of some of these isotopes, in which the isotopes separate themselves. Using compounds containing magnetic isotopes oxygen-17 and carbon-13, Nicholas Turro and Bernhard Kraeutler found reactions in which magnetic isotopes react differently from nonmagentic isotopes. This provided a means of separating the desired magnetic isotopes. It is hoped that similar techniques can be applied to the isolation of the nuclear fuel U-235 from U-238, which makes up 99 per cent of natural uranium.

The search for new drugs and new biological uses for known chemicals met with several successes. Upjohn Laboratory reported the successful synthesis of the antibiotic spectinomycin, important in gonorrhea treatment. This antibiotic, which is produced by the soil microbe *Streptomyces spectabilis,* has a somewhat unstable complex structure and has been the subject of synthesis efforts for about 20 years. Researchers now hope to produce variations of the drug that will be effective against a wide range of bacteria and have few or no harmful side effects. ■ A search for new antimalarial agents by Daniel Klayman and colleagues at the Walter Reed Army Institute in Washington, D.C. has resulted in the discovery of a new class of chemicals effective against a wide variety of diseases. Known as thiosemicarbazones, these compounds have been found effective against malaria, leprosy, gonorrhea, certain bacterial infections encountered after surgery, and some treatment-resistant atypical forms of tuberculosis.

Certain compounds have long been known to have antitumor properties, but they generally have been too toxic for cancer prevention or treatment in humans. Now nontoxic derivatives of vitamin A—retinylidene—1,3 diketones—have been reported to prevent chemical-induced cancer and reverse premalignant cell changes in some experimental animals. Research on the possible application of these findings to cancer treatment is being pursued. ■ Vitamin D and some derivatives may also have new uses—the treatment of osteoporosis and other bone diseases. ■ And as controversies about the role of vitamin C in combating viral infections continues, George Washington University biochemists Gary B. Thurman and Allan Goldstein added a new bit of data. Working with guinea pigs, who, like humans, cannot manufacture their own vitamin C, they found that vitamin C played a vital role in triggering the immune response to infection.

Some chemical reactions such as those involved in combustion in a car engine are so fast that it is very difficult to determine molecular and submolecular changes and energy states. Now IBM researchers, using sophisticated laser techniques, have obtained a glimpse of these reactions with "snapshots" following the process of an explosive reaction. The results of such studies may be applicable to petroleum-refining technology.

Barbara Tchabovsky

Physics Dept, General Motors Research Lab

An understanding of combustion is important in many fields. Here General Motors researchers use sophisticated laser techniques to study the step-by-step happenings of combustion.

IBM researchers Peter Sorokin (left) and Donald Bethune have taken "snapshots" of the rearrangement of molecules during a chemical reaction.

IBM

FIRE

by John F. Henahan

IN January, 1979, the underwater tunnel of the Bay Area Rapid Transit System (BART) between San Francisco and Oakland, California, became a fiery inferno. For several hours, more than 1,000 passengers, BART employees, and fire fighters were trapped by fire.

The fire was started by an electric short circuit beneath one car, and spread to the highly flammable polyurethane seat cushions. It gutted five cars and sent dense clouds of eye-searing, toxic smoke through the tunnel.

Analogous to the near disaster at the Three Mile Island nuclear plant, much went wrong that should not have gone wrong. Fire departments were called late. Vents that should have sucked out the smoke forced it back to the source. Trains were permitted to approach the fire zone. Fire fighters stumbled for kilometers through the smoke-filled tunnel, trying to reach and extinguish the fire before the air supply in their respirators ran out. Miraculously, the only fatality was a fire

fighter who had removed his empty respirator and quickly succumbed to the fumes. Everyone else was removed safely—confused, coughing, frightened, but alive.

FIRE, DEATH, AND DESTRUCTION

The BART incident was only one of roughly five million fires that destroyed homes, factories, hotels, high-rise buildings, and an estimated 7,500 Americans in 1979. The toll included another 50,000 people disabled by burns and other fire-related injuries. The toll also included about $12,000,000,000 in property losses, insurance costs, fire-fighting expenses, and loss of worker productivity. No other country does quite so badly. In Japan, where the fire hazards are much greater, per capita fire losses are a fraction of what they are in the United States.

Physicists concern themselves with the currents of air and hot gases that eddy through a fire and influence its spread. Chemists puzzle over the hundreds of chemical substances formed when flames tear down a material's molecular structure. Toxicologists measure how these combustion products affect the health of people caught in a fire. Behavioral scientists grapple with the victims' often erratic behavior. Fire remains today, however, a little-understood and unpredictable phenomenon.

In the United States, fire does not rank high on the national agenda. Fire research remains a poorly-funded backwater of the scientific enterprise. Despite the appalling loss of life and property, the federal government spends only about $20,000,000 a year in gathering fire statistics and promoting education. It also spends about $10,000,000 on basic and applied research on civilian fire hazards.

In the great Chicago fire that made a legend of Mrs. O'Leary's cow, the entire central portion of the city was leveled. In the aftermath of the 1923 Tokyo earthquake, fire consumed whole neighborhoods and killed 100,000 people.

INTENSELY COMBUSTIBLE PLASTICS

Such huge fires are a rarity now. New materials are changing the nature of fire hazard, especially in urban America. Wood has given way to concrete, glass, and steel. With "fireproof" structures, the unit size of most fires has decreased from the neighborhood block to the individual room. The hazard has not greatly diminished, however, because wood and cotton have also given way to plastics. Our fireproof buildings are increasingly filled with furnishings that burn with twice the intensity of traditional materials. Furthermore, they emit additional toxic fumes.

The evolution toward a more plastic and more combustible environment began in the late 1940's. The chemical industry began to make nylon, polyvinyl chloride, polystyrene, and other synthetic materials in great amounts. Among the most versatile of the new giant molecules, or polymers, was a material called polyurethane. Developed in the 1930's by German chemists, it has since been

A burnt-out house makes an eerie picture, after fire-fighters have put out the blaze and nature has taken over.

"Flashover" is demonstrated in this timed sequence (above). In only six minutes a small fire in a mattress can release toxic gases which accumulate under the ceiling, becoming so hot they cause an explosion. The extreme flammability of children's sleepwear (below) first prompted the search for safer materials.

used in hundreds of consumer products. These include stretch fabrics, rigid sheets of insulating foam, and furniture cushions.

Polyurethane was originally marketed as "non-burning" or "self-extinguishing." But in 1970, a newly completed concrete and glass terminal at Kennedy International Airport in New York sufered a devastating $2,000,000 blaze. Investigators established that the fire started in a small pile of construction debris, but was fueled principally by some 600 chairs clustered in waiting areas.

"We wondered what could do this," reported Joseph Klementowicz, a safety engineer with the Port Authority of New York and New Jersey. "What kind of fire could melt aluminum, explosively blow out huge plateglass windows, and cause patrons to run down corridors in mortal fear?"

The answer was the polyurethane foam used to stuff the chairs. At temperatures only slightly higher than that of boiling water, the foam began to decompose. This released flammable gases that rose to the ceiling and eventually exploded in a phenomenon known as "flashover." The burning foam also melted and dripped to the floor, spreading the fire.

The Port Authority later found that polyurethane has a flame-spread index of between 600 and 3,000. (The flame-spread index is a relative measure of how fast a flame spreads across a surface.) In compari-

son, the flame-spread index of red oak flooring is 100 and of latex foam rubber, about 1,000. The Port Authority banned polyurethane from the reconstructed terminal.

LIKE SOLIDIFIED GASOLINE

Polyurethane and many of the other polymer plastics, such as polyvinyl chloride and polystyrene, are potent fuels resembling solidified gasoline. Polyurethane ignites readily in the presence of an open flame. Then it releases twice the heat energy of equivalent weights of cellulosic materials such as wood and cotton. Controlled burns in fire-research laboratories have established that burning polyurethane mattresses reach higher temperatures than cotton mattresses. What is more, flashover occurs sooner, shortening time for escape.

Americans are increasing their use of polymer plastics in homes and offices. Plastic-based furniture and upholsteries are becoming more popular than wood and natural fibers because plastics are easier to care for and less expensive. Increasingly, however, they are implicated in fire statistics. Polyurethane cushions fed the fiery chaos that erupted in the BART tunnel. In January 1979, the National Academy of Sciences released a report recommending that polyurethane be banned from public transportation systems.

Burning is not the gravest hazard from fires. The Maryland study, conducted by

Walter Berl and colleagues at the Johns Hopkins Applied Physics Laboratory, showed that 80 per cent of some 400 fire deaths examined were caused by inhalation of toxic gases. When plastics smolder or burn, they introduce a complicated and deadly mix of gases to the air. In addition to large amounts of carbon monoxide, also released by burning wood, polyurethane produces hydrogen cyanide.

The effects of the two gases are thought by many investigators to be nearly additive. Together they deliver a one-two punch to the body. Carbon monoxide interferes with the ability of the blood to carry oxygen to the brain. Hydrogen cyanide seems to interfere with the ability of cells, including those in the brain, to use oxygen from the bloodstream. Both gases can cause unconsciousness quickly. Sublethal concentrations of toxic gases are believed to be partially responsible for the disorientation and frequently erratic behavior of fire victims that can often interfere with their escape.

How did polyurethane come to be marketed as "non-burning?" Small-scale tests of flammability—including those for polyurethane—were generally accomplished by briefly exposing a piece of the test material to a small flame in a laboratory setting. No attempt was made to simulate real fire situations, and particularly in the testing of polyurethane. The small-scale tests were misleading because they allowed much of the fire's heat to radiate off into the surroundings. In contrast, a real fire in an enclosed space, such as a room, burns with the benefit of reflected radiation. The radiation preheats the fuel, making ignition much easier and flame spread faster.

REGULATIONS STILL NOT ADEQUATE

The growing rash of polyurethane fires caused the Federal Trade Commission in 1974 to warn manufacturers that they could no longer market their products as non-combustible on the basis of small-scale testing. But the warning applied only to the rigid foams used in wallboards, not to the flexible foams used in chairs and mattresses. The Consumer Product Safety Commission's current flammability standard for mattresses, for example, requires only that the material resist ignition by a burning cigarette. It ignores the question of what happens with exposure to an open flame.

Federal efforts to regulate the sale of flammable materials has triggered an intensive search for fire-retardant compounds. The results, however, have been mixed. One of the best flame retardants yet found is a bromine- and phosphorus-containing compound popularly known as Tris. It seemed to fit the need perfectly when the Consumer Product Safety Commission decreed that children's sleepwear had to pass rigid flammability standards. Tris was very effective. Many fabrics not otherwise salable under the standard were suitably flame resistant when treated.

After years of use, Tris was found to cause genetic mutations in bacteria and kidney cancer in lab animals. These discoveries caused consternation in families with young children and forced Tris off the U.S. market.

With growing use of flame retardants, other problems have developed. Research has shown that polyurethanes treated with certain chlorine-containing retardants do not burn readily. They do smolder, however, and produce still another gas, hydrogen chloride, that can cause serious lung damage.

FLAME RETARDANTS NOT UNDERSTOOD

With an imperfect understanding of the chemistry of fire, the development of flame retardants remains only slightly advanced from a black art. Most flame retardants contain one or more of a few key elements. These include phosphorus, boron, antimony, and halogen atoms, such as chlorine and bromine.

Why these particular substances are so effective is still a matter of conjecture. Phosphorus and perhaps boron apparently help convert smoldering material to a carbonaceous char, which acts as a barrier to further attack by heat and oxygen. They may also help reduce the formation of combustible gases. Once combustible gases have been produced, halogen atoms seem to act as scavengers for highly reactive molecular fragments—called free radicals—that are crucial components of flame.

The search continues for fire-retardant materials. Dozens of new chemical retardants have been introduced in recent years. Several polymer materials that are themselves more flameproof have come into commercial use. However, they are generally much more expensive than the common polymer plastics—a factor that has precluded their widespread use. Short of government prohibition on a massive scale, the abundance of flammable plastics in the environment is not likely to change.

PROGRAMMING A FIRE

An alternative approach to fire prevention and control focuses on the physics of fire itself—how it interacts with architecture, furnishings, and air flows. The hope, championed by Howard Emmons at Harvard University, one of the pioneers of fire-disaster research, is to program simulated fires into a computer. This would predict the growth of fires in various settings and aid in planning buildings that would minimize disaster.

In pursuit of this approach, a generation of graduate students at Harvard, working with researchers at the Factory Mutual Research Corporation, has built ever more complex and realistic fires, measuring their course. Whole rooms, fully furnished, have been burned. The researchers have fed the information gained from these and other real fires, correlated in hundreds of mathematical equations, into a computer. According to

Emmons, the computer model already can predict what will happen if a fire occurs within a room of a given size and contents. He expects that within ten years, similar computer models will be able to predict the course of fire in a building.

Lax attitudes and individual carelessness about fire prevention can thwart the best technologies. Johns Hopkins researchers reported finding smoke detectors without batteries that therefore did not warn of fires that were subsequently fatal. Lars Lerup, an architect at the University of California at Berkeley, found in a study of nursing-home fires that patients could not respond to an alarm 50 per cent of the time because they were sedated or strapped down.

On a larger scale, the national apathy about fire prevention is an underlying cause of America's huge fire problem. The apparent national view is that fire is a natural disaster for which there are few preventive measures. "This public attitude is reflected in Congress, with its own inadequate perception of the problem and the low level of resources and legislation it makes available," says Joseph Clark, the former U.S. Fire Administrator.

FIRE IN JAPAN

Fire researchers find a completely different attitude in Japan. Japanese homes are made mostly of wood and bamboo and furnished with straw mats and other highly combustible furnishings. Fire losses, however, are only one seventh of those in the United States. This stunning difference is the result of several factors. In Japan the arson rate is almost negligible. In the United States it is a major contributor to fire statistics.

Furthermore, the Japanese attack the fire problem with more zeal, both at the national and the individual levels. Many households, for example, have specially designed water buckets at the ready.

The Japanese government supports a large array of fire projects, from television specials to street fairs, designed to keep the public informed. The Tokyo Fire Department is as large and expensive as that of New York City, even though it handles only one-sixth as many fires.

Milt & Joan Mann

In Japan, firefighting is a national priority. Firefighters exercise to keep in shape (above) and, from strategically-placed lookout towers (below), spot fires before they become unmanageable.

Milt & Joan Mann

The major portion of Tokyo's personnel time is spent in inspection, training, and public education. Fire research is well funded on both national and municipal levels and is, as the fire buckets suggest, often very practical in its focus. Japanese architects and designers are encouraged to work closely with the fire prevention community.

Emmons tells an anecdote that suggests the difference in national attitude. "If your neighbor's home burns down in this country, you try to be nice to him, cluck your sympathy, and invite him and his family in for a meal. In Japan, it's different. There the attitude is 'Those bastards. They let a fire get away. Get them out of our neighborhood!' As a consequence, boy are they careful."

Whether it is a matter of attitude or of national priorities, the results are effective. Yet for Americans, fire remains a hazard that cannot happen here—but does, on a tragic and preventable scale.

FLASHOVER: THE PHYSICS OF FIRE

From studies of the circumstances of fatal fires and from experimental "burns" of

A fire at an old factory reflects the often hopeless fight against public apathy and lack of funds.

Bill Noonan

instrumented rooms, fire scientists can now paint a detailed if still qualitative picture of the most common type of killer fire. The fire begins when a cigarette falls from a careless hand onto a bedroom mattress or living room couch. It scorches through the sheet or cover fabric and makes contact with the "foam rubber" mattress—actually made of a plastic foam known as polyurethane. The polyurethane ignites, producing a small and easily extinguishable flame. But the flame grows rapidly and quietly, too quietly to awaken a sleeping person. Smoke and partially burned gases rise from the decomposing mattress and are trapped within the room, accumulating at the ceiling. Heat radiating away from the flame begins to raise the temperature of everything in the room.

Within a couple of minutes after the fire begins, the thickening cloud under the ceiling is rich with toxic gases and hot enough that it acts like a huge space heater, intensifying the radiant energies heating the room's furnishings. For a person awakening at this point, it is possible to get out alive—the fire is still restricted to a small portion of the mattress and looks harmless enough. But it is essential to go quickly, on one's knees, avoiding lungfuls of the deadly, disorienting fumes near the ceiling.

As the temperatures of the room's furnishings pass 150° Celsius, decomposition begins, releasing volatile gases from wood, fabrics, paint, paper, and especially from many plastics. After four or five minutes, the room has become a tinderbox waiting for a spark or a tongue of flame from the original small fire to set off an explosion—the deadly phenomenon of "flashover." Almost instantaneously, all of the flammable objects in the room ignite. The small fire becomes an inferno from which there is no escape □

 SELECTED READINGS

"Fire and polymers" by G. Nelson. *Chemistry,* June 1978.

"Is that garment resistant to flame? Look again!" by F. Weinberg. *Science Digest,* May 1979.

"Toxic gases from fires" by J. Terrill. *Science,* June 23, 1978.

LOW-LEVEL RADIATION

by Walter Sullivan

THE exposure of perhaps two million Pennsylvanians to excess radiation from the accident at the Three Mile Island nuclear plant brought to a climax a prolonged and intense debate that began more than 20 years ago.

In 1979, a majority on a U.S. National Academy of Sciences committee that is assessing research on the effects of low-level radiation had come to believe that exposure to the type associated with Three Mile Island is less hazardous than many had previously believed.

The question is part of a broad debate that originally focused on whether there is a "threshold" level of exposure—a level below which there is no effect at all. No evidence of such a threshold has been found, however, any many specialists now doubt that one exists.

As a result of the Three Mile Island radiation leak, controversy has moved to the forefront. The dispute, which led to a sharp division in the National Academy of Sciences committee, centers on whether the effects are "linear"—that is, whether they decrease at uniform rates as dosage decreases.

In a linear situation a tenfold reduction of exposure should lead to a tenfold decrease in the incidence of cancer. Instead, some specialists say, the drop in cancer incidence at low-dose rates may be greater than that.

A dissent along these lines was appended to the draft of the Academy committee's report, a summary of which was made public on May 2, 1979. Five of the 18 committee members subscribed to this dissent. Since then, however, the number of dissenters has reportedly grown to a majority, and the report is being revised in an effort to achieve a consensus.

X RAYS, GAMMA RAYS, AND ELECTRONS

The type of radiation involved in the dispute is known as low LET, for linear energy transfer, radiation. This category in-

Keith Meyers/New York Times

The Three Mile Island accident in 1979 sparked new concern about effects of radiation exposure.

In 1898 Pierre and Marie Curie discovered radium, the chief source of the radiation used today.

cludes X rays and gamma rays—at the shortest wavelength end of the spectrum that includes visible light—and beta rays. The latter are electrons emitted by such radioactive substances as carbon 14.

The far more damaging high LET radiation consists of heavier particles, such as protons, neutrons, and alpha particles. People exposed to high LET radiation include uranium miners and radium-treated patients.

The effect of these heavier particles on molecules susceptible to genetic defects or to the genesis of cancer has been likened to a bulldozer tearing through a field of sprouting

X rays deliver about 40 millirems of radiation a year to the average medical patient.

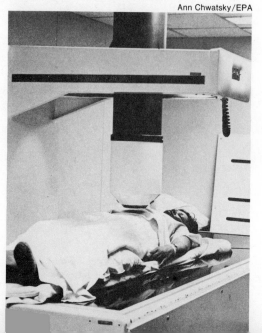

corn. The effect of low LET radiation is more like that of rabbits going through a field in that many of them would have to step on a corn sprout before it was damaged.

THREE MILE ISLAND REPORT

According to the preliminary federal report on the health effects of Three Mile Island, all of the radioactive material that escaped the plant was of the low LET variety. The report, prepared by specialists from the Nuclear Regulatory Commission, the Environmental Protection Agency, and the Department of Health and Human Services, estimated exposure to those within an 80-kilometer radius.

The report assumes that any added radiation exposure, no matter how small, leads to at least a slight increase in cancer risk. On this basis it suggests that, in addition to 325,-000 cancer deaths that would normally be expected in the area's population of two million, one fatality and one nonfatal case might occur as a result of the accident. If the effect is weaker, as suspected by dissenting members of the Academy committee, no one might contract cancer as a result of the accident.

The Academy report describes other forms of ionizing radiation and sums up the present state of knowledge concerning the effects of low-level exposure. Both high LET and low LET forms of radiation are ionizing. That is, with damaging energy they knock loose electrons within molecules, forming ions in the body.

Nonionizing radiation, as from ultraviolet light, microwave ovens, and very high-powered radars, can be damaging in other ways but does not figure in the nuclear-energy debate.

All life is in a constant crossfire of ionizing radiation, of both natural and artificial origin. Its biological effects are usually expressed in *rads,* for radiation absorbed dose. It is the term used for the amount of radiation absorbed by an organ of the body. One rad is equal to about 38 simultaneous chest X rays. Another unit for measuring the biological effect on a person from a dose of radiation is the *rem,* for roentgen equivalent per man. Exposures are measured in millirads (thousandths of a rad) and millirems (thousandths of a rem).

The dose received by those within 80 kilometers of Three Mile Island was estimated at 1.5 millirems. No one outside the plant received more than 100 millirems. In comparison, the average American receives about 100 millirems a year from natural sources.

High-level doses of radiation (doses of more than 100 rads), if received all at once, cause effects that appear within hours or days. These effects are called radiation sickness. The first symptoms are nausea, vomiting, and malaise. These are followed by hemorrhaging, diarrhea, and effects on the central nervous system.

SOURCES OF RADIATION

Exposure to naturally occurring radiation arises from three sources: radioactive material in the environment (rocks, soil, and building materials), cosmic rays, and substances in the body. All bone, for example, contains radioactive potassium, and virtually all tissue contains radioactive carbon.

The largest single source of artificial radiation is medical X rays. This form of medical treatment delivers an annual average dose of 40 millirems to the bone marrow. The accompanying chart shows the estimated average radiation doses for natural and artificial radiation. A third source of low-level radiation is uranium mines, their processing plants, and some phosphate mines.

Another source is fallout from weapons tests. Because fallout components, such as strontium 90 and carbon 14, become incorporated into the body, they may deliver radiation for an entire lifetime.

It was the question of fallout effects that, in the 1950's, began the early debate on low-level radiation. Initially the chief concern was genetic damage.

In 1958 Dr. Linus Pauling, who won a Nobel Peace Prize for his fight to halt atmospheric weapons testing, wrote to *The New York Times* that fallout from one year of tests "will ultimately be responsible for the birth of 230,000 seriously defective children and also for 420,000 embryonic and neonatal deaths."

Prominent among those of the opposing view was Dr. Edward Teller, "father" of the hydrogen bomb, who said that same year: "If you move from the seashore to Colorado, you expose yourself to considerably more additional activity than the accumulated effect of all past weapons tests."

Nevertheless, on August 10, 1958, the United Nations Scientific Committee on the Effects of Atomic Radiation concluded: "Even the smallest amounts of radiation are liable to cause deleterious genetic, and perhaps also somatic (body) effects."

At that time, a long-term study of the survivors of the Hiroshima and Nagasaki

UPI

Everyone is exposed to some natural radiation; industrial workers may receive additional doses on the job.

atomic explosions was well under way. Although the study has yielded many significant findings, some scientists have questioned whether the bomb survivors, exposed to high doses of radioactivity, provide a valid basis for conclusions about the effects of low-level radiation.

SUSCEPTIBILITY OF CHILDREN

Further complicating the surveys is evidence that some age groups, notably children, and some parts of the body are more susceptible than others.

An early indication of harmful effects

U.S. Army Photograph

Observers at an atomic test in 1957; such tests were later banned.

from low radiation levels developed from a survey initiated in 1955 to explain an alarming rise in leukemia in Britain. It located 14,300 people who had been treated with deeply penetrating X rays for arthritis of the spine, and confirmed that an abnormally high percentage had contracted cancer.

In 1970 Dr. Alice Stewart, then at Oxford University, reported that the Oxford Survey of Childhood Cancers, involving 15,298 persons, revealed a high incidence in those subjected to X rays before birth when their mothers were given pelvic X rays. The implication of this statistic is that the body is more sensitive to low LET radiation than had been assumed.

Later that year, however, Seymour Jablon of the Atomic Bomb Casualty Commission and Hiroo Kato of the Japanese National Institute of Health reported on a follow-up of 1,292 persons prenatally exposed to bomb radiation. There was, they said, "no significant excess of mortality from leukemia or other cancers." Their findings, they added, indicated less of a dose effect than expected from a linear response.

Meanwhile, after years of reassurance from official quarters that radiation by-products of nuclear energy were safe, there began to be defections from within the atomic-energy establishment.

The controversy intensified in 1976, after Dr. Thomas F. Mancuso of the University of Pittsburgh teamed with Dr. Stewart and one of her colleagues, Dr. George W. Kneale, to examine the death certificates of former employees of the Hanford Works in Richmond, Washington. The plant produces plutonium for nuclear weapons.

Initially the death certificates of 2,184 "exposed" workers, all of whom wore radiation badges, were examined, as well as a comparison group of 1,336 "nonexposed" workers.

The researchers found that among the exposed workers cancer deaths were eight per cent above normal. There were markedly high rates for cancers of the pancreas, lung, bone marrow, and lymph systems. The records of 4,033 exposed workers who had died by 1977 were examined later, with similar results.

As with Dr. Stewart's earlier Oxford study of prenatal exposure, the incidence of cancer seemed higher than expected from surveys of Hiroshima and Nagasaki survivors and of those who had undergone medical X rays. Dr. Stewart and her colleagues attributed this to the prolonged, low-intensity exposure of the Hanford workers, in contrast to the more intense, short-term exposure of the other subjects.

SIMULATING ATOMIC BLASTS

In compiling its recent report, the National Academy of Sciences committee studying the effects of radiation considered many earlier findings. The most pertinent of these come from continued observation of those who survived the atomic bombs over Hiroshima and Nagasaki.

The study, under international auspices, has involved 109,000 of 284,000 identified survivors and another 2,800 who were in their mothers' wombs at the time of the explosions.

In the course of the research, typical Japanese houses were constructed at the United States weapons testing site in Nevada. Measurements were taken in and near them as bombs comparable to those dropped on Japan were detonated. When the partial test ban treaty ruled out such tests, a particle accelerator was hoisted to the top of a 450-meter tower to simulate the radiation.

It is estimated that 22 per cent of the Hiroshima survivors and 33 per cent of the Nagasaki survivors received less than 10 rads. Both explosions emitted primarily low LET radiation.

Follow-up studies of the survivors have led to several surprises. No genetic effects have been identified in the next generation. Also, death rates from all causes have been slightly less than for Japanese not exposed to the bombs. There proved, typically, to be a lag of many years before the appearance of cancerous tumors, whereas leukemia cases appeared much sooner.

Some specialists, such as Dr. Joseph Rotblat, past president of the British Institute of Radiology, believe that the survivors may be living longer than other Japanese because weaker residents of Hiroshima and Nagasaki were killed by the explosions. The follow-ups, nevertheless, have led researchers to believe that body cells have often been able to repair damage from low LET radiation.

Some researchers believe that the dose-effect relationship is distorted in a situation involving very high exposures—such as Hiroshima and Nagasaki—because such exposure kills cells most susceptible to becoming cancerous □

Estimated Annual Average Radiation Doses

Source	Dose (Equivalent rate in millirems per year)
NATURAL RADIATION	
Cosmic rays (sea level)	23
Cosmic rays (5,000 feet)	50
Cosmic rays (air travelers)	65
Cosmic rays (plane crews)	160
Radioactive constituents of body (potassium 40, rubidium 87, carbon 14, radium 226 & 228, tritium)	28
Gamma radiation from terrestrial sources	26
ARTIFICIAL RADIATION	
Medical and dental X rays	
Patients	20
Occupational	0.4
Radiopharmaceuticals	
Patients	2–4
Occupational	0.15
Nuclear Power	
Environmental	1
Occupational	0.15
National laboratories and Contactors	0.2
Industrial applications	0.01
Military applications	0.04
Weapons testing fallout	4–5
Color television	4–5
Air travel	0.5

Source: Report of the Committee on Biological Effects of Ionizing Radiations, 1979

The New York Times/July 2, 1979

 SELECTED READINGS

"How radiation affects us" by M. Browne. *Science Digest Special,* Winter 1979.

"Low-level radiation: just how bad is it?" by J. Marx. *Science,* April 13, 1979.

"Primer on radiation" by W. Rados. *FDA Consumer,* July–August 1979.

"Radiation in daily life" by E. Komarov. *World Health,* June 1979.

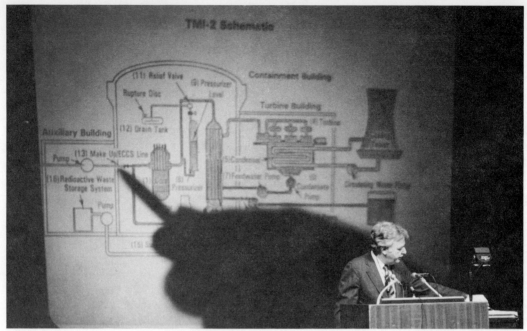

Hathorn/Olson Photography

John Kemeny describes the basic workings of a nuclear-power plant while giving the report of the President's Commission on Three Mile Island.

THE KEMENY REPORT

by John G. Kemeny

AT 4:00 A.M. on the 28th of March, 1979, an extremely small and unimportant malfunction happened at a nuclear plant in the state of Pennsylvania. Within a very short period of time, it would turn into an event of momentous impact, with repercussions felt over most of the world.

Two weeks after that accident, the President of the United States appointed a 12-member commission. When we first met, in late April, I looked around the room and found one of the most diverse groups I have ever worked with—diverse in every possible way. The opinions on nuclear power ranged from the strongly pro-nuclear to the strongly anti-nuclear. The members had a wide variety of backgrounds: There were representatives of several academic specialties, a governor, a well-known environmentalist, a Washington lawyer with significant government experience, and Anne Trunk, the one member of the commission who lived through the accident.

Finally, there was the chairman. I did not fit any of the categories for membership on the commission. I am not quite sure whether I was there as a generalist, which is possible, or whether I was there because they felt that with so diverse a commission, my having had ten years' experience chairing faculty meetings would be an ideal background.

THE WORKINGS OF A NUCLEAR POWER PLANT

Of course, we quickly needed to find out how a nuclear power plant works, a process that can be described here in fairly simple terms. In the right side of the diagram, the feedwater pumps drive water into the steam generator where the water is heated up and turned to steam, and that steam drives a turbine (or several turbines) to generate electricity. Then the water is cooled down again, condensed, pumped back in, and re-heated, and it keeps generating electricity. Incidentally, this part of the plant, I am told, is no different from any other kind of electric generating plant. It could be driven by coal or oil or whatever the fuel might be.

I want to call particular attention to the cooling towers. Because of the many ironies connected with this particular accident, the commission would spend a lot of time talking about the cooling towers, which became the symbol of Three Mile Island. They are tremendously impressive. They are frightening. They are probably the least important part of the entire plant. All they do is provide a third water system to cool off the steam, and they are used purely for cooling that water which has no radiation in it. All you see coming out of the towers is harmless steam. This is not where the danger is. They look huge, and they are totally unimportant.

But what is special about the plant? What is special is that it is not coal or oil or wood that heats this water but a nuclear reactor. That means there are uranium pellets in a metal casing, in something called zirconium . . . lots of them sitting around . . . and a very carefully controlled chain reaction, a reaction in which the very basic energy of the atom is used. In this particular case it is used for nothing more exciting than heating up water in the primary loop, which in turn heats up the water in the secondary loop (center section), which then drives a turbine. Enormous amounts of heat are created, and therefore a great deal of electricity can be generated.

Why are there two separate water systems? That is because the primary system comes in contact with nuclear materials and can pick up radioactive materials, while the secondary system never comes in direct contact with nuclear materials. It becomes heated by running through neighboring tubes, so it is free of radioactivity.

Now, the little things at the top of the reactor are absolutely crucial. They are called control rods. If anything goes wrong, they drop into the middle of all the nuclear material, and they are able to capture enough of the neutrons that are running around so that the chain reaction stops. That is the single most important safety feature of a nuclear power plant.

HOLDING IN ANY RADIATION

The whole primary system is enclosed in an enormous reinforced structure called the containment building. The theory is to contain within that area any radiation that might escape. It can be isolated so that no radiation can escape to the outside world.

The part on the left of the diagram is normally the least important part. It is called the auxiliary building, for miscellaneous equipment. It would turn out to be terribly important in this particular accident because all the radioactive material that escaped went out through the chimney of the auxiliary building.

The final piece of equipment I want to describe is something called a pressurizer (center). It serves the following purpose: The water that cools the reactor and, in turn, heats the water in the pressurizer is at quite high temperatures, between 500 and 600 degrees Fahrenheit. Since water boils at 212 degrees, you might ask how can there be water at that kind of temperature? The answer is that by keeping it under high enough pressure, as in a pressure cooker, for example, it will not boil even at much higher temperatures.

The purpose of the pressurizer, which contains part water and part steam, is to maintain an equilibrium to keep things at the right pressure. The operators are carefully trained to keep watching the water level in that pressurizer. If it is high enough, there is enough water. If it goes too low, it needs more water. That turned out to be one of the most important things in this particular accident.

WATER STOPPED CIRCULATING

Let me now turn to what happened. Just before 4:00 A.M., some of the crew were

Aerial view of Three Mile Island, the site of the worst accident in nuclear-power history.

Maps Inc

working on repairing an extremely unimportant part of the system—the polishers. (They are so unimportant, they are not even shown on the diagrams.) Water that runs through the turbine is circulated so that any "gunk" in it is removed by these polishers and therefore they have to be cleaned periodically.

Something went wrong as they were being cleaned. We think, but are not absolutely sure, that a little bit of water from the polishers got into an air line, which in turn triggered something else that turned off a pump, and all of a sudden water stopped running into the steam generator. As a result, the turbine was shut off by the safety machinery, and there was no water circulating on the right side.

As I pointed out, there is a dual function in the steam generator. The water in the primary loop heats up the water in the secondary loop to generate electricity. At virtually the same time, by passing its heat along to the secondary side, the water gets cooled off and can go back and keep the reactor cool. All of a sudden, with water not running into the steam generator, not very much heat was being removed from the reactor, and things began to heat up where it really counted. As the water got hotter, the pressure rose. But there is a provision for just such an event.

Right above the pressurizer is a valve, the pressure-operated (or pilot-operated) relief valve, which acts like the lid of a steam kettle which, if the pressure gets too high, lifts up and lets out some steam. That valve lifted to release the pressure as it was supposed to do. When the pressure kept rising even higher, the next safety device was triggered: The control rods dropped into the reactor, just as they were supposed to, and the chain reaction stopped within a second.

So, ten seconds into the accident, and given the original malfunction, everything had gone perfectly. Everything seemed to be completely under control. It was like hundreds of previous incidents that had happened with no bad effects.

HEAT CONTINUES TO BE GENERATED

One more thing about the reactors: When the operators turn off the chain reaction, not all the heat generation stops. About 94 per cent of it does, but not all of it, because the process of nuclear fission creates radioactive by-products—wastes—that continue to give off radiation, which in turn generates heat. After the fission is shut off, only six per cent of the original amount of heat remains. But the original amount was horrendously large and six per cent is still quite a large quantity, and it is extremely important to keep removing that heat.

The operators have two ways of doing that. One is through the steam generator. The other involves special emergency water systems that are designed to be much more than enough to remove all that heat. It is at this point in the Three Mile Island accident that things go wrong.

In this system practically everything

In the days immediately following the accident, many children and pregnant women were bused out of the vicinity.

exists in duplicate; when the water stops running, a whole second system is designed to start pouring water into the steam generator. That came on automatically as it was supposed to, but no water reached the steam generator. One operator madly scurried around trying to find out what was happening. Eight minutes later he discovered that some valves which were always supposed to be open under normal operations were left closed at some unknown time.

We never did discover when they were left closed. The most likely time was during a maintenance operation two days earlier. And, although the people who were involved swear that they reopened them, we are not absolutely sure that their memory is right. At any rate, that is one of the minor mysteries. It is not of vast importance, because our analysis showed that the emergency water system coming on would not have made a great deal of difference in view of everything else that happened. But it was very important in terms of one operator's total confusion—scurrying around watching one side while horrible things were happening over on the other side.

A VALVE STUCK OPEN

The second thing that happened is that when the reactor shut off, the pressure started dropping. As the pressure dropped, the valve that opened under too high pressure was supposed to fall back into place. There was an electric signal to open it and an electric signal to close it, and there was the light in the control room that said the signal went out for the valve to close. What the operators did not know was that although the signal went out, the valve stuck open.

Now, valves do stick open, and this particular valve had some history of sticking open. As a matter of fact, because of that, there was another valve behind it that they could close from the control room if this one ever stuck open. But they did not know that this valve had stuck open.

Things were getting to be quite serious because with the valve stuck open, precious water was running into a drain tank instead of staying inside the system to cool it. It would be well over two hours before the op-

erators realized that that valve was open. By that time tens of thousands of gallons of water had gone out through the valve and through one other route.

Since the pressure was not diminishing to proper levels, two minutes after the accident started the main safety system came on by itself. It is called the high pressure injection system. It pumps in, through two pumps, a thousand gallons a minute—vastly more than is normally needed to cool everything off. We have carefully checked the calculations. Even with that valve stuck open, there was plenty of water to bring everything under control.

HUMAN ERROR

But now the third thing went wrong. The operators turned off one of the pumps and cut the other one way back, so that instead of a thousand gallons a minute there were less than 100 gallons a minute. This created a situation where the amount spilling out of the system was significantly more than the amount being let in. That is the fundamental and direct cause of why a minor incident turned into a major accident.

The operators realized none of this. Their supervisors who came to help out did not recognize the problems, and about 100 minutes into the accident—a little over an hour and a half—they had a very serious problem. Water was boiling. There was not enough water to cover the core. The metal casings that held the uranium started bursting, and eventually enormous damage was done to the entire core.

For hours they kept trying to deal with it. They tried one thing after another, and from analysis done a month later it is clear that some of their efforts made things better and some made things even worse. It took most of that day before they got the system even roughly under control. That is how the worst accident in the history of commercial nuclear power happened.

It was quite natural, I suppose, that given those facts all the early reports said: "It is very simple. The equipment had only minor problems. It is all the fault of the operators. It's what they did wrong that caused the accident."

Wearing protective overalls, gloves, and boots, members of the Commission peer down at one of the Three Mile Island nuclear reactors during a tour of the plant.

It certainly looked that way to us, too. At our first public hearing where we could take testimony under oath, we called all the operators and their supervisors to tell us why in heaven's name they did what they did. And, to a man, they testified that they had never been prepared for anything like what they faced there. We pushed them very hard, and we could not shake them.

At that hearing our investigation, which had concentrated on equipment, took a very sharp turn. From that point on—although we continued to look at the equipment and made a number of recommendations for improving it—we followed a path leading to our major conclusion: That the real problem was not the equipment but the people. Before we were through, we would find "people problems" in more different places than we would ever have guessed at the beginning.

There was one incident from which we probably learned more than from anything else. We learned it because of one single document that our legal staff found in an enormous mound of papers from one company.

A top engineer in Babcock and Wilcox, the company that manufactures the steam-supply system, had, after studying an accident at a nuclear-power plant in Ohio in 1977, realized that operators must be told that under certain circumstances watching the water level in the pressurizer, as they had been instructed to do, was not enough and might be misleading—that even if the water

level showed high, they should keep the water pouring in. He wrote a memo to this effect—a memo lost in a bureaucratic maze. Others also became aware of the problem and wrote memos—to the utility involved, to Babcock and Wilcox, and to the Nuclear Regulatory Commission. For all kinds of reasons none of them did anything about it.

THE TRAINING OF OPERATORS

We then started looking at the training of operators. I will give just a slight idea of what we found. There seemed to be no minimum educational qualifications for somebody entering operator school. It is essentially an on-the-job training program; it has no precise curriculum. There is shared responsibility between the utility and the steam supplier, with no precise rules as to exactly what is to be covered by each one. Neither teaches the fundamentals of nuclear power.

It is a sort of button-pushing school. Even when they do receive practical, hands-on experience, there are some serious deficiencies. For example, a key training device is something called the simulator, which is a computer that can reproduce what happens in the control room. NASA used simulators for its space flights, and they are used for training airplane pilots. This simulator was a perfectly good one for ordinary operations. But our investigation showed that when they tried to reproduce on it the conditions of the accident at Three Mile Island, they found it was not programmed to reproduce those conditions. Therefore, the operators had to be right in saying that they had never been trained for anything like that.

The control room is the biggest Tinker Toy you have ever seen in your life. There are hundreds of flashing lights all over the place. Each one suggests a certain kind of alarm. I have never quite gotten over an incident that happened while we were touring the plant. Alarms went off, and people did something about them, called somebody, pulled a lever, and pushed a button. There are little transparent labels, and behind each label is a light that blinks to show which alarm has gone off.

After the third alarm during our tour, I looked to see where the alarm was. Nothing was blinking. So I finally raised my hand and asked the person who was giving us a fascinating lecture if he would mind telling what was going on. He asked the operator, who said, "Oh, it is very simple. One of the light bulbs must have burned out, and therefore we don't know which alarm went off." I then watched for five or ten minutes while an auxiliary operator removed those little labels, one at a time, until he found the burned-out light bulb, and screwed in a new light bulb. It started blinking, and then he knew which alarm went off. Then they did something about it. I am afraid I did go so far as to say publicly that I did not think that was modern technology at its most glorious.

THE NUCLEAR REGULATORY COMMISSION

From there we took a very intensive look at the Nuclear Regulatory Commission.

In terms of operator training, I should tell you that section has a minute staff—I think there are eight or nine full-time employees in it, plus some part-time people. They really just did a token sampling and administering of quite routine exams. Even there we found, for example, that an operator could fail badly that part of the exam having to do with the safety systems, but get a good enough overall grade to pass the examination.

We looked at their licensing and found all kinds of difficulties with the licensing process. Perhaps the most troublesome was that in the licensing of a given plant, if there was a serious problem that was applicable not just to that plant but to a lot of plants, they would label the problem "generic." Then the plant did not have to worry about that problem because it would go through a different machinery. Some of those "generic" problems have been sitting around for years and years.

We looked at their enforcement arm, because all their rules and regulations mean nothing unless somebody enforces them. We found that this was probably the weakest part of the commission.

As we studied the N.R.C. overall, our most important judgment was that it is an agency hypnotized by equipment. It had a firm belief that equipment can be made failsafe. As a result, the N.R.C. totally ignored the human element in nuclear power.

The March 28, 1979 accident at Three Mile Island could clearly have been prevented. But the President's Commission has overwhelmingly concluded that given all the problems—the human problems that we found within the utility, its supplier, and par-

The biggest Tinker Toy ever—hundreds of flashing lights, levers, and buttons characterize the control room at Three Mile Island.

Courtesy, Metropolitan Edison

ticularly the Regulatory Commission—if this particular accident had been prevented, an accident like it was eventually inevitable.

It is on that that we based our overall conclusion: "To prevent nuclear accidents as serious as Three Mile Island, fundamental changes will be necessary in the organization, procedures and practices—and, above all—in the attitudes of the N.R.C. and, to the extent that the institutions we investigated are typical, of the nuclear industry."

RECOMMENDATIONS

Where did we go from there? Our commission then entered its very difficult decision-making stage. Of course, there were many things that we could not do. We did conclude that our evidence was not such as to recommend that nuclear power should be abolished. But we did not feel that we could say go full speed ahead with nuclear power, either.

We started with a restructuring of the N.R.C. because that agency must be changed. We recommended that it go to the form of a strong administrator, who would be chosen from outside the present agency. We feel that this is crucial. We want him or her to have enough freedom to bring a great deal of new blood into the agency.

We recommended sweeping changes for how this agency should function, which I hope will be accepted whether or not our single administrator is accepted. I'll provide just two examples:

• On licensing we have recommended vastly higher qualifications for a utility before it is allowed to operate a nuclear power plant—qualifications stringent enough, I suspect, that a number of present utilities would not be allowed to operate such plants.

• Regarding enforcement, we issued a long list of recommendations for strengthening that area, one of which is that every single licensee should be periodically reviewed in depth as to whether it is performing up to the standards of that license.

We also made a number of recommendations to the utilities on organization, on procedures, and on standards of maintenance that were certainly not satisfactory in this particular plant:

• We recommended a completely new approach to operator training so that candidates would first have to graduate from a training institution, where they will learn the fundamentals of nuclear power before they get on-the-job training.

• We recommended very strongly that utilities pay a great deal more attention to the procedures given to operators, particularly emergency procedures, because some of the ones we reviewed were at best confusing and possibly totally wrong. (For example, we had a half-hour argument in one of our public hearings, just to try to figure out which of two procedures the operators were supposed to follow during that particular accident.)

• We made a number of recommenda-

One week after the accident, former Health, Education, and Welfare Secretary Joseph Califano (left), Environmental Protection Agency Administrator Douglas Costle, and Nuclear Regulatory Commission Chairman Joseph Hendrie, appeared at a Senate inquiry.

UPI

Scene from *The China Syndrome*, a dramatic film about a nuclear-power plant accident—released just days before the Three Mile Island accident.

tions on equipment, the most important of which has to do with modernization of the control room.

IN CASE OF ACCIDENT . . .

Then we turned to the mitigation of accidents once they happen. There is the question of emergency preparation and response. Fortunately, in the case of Three Mile Island, although that plant is now a total mess, the containment building worked well enough so that most of the radiation did not get out.

But if there had been significant releases of radiation, we felt that the preparation was atrocious and the response was worse. The N.R.C. had come up with a magic number for establishing a safety zone. Through a crazy calculation that we tried to explain in our document, they somehow established a two-mile safety zone as a magic radius around this plant.

Fortunately, Pennsylvania has tougher laws. That state requires five miles. And those zones were for much worse accidents than this one. In the middle of this accident, where people suffered very little direct harm, authorities were planning for an evacuation of up to 20 miles from the plant, and we noted that the way that planning was done had absolutely nothing to do with real life.

We have recommended that, where feasible, plants should be located as far away as possible from major population centers, and the states in which they are located should be required to have emergency plans. We also recommended significantly better public education.

AFTERMATH

The sad thing that happened was described by one congressman at the end of the joint hearing. He pointed out that the biggest story never got proper coverage. That story is the vote we unanimously adopted that says no license—neither a construction permit nor an operating license—should be issued until three separate requirements are satisfied:

• That the new safety requirements that we and others recommended have been implemented;

• That the applicant fulfill the much higher qualification for running a nuclear power plant, including having an acceptable operator training program;

• That those licenses should be made conditional on the approval of state and local emergency plans.

We have no way of enforcing these requirements, as we have no way of enforcing any other recommendation. But if this recommendation should be given teeth, let's say, by the President and Congress, it could be the most powerful recommendation that we made □

 SELECTED READINGS

"The safety of fission reactors" by H. Lewis. *Scientific American,* March 1980.

"Kemeny report: abolish the N.R.C." by E. Marshall. *Science,* November 16, 1979.

"Nuclear power-plant performance; an update" by R. L. Goble and C. Hohenemser. *Environment,* October 1979.

Joel E. Arem

The metal bismuth shows its orderly arrangement of crystals. Tarnish gives the iridescence.

SYNTHETIC CRYSTALS

by Joel E. Arem

UNTIL recent times nature almost had a monopoly on growing crystals. This is no longer true. The way crystals grow in nature and the constituents they grow from have been extensively studied in the laboratory and imitated—and for very good reasons.

Synthetic crystals are at the heart of our technological society. They are essential in computers and other electronic equipment. In the form of lasers, they may provide the key to the production of limitless energy on earth. Yet relatively few people know that the technology of crystal-growing exists, let alone that it has spawned a multibillion-dollar industrial offspring. This is understandable because most crystals produced by industry are used by industry, not by consumers.

Until recently little systematic effort had been made to document achievements in synthetic crystal growth, or to preserve first-grown and unusual crystals for future generations. This situation changed with the inception in 1971 of the National Synthetics Collection in the Smithsonian's Department of Mineral Sciences. It includes the specimens illustrated in this article, plus hundreds more from almost every major crystal-growth laboratory in the United States.

A PATTERN OF ATOMS AND MOLECULES

A crystal is solid material—and all true solids are crystalline. Every atom in a solid has definite neighbor atoms, all at fixed distances and relative positions.

The fixed pattern of atoms in a specific crystal gives it constant and recognizable properties. Occasionally "mistakes" occur when a crystal grows in nature: atoms that do not normally belong are incorporated. These are termed impurities, and they have a great effect on the properties of the host crystal. After much experimentation in synthesizing crystals, scientists have learned how to add impurities selectively and in controlled amounts. This is a process called "doping," in which the additives are termed "dopants." Crystalographers can thus tailor the properties of crystals for specific purposes.

It is important to differentiate between *synthetic* and *imitation* materials. Synthetic crystals are manufactured from simple components, and the very word synthesis means "put together." A synthetic gemstone can be chemically, structurally, and physically the same as its natural counterpart. The same mineral constituents must be mined from the ground and purified and, when placed in the proper conditions, their atoms will be rearranged into the desired crystal.

Synthetic ruby, for example, is ruby. The laboratory process used to make it may not be

acteristics. A major emphasis has centered on finding a substitute for diamond.

IMITATION DIAMONDS

Diamond is not only a woman's best friend, it is also the friend of the industrial machinist, for it is one of the finest abrasive materials known. The demand for industrial diamond is so great that it could swallow up all the stones mined, including the mere five per cent suitable for gem use.

When cut as a gem, diamond has a dazzling display of colors. The colors are due to

A diamond imitation, synthetic rutile sparkles with a dazzling array of colors.

Joel E. Arem

the same as that used by nature (as explained later) but the end result is material that is the same. In fact, the synthetic product is generally finer in color, purity, and transparency than that made by nature.

An imitation, on the other hand, is a material with properties that mimic those of a different, more costly material. Glass, for example, has long been used as an imitation—and a very poor one—for ruby, sapphire, zircon, emerald and other stones. Recent technology, however, has produced some remarkable crystals with much better imitative char-

dispersion, the ability of a material to separate white light into its component colors. Diamond is not the only material with high dispersion, but it has the best combination of dispersion, hardness, and transparency.

In the late 1940's imitation gems with incredibly high dispersion appeared on the market under a wide variety of trade names. These gems were made of titanium dioxide, which occurs in nature as the mineral rutile. A disadvantage of synthetic rutile as a gemstone is its relative softness and distinct yellowish body color.

In the late 1960's a completely different material emerged victorious among diamond imitations. Yttrium-aluminum garnet, known in the gem market by its acronym, YAG, was originally grown for use in lasers. YAG, doped with the rare earth element neodymium, yields lasers with very high efficiencies. When carefully cut, however, YAG affords gems that have the brilliance and colors of diamond. In addition, YAG is quite hard and durable. Unfortunately, YAG lacks the tremendous dispersion, or prismatic effects, in which light is broken up into its component colors, that makes diamond so attractive.

thetic diamond have been produced for industrial use. Gem-sized crystals, however, are so expensive to make that they cannot be profitably marketed. The largest synthetic-diamond-gem crystals weigh only about one carat, and gems cut from such crystals weigh less than half a carat.

OTHER SYNTHETIC GEMS

All the "precious" gems have been synthesized—emerald, ruby, sapphire and diamond, as well as opal, quartz, and others. In most cases the synthetic product is more

YAG, a diamond imitation, has the brilliance and color of diamond. It is also hard and durable and used for lasers.

Joel E. Arem

ponent colors, that makes diamond so attractive.

Technology continued to work on producing a better imitation diamond. Eventually a material known as "zirconia" (cubic zirconium oxide) was developed. This material has the hardness of YAG plus the dispersion of diamond. It is by far the best diamond imitation ever produced.

Diamond itself has been synthesized also by an elaborate and costly method first announced by the General Electric Company in 1955. Since that time millions of carats of syn-

transparent, freer of inclusions, and finer in color than the natural counterpart. Ruby is simply the red variety of corundum (aluminum oxide), a mineral that occurs in many colors. The rest are called sapphire. Star sapphire and star ruby have both been synthesized. The mysterious stars in gems are due to the presence of minute inclusions. Light reflecting from such inclusions creates a "sheen," which is concentrated into sharp lines when the gem is cut. In corundum the inclusions are tiny needles of rutile, oriented within the host material according to the symmetry of the host's structure. The symmetry of corundum is hexagonal, so that the resulting star in the crystal is six-rayed.

Occasionally, despite careful control of the growth process, accidents occur. These events produce strange, deformed crystals, or aggregates, which owe their existence to essentially random growth conditions. Since natural crystals grow in similar circumstances, the "misfits" of laboratory growth often resemble natural mineral specimens. In such cases we can study the synthetic for insight into natural conditions. Most synthetic crystals, however, have distinct and predictable characteristics that reflect the growth technique that produced them.

GROWING CRYSTALS

The trick in growing a crystal is to get the atoms and molecules that make up the crystal to arrange themselves in the periodic, orderly arrangement characteristic of the solid material. This can be done in several ways. If the atoms are bouncing about in the form of a vapor, they must be condensed. If they are sliding over one another in a pot of molten material, the melt must be chilled and solidified. If the atoms are floating about in solution, they must be precipitated out. This gives us three basic methods of crystal growing: from a vapor, from a melt, and from solution.

Growth from vapor is usually very rapid. The growing crystal tends to spread out rapidly into the nearest, coolest part of the environment surrounding it, resulting in elaborate spikes and branches. This accounts for the lacy spider-web appearance of snowflakes, which grow from water vapor high in the atmosphere. Such intricate, branched crystals are called dendrites, and dendrites are characteristic of vapor growth. Dendrites can also form from a melt, as a result of rapid cooling.

Metals are the most familiar crystalline materials grown from melts. Every time a steel mill pours ingots it is creating masses of crystals in the molds. There is no control over the cooling process, so many crystals form simultaneously and grow against each other—a state of affairs that is undesirable to the crystal-grower. His aim is to control carefully the growth process and thus allow the for-

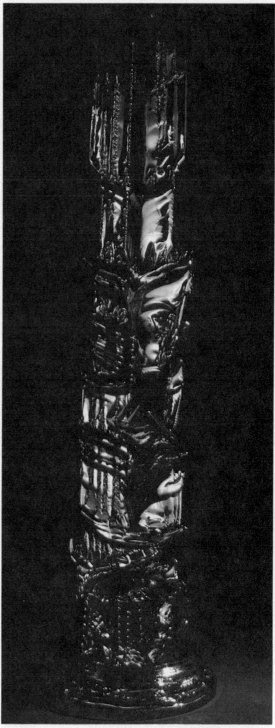

Joel E. Arem

Crystal pulling from molten material must be done carefully or a bizarre form such as the silicon crystal shown above can occur.

mation of only a single crystal. There are three basic techniques of melt growth currently in use to do this job.

GROWING SINGLE CRYSTALS

The simplest is called the Bridgman-Stockbarger method after the scientists who invented it. In this technique a powder of the desired crystal (or a mixture of components) is poured into a specially shaped container, lowered into a furnace, and melted. The container has a conical bottom that tapers to a small point. When this vessel passes through the furnace and emerges at the bottom, the tip is the first part to cool, and a single crystal generally forms there. The pot is lowered slowly from the furnace and, as the melt solidifies, atoms from the melt attach themselves to the solid, extending the growing crystal. Eventually the whole melt solidifies, and the result is (ideally) a single crystal.

Many substances are grown by the Bridgman technique. Halite (table salt) is vital not only to life, but to the chemical industry as well. Large, transparent masses of halite are needed from which to cut lenses and prisms. These are incorporated in specialized optical devices used in chemical analysis and quality control. Such masses are grown from a melt, in the form of ingots that may weigh hundreds of kilograms. A related material, cesium iodide, is grown in Bridgman ingots weighing more than half a ton.

These behemoths are the largest crystals yet grown in the laboratory.

One technique for ruby synthesis, first developed in France in the 19th century by Auguste Verneuil, involves growth from a melt. In the Verneuil method, powdered material is dribbled from a hopper through an intensely hot oxy-hydrogen torch flame. (For ruby and sapphire the powder is aluminum oxide containing a trace of the proper impurities to produce the color.) The powder melts and forms tiny droplets that fall, in a kind of "molten rain," onto a ceramic rod. The rod is rotated and slowly lowered as the crystal builds up on its tip.

Verneuil crystals up to 20 centimeters long are routinely made. This process can be automated, and some gem crystal factories boast more than a thousand simultaneously operating crystal furnaces. The output of such factories is measured in tons, rather than carats. Verneuil growth accounts for most of the rutile, strontium titanate, gem ruby and sapphire, spinel, and many research crystals produced today.

A third, and vitally important, melt-growth technique is generally called "crystal pulling," or the Czochralski technique (named for its inventor). A rotating rod containing a slice of the desired crystal is lowered down to a vessel containing the same material in molten form. The rod is touched to the melt, held there briefly, and then slowly

Ruby crystals produced by dribbling powdered chemicals through a flame onto ceramic rods can be cut to produce a perfect, synthetic star ruby, shown at right.

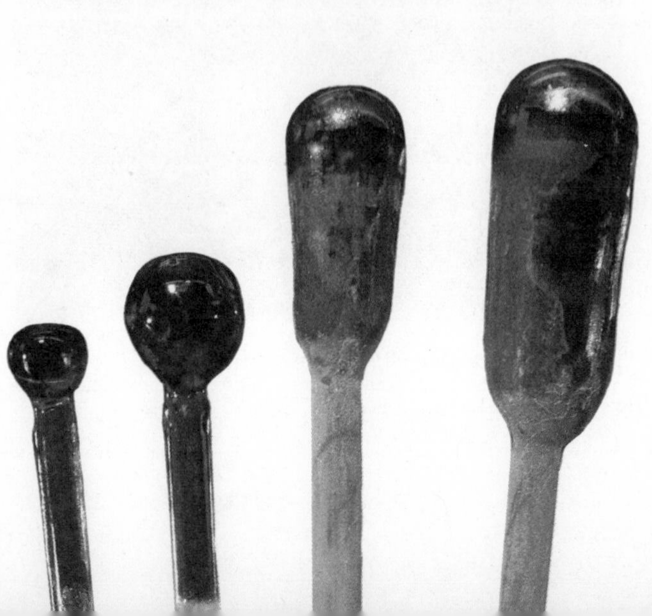

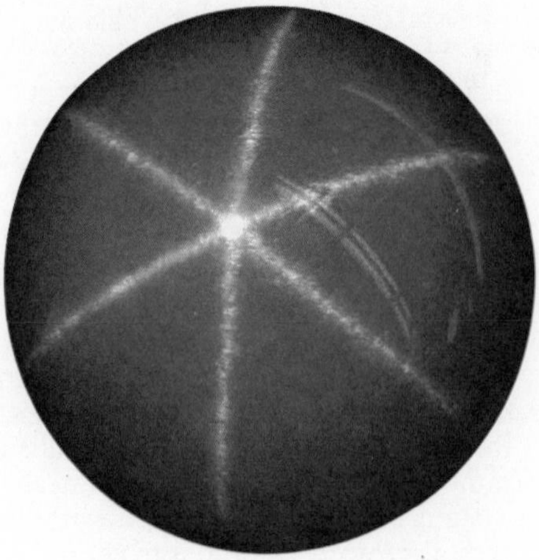

Joel E. Arem

Joel E. Arem

In the Bridgman-Stockbarger method of crystal growing, powder is used to make single crystals like the red crystal KRS-5 and the two fluorite crystals shown.

withdrawn. Some material from the melt adheres to the rod and is pulled sufficiently out of the melt to solidify. This process continues as the rod is withdrawn. The solidifying material builds up a single crystal on the end of the rod.

Czochralski growth accounts for some of the largest and finest crystals yet produced. Ruby crystals more than seven centimeters in diameter and 50 centimeters long, sapphires weighing about seven kilograms, and silicon crystals many meters long are typical of routine industrial production. Silicon is extremely important, because it is the basis of much of the technology of transistors and a major component of solar cells.

FROM SOLUTION TO CRYSTAL

Crystal growth from solution is the most familiar to all of us. If you swim in the ocean and then sun on the beach, your skin is soon covered with a fine crust of salt. This crust is made up of tiny crystals that grew from the ocean water as it evaporated from your skin.

Growth from solution is the way most natural crystals grow. Even in the human body, the growth of bone occurs through the deposition of a mineral material from solution (as do, less happily for us, gallstones and kidney stones).

On a larger scale, and with considerable modification, this process can be controlled to produce a wide variety of extremely large and perfect crystals used in the electronics industry. For example, since the 1940's, quartz

has become an increasingly vital material: large perfect quartz crystals are needed to make oscillators in communications equipment and the production of these has become a considerable industry.

Synthetic crystals of quartz are grown from solution at high temperatures and high pressures—a process called hydrothermal growth. A hydrothermal "bomb" is a steel can that is filled with water, seed crystals, and feed material (lumps of impure natural quartz) and placed inside a furnace. At temperatures of several hundred degrees the water vaporizes and creates high pressures inside the can. Under these conditions water is a powerful solvent. It dissolves the impure quartz, circulates inside the can, and deposits the dissolved material on the seed crystals.

Whatever the future holds for society, there is little doubt that synthetic crystals will play an increasingly important part in the emergence of the technology that keeps it running □

 SELECTED READINGS

"Decline in crystallography" by G. Jeffrey. *Physics Today,* November 1978.

"Elegant symmetry of crystals" by R. Ewing. *Natural History,* February 1978.

"Bell Labs reports manmade single-crystal monolayer alloys" by Gloria Lubkin. *Physics Today,* February 1977.

"Thin-layer crystal growing" by E. Keller. *Chemistry,* September 1978.

Harvard University
Sheldon L. Glashow

UPI
Steven Weinberg

Wide World
Abdus Salam

UPI
Georg Wittig

THE 1979 NOBEL PRIZES IN PHYSICS AND CHEMISTRY

by Barbara McDowell

Purdue News Photo
Herbert C. Brown

RESEARCH helping to unify two of the fundamental forces of nature earned U.S. physicists Steven Weinberg and Sheldon L. Glashow and Pakistani physicist Abdus Salam the 1979 Nobel Prize in Physics from the Swedish Royal Academy.

The 1979 Nobel Prize in Chemistry was shared by Herbert C. Brown of the United States and Georg Wittig of West Germany for their different but related discoveries facilitating the mass production of industrial and pharmaceutical chemicals.

THE PRIZE IN PHYSICS

Physicists—not the least of them being Albert Einstein—have long sought a single theory unifying the four basic forces of nature. These forces are gravity; electromagnetism, which accounts for such phenomena as sunlight and radio waves; the strong nuclear force that holds the nucleus of an atom together; and the weak nuclear force, which is responsible for some forms of radioactive decay. That still distant theory was brought one step closer by Weinberg, Salam, and

Glashow, whose separate but complementary research explains the unity of two of these forces—electromagnetism and the weak nuclear force. Their finding has been ranked by many of their colleagues among the most significant of the 20th century. It has been compared with James Clerk Maxwell's 19th-century explanation of how electric and magnetic forces are related. As Glashow notes, "One talks now of the fundamental forces of nature being gravity, strong nuclear force, and something called electro-weak force. Before, people had spoken of electromagnetism, which is heat and electricity and magnetism, and weak nuclear force as separate entities. Not any more."

It was Weinberg who in 1967 first succeeded in linking the electromagnetic force and the weak nuclear force. He did it through a series of complex mathematical concepts. Salam was simultaneously arriving at virtually identical conclusions, which he published the following year. Only one class of elementary particle was initially covered by what came to be known as the Weinberg-Salam Theory of Weak Interactions. In 1970 Glashow extended the theory to all elementary particles through his identification of a new type of quark, which he dubbed charm. Quarks are theoretical particles thought to make up certain elementary particles, including protons and neutrons. Charm is a complex combination of mathematical properties involving the way a particle is produced and the means by which it splits up.

The three Nobel laureates are theoretical physicists. Others had to prove their theories in the laboratory. First to be tested was the predicted existence of neutral current in an atomic nucleus, a previously undetected form of the weak nuclear force through which particles could interact with one another without changing their charge. A similar neutral current had already been observed in interactions governed by the electromagnetic force.

Explains Glashow, "The neutral currents we described and predicted are the things that let neutrons become protons even though they look very different." This neutral-current interaction was verified in 1973 after what Weinberg described as "very heroic experiments" at the European Center for Nuclear Research in Geneva, Switzerland. Other portions of the Weinberg-Salam Theory have been upheld by subsequent tests.

The theory has no immediate practical application, though it does provide science with a clearer understanding of the behavior of everything from an exploding star to the atomic nucleus. "Like politics, music, what have you, this should be part of human culture," says Glashow of the theory. "After all, we have an obligation to try to understand how the world is made up."

The new laureates seem agreed that Einstein's "unified field theory" is not yet in sight. Weinberg and Glashow have speculated, however, that the strong nuclear force might be unified with the weak and electromagnetic forces through detection of a supermassive particle some millions of millions of times more massive than the proton or neutron. "Gravity is the big enigma," says Weinberg of the fourth basic force of nature. There is no satisfactory theory of gravity in the very small."

"Theories are built out of little pieces of the puzzle," adds Glashow on a more hopeful note. "All the parts are different fragments of the same fundamental theory."

Steven Weinberg was born May 3, 1933 in New York City. He attended both the Bronx High School of Science and Cornell University with his fellow Nobel laureate Sheldon Glashow. He then pursued advanced studies at the Copenhagen Institute for Theoretical Physics and at Princeton University, where he earned his doctorate.

Weinberg joined the Harvard faculty in 1973 after teaching at the Massachusetts Institute of Technology and the University of California at Berkeley. Also since 1973 he has been senior scientist at the Smithsonian Astrophysics Laboratory. In addition to scholarly publications, Weinberg is the author of *The First Three Minutes,* a book for the layman describing the events thought to have taken place immediately after the beginning of the universe. The book, which won two awards in 1977, has sold 33,000 copies in the United States, and has been translated into 16 languages.

Abdus Salam was born in Jhang, Pakistan, on January 29, 1926. He received his doctorate in physics from Cambridge University in England. He is professor of theoretical physics at the Imperial College of Science and Technology of the University of London, as well as director of the International Center for Theoretical Physics in Trieste, Italy. He also chairs the United Nations Advisory Committee on Science and Technology. The first Pakistani to win a Nobel Prize, Salam is reportedly seeking to train more scientists to work in the third world.

Sheldon L. Glashow was born December 5, 1932, in New York City. After undergraduate study at Cornell University, he received his master's degree and doctorate from Harvard University. He served as a research fellow at the California Institute of Technology and as a professor at Stanford University and at the University of California at Berkeley before joining the Harvard faculty in 1966.

THE PRIZE IN CHEMISTRY

The work that won the chemistry prize for Brown and Wittig was as practical as the work that won the physics prize for Weinberg, Salam, and Glashow was theoretical. Many chemicals vital to modern medicine and industry would be prohibitively expensive to produce without the basic discoveries of Brown and Wittig—Brown in boron chemistry, Wittig in phosphorus chemistry.

Both men contributed to the development of reagents, chemicals that help other chemicals to react. These compounds act as intermediate links in the synthesis of complex materials, holding large molecules in place until the chemist is ready to replace them with permanent links.

Brown's reagents are boranes, some 50 combinations of the elements boron and hydrogen that are easily joined with many large organic molecules. The practical fruits of this research range from the arthritis medicine hydrocortisone to a uranium compound Brown developed during World War II for possible use in fueling the atomic bomb.

Wittig developed the so-called Wittig reaction that is used extensively in chemical synthesis. His work has involved primarily chains of carbon, hydrogen, and phosphorus atoms. Vitamin A is one of the substances that can now be mass produced as a result of Wittig's efforts.

The full potential of boranes and similar reagents is only beginning to be seen, suggests Brown, who is currently trying to use boranes to produce a new type of pesticide whose perfume sexually attracts male insects and prevents them from mating with females of their species. "We found a totally new continent in the discovery of boranes," says Brown. "Now we are exploring its mountains and rivers, but it will take another generation of chemists to settle it and bring back all its many riches."

Herbert C. Brown was born in London on May 22, 1912, and immigrated to the United States two years later. He is a naturalized U.S. citizen.

"I grew up very poor in a very rough section of central Chicago," recalls Brown, whose many borane patents are said to have made him a millionaire. "I think that's why I'm on the move all the time."

Brown earned his B.S. and doctorate at the University of Chicago, where he first became interested in boron chemistry. He remembers that boranes were then so rare that they were doled out "by the thimbleful."

Brown taught chemistry at his alma mater and at Wayne State University before joining the Purdue University faculty in 1947. In 1958 he was named to the university's top chemistry professorship.

Georg Wittig was born in Berlin on July 16, 1897. He received his doctorate in 1923 from Germany's Marburg University. His professorial career included stints at Marburg, Braunschweig Institute of Technology, and Tubingen University. He joined the faculty of Heidelberg University in 1956 and was granted emeritus status in 1967.

Wittig has not yet retired from the research on phosphorus chemistry to which he has devoted some 60 of his 83 years. He reports that he advises his younger colleagues "to never give up, always challenge the impossible" ☐

The Gossamer Albatross, a 75-pound machine powered by a 140-pound ''engine'' (pilot Bryan Allen) made aviation history as the first man-powered craft to cross the English Channel.

TECHNOLOGY

Auburn University researchers Kuan, Melius, and Lee have found that *Bacillus subtilis* bacteria may provide an economical source for a new photographic emulsion sensitive to ultraviolet light.

TECHNOLOGY
REVIEW OF THE YEAR

Many technical advances during 1979 related to energy—ways to conserve energy and ways to dispose of some of the hazardous wastes of energy production. Among the numerous other developments were some related to transportation and manufacturing processes.

Radioactive Wastes. The disposal of high-level radioactive wastes—from nuclear power plants, from nuclear-weapons facilities, and from medical and scientific centers that use radioactive materials—is a serious and growing problem. In recent years the packaging of the radioactive wastes in borosilicate glass and burying them in geologically stable formations of rock and salt has gained wide acceptance. Now a new method—synroc—has been proposed. A. E. Ringwood, a geochemist at the Australian National University's Institute of Advanced Studies in Canberra, proposes to bond the atoms of the radioactive waste into the crystalline structure of a stable synthetic host rock. Melted constituents of the rock—primarily the minerals perovskite, hollandite, and celsian—would be mixed with melted radioactive waste in a ratio of nine parts rock to one part waste. The mixture would then be packed in thick-walled nickel canisters and pressed with heat and cold treatments to reach its "theoretical density." Since the minerals make up 90 per cent of this synroc they determine its structure and geochemical properties. Ringwood cites other advantages of his plan: synroc maintains its integrity better than borosilicate when subjected to high temperatures, pressure, and water; and the packaging and sealing of the wastes in synroc eliminates the release of volatile elements that accompanies the production of borosilicate. Ringwood envisions storage areas with nickel canisters buried in granite, with impermeable clay and mudstone between the canisters and above them for the top 1,000 meters to the surface.

GE's new "Electronic Halarc" bulb produces as much light as today's 50/100/150 three-way bulb on its highest setting but uses only one-third the energy.

Energy-saving steps. Scientists have also found ways to conserve energy in many fields—metallurgy, to cite one. Chemical engineers from the University of Connecticut have found a way to reduce the amount of energy needed to refine certain industrially important metals. A process known as electrowinning is used to recover some 75 per cent of chromium, 53 per cent of zinc, 50 per cent of cobalt, and more than 10 per cent of copper and nickel in the United States. This process involves the use of an electric current to deposit the metal on a negatively charged electrode. Mohammad Farooque and Robert Coughlin have found that the addition of pulverized coal to the positive electrode greatly reduces the amount of electricity needed to power the reaction. In one test involving copper the coal reduced by two thirds the amount of electricity needed. ■ There was also an important energy-saving step in metal processing. Heat loss—and thus energy loss—is a serious problem in many facets of metal processing. Metals must often be heated to temperatures well over 500° Celsius and kept at those high temperatures through several processing steps. Meanwhile, as the processing proceeds, the metals lose heat from their surfaces—enough to equal 60 barrels of oil a day from large open furnaces. Now Charles A. Berg of Pyreflex Corporation of Buckfield, Maine, has developed and patented a multifaceted reflector panel that reduces this heat loss. The panels are highly reflective, sending the heat back to its source in much the same way a bicycle safety reflector reflects car lights. Tests have revealed that the panels reduce heat loss from a 800° Celsius metal by 46 to 90 per cent. This means that less heat must be generated to maintain the metal at the required temperature—and thus that less energy is used. Added benefits: less chemical degradation of the metal as it is repeatedly cooled and reheated and faster production times.

You may not have to turn off your lights to save energy in the near future—just change bulbs. General Electric is developing a light bulb that, it claims, will be as bright as a typical 1,000 watt bulb but last five times longer—five years of average use—and consume one third the power. The bulb uses incandescent filaments for initial illumination and then, after 30 seconds of warm up, a metal-halide system. The hybrid bulb is expected to retail for about $10.00, and, according to GE, will save about $20.00 in energy costs during its lifetime.

Transportation. Develop new transportation—or go back to the old? A growing number of naval architects believe that they can build improved sailing ships and that rising costs of fuel and machinery for diesel ships are making sail power very attractive economically. Most plans for modern merchant sailing ships call for ships with sophisticated weather and navigation equipment, stabilizers, computers to control the driving sails, and an auxiliary motor for use on calm days. Proponents say that the costs of running such a ship would be one fifth less per ton of cargo than diesel shipping. To bolster their arguments they point to the long evolution of sailing knowledge and to the fact that merchant sailing ships are still used in many parts of the world. ■ Pedal an airplane? On June 12, 1979 bicyclist Bryan Allen became the first person to fly the English channel under his own power—pedalling to drive the plane's propeller. The fragile craft—the Gossamer Albatross I—skimmed over the waves at heights less than five meters and at speeds of less than 22 kilometers per hour. But the U.S. National Aeronautics and Space Administration became interested in the craft and in its possibilities for use in communications, atmospheric monitoring, and ground observation. They plan to begin testing Gossamer Albatross II in the near future. This more sophisticated model, designed and built by Paul MacCready who also built the original, can attain altitudes of 20,000 to 26,000 meters and speeds of nearly 160 kilometers per hour. Although some human-powered tests will be undertaken, NASA plans to use an electric motor to drive the craft.

Bacterial production of protein. Bacteria are entering the factory. Several companies throughout the world are working on the bacterial production of protein as a feed supplement to animal fodder. According to some reports, such bacterial protein is already economically competitive with fish meal. ■ And bacteria may soon be used to produce photographic emulsions sensitive to ultraviolet light. Researchers have developed such a new photographic emulsion using enzymes from a cow's pancreas but report that bacteria (*Bacillus subtilis*) will provide a simpler, more economical source.

Barbara Tchabovsky

DOE photo by Jack Schneider

The U.S. Postal Service is using electric mail trucks in one part of California in an effort to save energy.

SCP yeast, at 23,000 times magnification, is a single-cell protein that may become an increasingly important source of animal feeds.

Provesta Corp., Phillips Petroleum

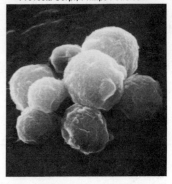

Victor Scheinman, the developer of Puma robots, watches as small Puma 250 model installs light bulbs in an automobile instrument panel.

Christopher Springman/Black Star

THOSE SMART YOUNG ROBOTS

by Gene Bylinsky

IN the spring of 1980, a U.S. sheepshearer nicknamed "Puma" joined the itinerant army of highly paid specialists who separate Australia's 135,000,000 sheep from their coats. But unlike the 10,000 other shearers, Puma is a robot, attempting for the first time to perform a task that until now has defied mechanization.

Puma—an acronym for Programmable Universal Machine for Assembly—does not resemble *Star Wars* robots, the anthropomorphic "C3PO" and his barrel-shaped sidekick "R2D2." More like a grasshopper in appearance, Puma duplicates the function of only one part of the human anatomy—the arm. It is generally bolted to the floor and incapable of locomotion. Puma is in the vanguard of an army of small and relatively inexpensive robots. These are taking over more and more jobs that were previously performed by humans.

PROGRAMMABLE AUTOMATION

Robots have been on the industrial scene since the early 1960's. The first models were designed mainly for difficult and hazardous jobs. In contrast to these hulking brutes, the newer breed are sylphlike—and far brainier. Thanks to new microelectronic technology, today's robots are equipped with computers that enable them to learn a succession of tasks. Moreover, they have a versatility that promises to render obsolete a good deal of what is currently thought of as automation.

Robots, in fact, are the latest form of automation—a "programmable," or "flexible," variety. These differ from the fixed type, best exemplified by a battery of machines designed solely to drill automobile-engine blocks. Compared with those forerunners, the new robots are nimble jacks-of-all-trades. A typical model can be fitted with a variety of "hands"—for example, a mechanical gripper that enables it to pick up parts and pass them along, a spray head that converts it into a painter, or an electric arc that turns it into a welder. Such robots load and unload parts from furnaces, stamping presses, and conveyors. They also quench red-hot parts, lubricate dies in stamping machines, drill holes, insert screws, and grind parts. A few of them even perform their jobs while riding conveyors.

Robots are even involved in the inspection of finished products. At Texas Instruments, for example, there are dozens of computer-controlled small robot arms with television camera eyes. They spot pocket calculators moving down a conveyor belt, pick them up, and place them in an automatic electronic inspection station.

Most wondrous of all, robots are starting to assemble components in factories. During 1980 General Motors plans to install ten Pumas, which, among other things, will partly assemble armatures for electric motors, screw small electric bulbs into instrument panels, and help put windshield washers together.

SALES BOOM

These simple assembly chores may be the beginnings of what lies ahead. Robots are getting smarter all the time, and some already have a sense of "touch" as well as "sight." Contrary to general belief, 75 per cent of U.S. industry's products are not mass-produced in long production runs. Rather, they are assembled in small batches as styles and sizes change. At present, these products are put together largely by hand because extensive mechanization of the traditional kind does not pay. It is now believed, however, that robots could one day take over many of these batch-assembly jobs.

Many corporations are awakening to the possibilities, and their interest has kindled a sales boom at Unimation Incorporated of Danbury, Connecticut, the world's largest robot maker. It has more than half of the $60,000,000 U.S. market. Unimation, which developed the Puma, already has orders for 80 of them.

FOR DANGEROUS AND MONOTONOUS JOBS

Robots have come a long way from their early days. Joseph F. Engelberger, a Columbia University-trained physicist who founded Unimation in 1958, recalls that he first had to beg potential users to buy his contrivances. Now, however, industry's quickening interest is directly related to its concern about productivity and profits.

As a rule, robots' higher productivity has little to do with higher speeds. They are generally designed to work at human tempos so that they will mesh with existing factory operations. The productivity increase comes rather from a robot's ability to work more consistently at a monotonous or dangerous job than a human. A robot doesn't get hangovers, and it can work three shifts.

In die casting, robots feed metal blanks into a furnace and pick up hot castings. There, they have increased production by as much as 10 per cent. They have also reduced labor requirements by 70 per cent, and have cut rejects by as much as 15 per cent. In this particular operation, with its noxious fumes

At Texas Instruments, computer-controlled robots used to run tests on handheld calculators have increased testing productivity sixfold.

and stifling humidity, workers are only too happy to step aside in favor of robots.

ECONOMICAL, TOO

Perhaps the most endearing fact about the money-saving robots, from industry's standpoint, is that their labor has grown cheaper in relative terms. Robots range in price from $10,000 to $120,000. Auxiliary equipment can easily double the installed cost. Unimation's Engelberger estimates, however, that it costs no more to maintain a typical robot than it did in the early 1960's—about $4.60 an hour.

Australia's sheepmen dream of realizing great savings, too. Engelberger was initially skeptical of the proposal to use robots for shearing. When a scientist from an Australian research institute telephoned to inquire about the possibilities, Engelberger blurted out: "You're nuts!" A few weeks later, though, the persistent Australian called again—this time from Danbury—to inform Engelberger: "Here I am, with a friend."

It turned out that the Australians were dead serious. They already had done preliminary research on ways to immobilize a sheep temporarily with an electric shock, so that a robot could go to work. The Australians had been thinking of a small robot the size of a Puma. When they were shown one, they ordered it on the spot. Meanwhile, a company in Perth, Australia had developed sensors to be incorporated into the clippers so that the robot won't skin the sheep it is shearing.

Automobile manufacturers are the biggest users of robots in U.S. industry. The robots are most widely used in welding, with painting a close second. A group of robots welding car bodies on a moving line looks like a swarm of unearthly insects pecking at an enemy. Their work is punctuated by the grinding of gears and puffs of air released by their pneumatically powered "hands."

ASSEMBLING PARTS

Even as it expands the use of robots in simple tasks, General Electric is studying ways to use them in assembling small parts, such as those used in electronic devices and small appliances. Minnesota Mining & Manufacturing, meanwhile, is exploring the possibility of using Pumas to assemble tape cassettes. Three robots already assemble typewriter-ribbon cartridges at an Olivetti plant in Pennsylvania.

The development of Puma is a direct outgrowth of G.M.'s intensive interest in robot assembly. The company's long-term objective of using robots interchangeably with people in its assembly lines began to take shape around 1976. At that time G.M. discovered that parts weighing only one to three kilograms constitute 95 per cent of the components of a passenger car. The only robots then available were big ones unsuitable for assembly chores. So around 1977 G.M. handed the assignment of developing a small robot to Unimation. The first Puma, priced at $35,000, was delivered early in 1979. It took over a number of jobs at G.M.,

A robot hand, equipped with a spray head, becomes a painter at General Motors and other facilities; equipped with an electric arc, it becomes a welder at a Chrysler plant.

including fairly complex ones that involve putting things together.

At a Delco Products plant in Rochester, New York, Puma will be programmed to do several jobs. It will reach out to pluck a tiny electric-motor armature out of a furnace in which the temperature is running at 233° Celsius. Then it will attach a commutator ring to the armature, put on some resinous material, and replace the armature in the furnace for curing. This is an unpleasant task for human workers.

ROBOT LANGUAGE

Computer programming is the key to turning robots into assemblers. The more advanced robots, such as Puma, can be told what to do by typing in the instructions on a computer keyboard. This is typed in a "language" that includes about 100 English words such as "here," "move," and so on. Eventually, enthusiasts say, the evolution of robot language will make it possible to give robots spoken or typed commands such as: "Assemble the carburetor." This is no pipe dream. At SRI International, to cite one instance, robots have already been taught to obey one-sentence spoken commands relating to portions of an assembly job.

It has been demonstrated that even fairly "stupid" robots can be used to assemble fairly elaborate components. Scientists at the Charles Stark Draper Laboratory in Cambridge, Massachusetts, built a robot station that assembled a commercial automobile alternator consisting of 17 parts. The robot did the job somewhat more slowly than people do. The project's aim, however, was not to develop an economical assembly process. It was to gather data on the basic principles of parts assembly.

The Draper Laboratory scientists took apart a number of typical small products, including an electric motor, a refrigerator compressor, a bicycle brake, and an alternator. They found that these products consist largely of parts arranged in a stack atop a main body. Stacking, they concluded, is a promising area for robot assembly. A relatively simple robot arm moving in three perpendicular planes can accomplish all the necessary motions. More complex products,

Cincinnati Milacron

A computer-controlled robot with a mechanical gripper can pick up parts and pass them along.

the scientists found, would require complicated robots equipped with special inserting and holding tools.

ARTIFICIAL VISION

Before full-fledged assembly by robots becomes a reality, a number of important obstacles must be overcome. First and foremost is the so-called parts-presentation problem, which begins with the factory bin. It's a giant step for a robot. Artificial vision systems have no problem recognizing objects lying singly on a flat surface. When the parts are jumbled atop one another, however, recognition of individual parts becomes a horrendous computational problem for robot computers.

The closest researchers have come to solving the problem is to make a robot grasp a part from a bin and hold it in front of a television camera for recognition. But this approach, which is being tried out at the University of Rhode Island, is too slow for production-line use.

Another presentation problem is how to orient parts correctly on a conveyor so that robots can pick them up. Even when the "bin picking" problem has been eliminated with mechanical chutes and vibrator pans, the parts don't always tumble out in exactly the right position.

Mating parts with extremely close tolerances presents another major challenge. At the Draper Laboratory, the most difficult operation in the assembly of alternators was the insertion of a bearing into the main body.

The clearance is only one hundredth of a millimeter.

Before arriving at a solution, the scientists spent several years analyzing close-clearance insertions and deflection forces that can cause parts to jam or get scratched. The studies resulted in the invention of an ingenious device called "remote-center compliance." This device permits the main workpiece to tilt its tip and allows for some play in robot movements. As one researcher puts it: "It helps the robot to wiggle and try."

"SEEING" AND "TOUCHING"

How can robots take over more tasks in existing factories and work alongside people? They have to be given better vision and a sense of touch. Some clever approaches are being explored. At the U.S. National Bureau of Standards, researchers have put a small television-like camera on a robot arm along with a light that shines from inside the claw.

The robot can infer the size and shape of objects and their distance by the way light strikes their angles and surfaces. This creates simple images already "familiar" to the robot's computer.

Interesting solutions are in the works for the "touch" problem, too. Victor Scheinman, who started the movement to small robots by building both the predecessors of Puma and Puma itself, says that assembly robots probably require an anthropomorphic hand. It might have only two or three fingers, but the fingers would be equipped with sensors to measure the force of their grip.

Scheinman's goal is to develop a general-purpose robot hand sensitive enough "so that Puma will be able, essentially, to pick up an egg at one moment and not crush it and then pick up a lead brick in the next motion and not drop it."

One way to provide a sense of touch is to equip robot fingers with microswitches that can sense pressure and make the robot hand

Robots with improved "seeing" and "touching" ability would have many uses. At left, bright lights around a camera help a computerized robot to recognize the part it is holding. At right: a plastic skin for robot hands is being tested. The skin would register different pressures as indicated by colors on a television monitor.

John Marmaras/Woodfin Camp   Christopher Springman/Black Star

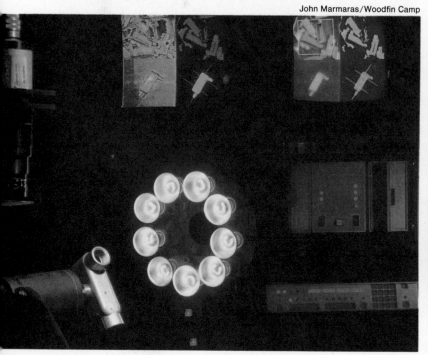

Factories in which human workers mainly supervise robots that perform the manufacturing, testing, and packaging functions? A distinct possibility, according to some proponents of robotics.

Magnussons i Genarp AB

close. Another is to cover the hand with a rubberized material whose electrical resistance would change with varying pressures.

AUTOMATED FACTORIES

It is just a question of time, the apostles of robotics say, until highly automated factories with platoons of robots are commonplace. The U.S. Air Force is sponsoring efforts that could lead to the construction of a large automated factory—one that would produce military airplanes. Nearly 80 companies and university organizations are participating in the Air Force's Integrated Computer-Aided Manufacturing (ICAM) program. It envisages the use of computers to organize every step of manufacturing. Batch assembly is the rule in the aircraft industry, and production runs for parts rarely exceed 100. Every time they build a new airplane, or make changes in an existing one, the manufacturers have to make new tools that may never be used again.

When a production run is completed in an ICAM plant, smart robots equipped with vision and touch would simply be taught new tasks. An inventory of tools—that is, learned tasks—would thus reside in the memories of robots, replacing warehouses full of machine tools. The ICAM program aims to have its first integrated manufacturing center in production in 1985.

AND PEOPLE?

Does all this mean that robots are on the verge of displacing people *en masse?* Unions such as the United Auto Workers are already voicing concern. Says James S. Albus, who is involved in the work on robot vision at the National Bureau of Standards: "In a few years we can have factories where workers are primarily involved in supervising robots." If the robot industry goes the way of the computer industry, adds Albus, "we would see robots making robots. This would bring machines costing thousands now down to less than $100 each. This could mean an effective labor rate, in many operations, of only pennies per hour." However, Unimation's Engelberger estimates that even at the highest projected growth rate, robots will replace no more than five per cent of the Western world's blue-collar work force by the end of the 20th century □

 SELECTED READINGS

"Advanced interactive technology: robots in the home and classroom" by M. Freeman and G. Mulkowsky. *Futurist,* December 1978.

"Blue-collar robots" by T. Nicholson and others. *Newsweek,* April 23, 1979.

"Extra! Man takes over: robots and people in parts assembly work." *Science Digest,* January 1979.

"Robots are coming" by D. Colligan, *New York,* July 30, 1979.

LASER LIGHT SHOWS

by Annabel Hecht

THE dazzling imagery called forth by reviewers is nearly as colorful as the show itself: "a spiral-like Mobius tornado unwinding along itself," "gauzy underwater dream shapes," "clusters of jewel-like webs," "a vertiginous celestial traffic jam." Such extravagant word pictures are being used to describe the latest thing in show business. This is the use of lasers for spectacular visual effects at concerts—both the symphony and rock-music varieties—discotheques, and in planetariums.

To create these unusual effects, laser beams are diffused and refracted optically and often played against a ceiling or projected on a screen. The laser operator can make the beam change its shape and dance and weave to match the mood and tempo of a musical accompaniment. Introduced in Los Angeles in 1973, the laser-light show was an instant success. Planetariums in at least 20 cities in the United States, Canada, Britain, and Japan, have featured the light-and-music entertainment. Meanwhile, the number of rock bands using laser light to enhance their presentations has nearly doubled since 1978.

But beautiful as they are, these unusual "fireworks" are not without danger. If a laser beam strikes a person's eye, it can impair vision and even cause blindness. The chances of this happening in a planetarium show are small. The reason for this is that this type of installation plays the laser images on a domed roof over the viewers' heads. What does concern the Federal Drug Administration (FDA) are laser-light shows produced in discotheques and by touring rock music groups. In these places high-power lasers are sometimes used in uncontrolled and unsafe ways. (The FDA has authority to regulate radiation-emitting devices, including lasers.)

As every science-fiction buff knows, lasers are devices that produce very concentrated beams of light. The beams range from microscopically small to several centimeters in diameter. Some lasers produce relatively low-power beams that generally are not considered dangerous. High-intensity laser beams, however, can be powerful enough to bore through heavy steel plates.

LASER USES

Lasers have a wide variety of uses. Their light has been bounced off the moon in sophisticated measurement experiments. It is used on the ground as highly accurate surveying tools. They have been aimed into some patients' eyes to perform delicate surgical procedures and into others' throats to remove warts on the larynx. Low-power lasers are used in supermarkets to "read" coded labels at the checkout counter. High-power lasers are used for drilling, cutting, and welding metals. Communications, fingerprint identification, pollution detection, cell measurement, even tailoring are all fields where lasers are being used.

As more and varied uses for lasers developed, FDA became concerned about the danger of consumer exposure to laser radiation. In 1973 a survey showed serious deficiencies in safety practices among users of lasers and in laser-producing equipment. The Agency then issued a safety standard for lasers, which became effective in August 1976.

CLASSES OF INTENSITY

The standard divided laser products into four classes. These are based on the intensity of the radiation and the potential for producing biologically harmful effects. Class I products are those which limit laser radiation to levels that have not been found to produce biological damage. Class II products emit visible light that could cause eye damage after long-term exposure. Class III laser products emit rays strong enough to cause damage to human tissue from one short, direct exposure. Class IV products are those that produce laser beams that could cause biological damage by diffuse reflections as well as direct exposure.

The standard requires that all laser products be equipped with various radia-

Courtesy of Laser Images, Inc.

Spectacular colors and patterns are produced in laser light shows. These "fireworks" are not without danger, however.

Courtesy of Laser Images, Inc.

Lasers are the latest thing in entertainment. Here laser-produced colors and patterns are being used to help create a particular mood and tempo at a popular discotheque.

Adam Scull/Black Star

tion-safety features such as protective housings, safety interlocks, key switches, emission indicators, beam-control devices, and warning labels. The safety devices required depend on the class of the laser. High-power products need more safety devices because of their greater potential for producing biological damage. Additional safety requirements have been set for medical and demonstration (including entertainment) lasers and for surveying, leveling, and alignment laser products.

When these standards were developed, the use of lasers in the entertainment world was concentrated in artistic displays (light sculptures and holographic exhibits) and in planetariums. Products normally intended for classroom or entertainment use are included in the standard as "demonstration" laser products. They must meet the emission and labeling requirements of Class I or II lasers.

THE DISCO-LASER SHOWS

Because of the low visibility of their beams, however, these lasers aren't effective

with large crowds. Therefore, producers of laser-light shows are using the higher-power Class III or even Class IV lasers. These systems can easily exceed the radiation limits for products classified as entertainment lasers if the beams are accessible to people or can hit them. Moreover, investigations by electro-optics specialists have revealed that some of these light shows are being operated in an unsafe manner.

In one instance a laser beam was sprayed directly on the audience from a fiber-optic device on the wrist of a performer. In another show, beams were bounced from mirrored walls and mirror balls hanging from the ceiling. One rock-music group has been using lasers so powerful and so accessible that a stagehand is reported to have been able to light a cigarette with the beam.

A visible laser beam, aimed over the audience at a dull surface, presents few problems. The beam is dispersed or scattered, reducing its brightness. But if the beam strikes a shiny, reflective surface, it can bounce back at full strength or close to it. Keeping the beam moving rapidly doesn't assure safety either. It could unexpectedly hit a shiny surface, reflecting the ray into the faces of viewers. Breaking up the beam and spreading it out can reduce its harmful potential. However, it takes technical know-how to calculate how this can be done without hazard. Usually the people in charge of producing rock-music shows know more about the music than about laser technology.

EYE BURNS

Contrary to the impression given by a popular James Bond movie, laser beams flashed about in a light show will not cut a person in half. What can happen may be so subtle the victim may not even realize it has happened. A laser beam entering the eye can burn the retina. If this occurs in the area of the eye's peripheral vision it may not be noticed immediately. A number of burns, however, in this part of the retina might produce some visual problems.

If the laser beam makes a direct hit in the area of sharp vision, the burn would cause a very noticeable blind spot, resulting in serious vision impairment. It is even possible, though a small probability, that a laser beam could enter the eye at just the right angle to hit the optic nerve, causing total blindness. All it takes is a fraction of a second for damage to occur.

GENERAL-PURPOSE LASERS

Most manufacturers of laser products intended for use in light shows are fully aware of the potential hazard of their equipment. They have taken precautions to prevent accidental exposure to laser beams. In addition to government standards, they have as guidelines a voluntary standard for safe use of lasers developed by the American National Standards Institute.

More and more light shows are using general-purpose lasers, which were not designed or manufactured for this purpose. In addition, these shows often add components

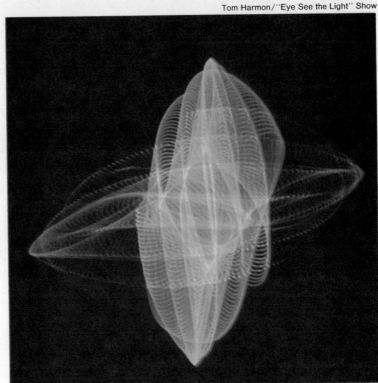

Twirling color pattern from "Eye See the Light," a planetarium laser light show.

such as scanners, display screens, and optical devices. Many operators and designers of such shows do not understand the power or the hazards of their equipment. The problem is compounded in the case of touring musical groups that play each night in different locations, each having different structural features.

There is virtually no local regulation of light shows. Twenty-three states have authority to regulate such shows under laws governing radiation other than X rays. Only a few states, however, have specific legislation covering lasers. In two of these states, action was taken to close down unsafe light shows. But it is often difficult to arrange to inspect the equipment before a show plays its one-night stand and moves on.

STRONGER REGULATIONS

The potential hazards of laser-light shows have now become apparent. Therefore, FDA has been conducting an intensive search to find out who is producing the shows, who is manufacturing the equipment, and what the specific hazards of the equipment are. FDA has inspected the equipment used by a number of touring groups, as well as some fixed installations.

FDA plans to work closely with state radiation-control agencies to share information on the use of lasers in the entertainment field. Data gathered in inspections have been passed on to these agencies. In addition, information materials are being developed to help light-show operators recognize potential hazards and prevent them.

A laser-light show can operate if it meets federal performance standards for its class. Furthermore, the equipment must be designed and operated in accordance with strict safety criteria spelled out in the guidelines.

One of these criteria specifies that the total radiation exposure in the area where the audience will be located cannot be more than the limits of a Class I laser. This includes radiation reflected from targets and scattering devices such as mirrors.

Another requirement of the guidelines is that if the equipment doesn't need an operator to run it all the time, the path of the laser beam must be at least 6 meters above any place the audience might stand. This distance is lowered to 3 meters if there is an operator on hand all the time to control the equipment.

Another specification is that there must be one or more controls to shut the equip-

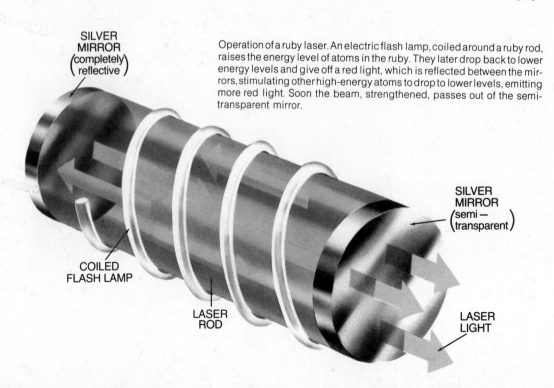

SILVER MIRROR (completely reflective)

COILED FLASH LAMP

LASER ROD

SILVER MIRROR (semi-transparent)

LASER LIGHT

Operation of a ruby laser. An electric flash lamp, coiled around a ruby rod, raises the energy level of atoms in the ruby. They later drop back to lower energy levels and give off a red light, which is reflected between the mirrors, stimulating other high-energy atoms to drop to lower levels, emitting more red light. Soon the beam, strengthened, passes out of the semitransparent mirror.

All laser products, including this desk-model, must be equipped with radiation-safety devices such as emission indicators, beam-control devices, and warning labels.

ment off in case something goes wrong or the audience gets overly enthusiastic. In case there is no operator running the show, someone must be assigned responsibility for stopping the performance if problems develop. The laser-light show must meet any other radiation safety standards FDA believes are necessary. The operator of the show should also check with local or state officials to make sure that their requirements are met and clearances obtained before the show goes on.

IF YOU GO TO LASER ENTERTAINMENT

There have been rumors, but no confirmed reports as yet, of eye injuries suffered at laser-light shows. Through a letter in a professional medical journal, FDA is asking physicians to report any such injuries that come to their attention.

Even with these new guidelines for laser-light shows, there is always the possibility that a performance will take place using equipment that hasn't met all the safety criteria. People planning to attend a laser-light show may wish to call their local health department to find out whether safety checks have been made and all local ordinances are being met. If there is any doubt, it may be better not to attend the show.

To avoid the risk of eye damage it is a good idea to follow one simple rule: never look directly, or through binoculars or cameras, into any intense light beam whether it comes from a laser or another source □

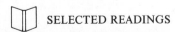 SELECTED READINGS

"The lighter side of lasers" by R. Horn. *The New York Times Magazine,* September 30, 1979.

"Traveling laser shows: danger under the rainbow" by H. Fantel. *Popular Science,* April 1979.

U.S. Dept. of Transportation

A police officer is using a radar gun that provides a digital readout of the speed of the vehicle being tested.

POLICE RADAR

by Marshall Schuon

WHEN Florida police clocked a speeding banyan tree and a house moving at 28 miles an hour early in 1979, the reports sparked a court hearing and widespread questioning of what had previously been an accepted fact of life behind the wheel—the absolute accuracy of police radar. The hearing did in fact document radar's fallibility: 80 cases based on radar evidence were dismissed and police in at least one Florida county are now required to support the arrest of speeders by pacing them.

In the months since Judge Alfred Nesbitt found that a precise scientific principle had become imprecise in practice, other states and municipalities have taken a new look at the primary weapon in the arsenal against speeding. It has reached the point where praise for radar is unusual, said Marshall Treado, the man responsible for a recent U. S. federal government radar testing program.

MILLIONS OF TICKETS

Mr. Treado, radar program manager in the Law Enforcement Standards Laboratory of the U. S. National Bureau of Standards, said the testing predates the Miami hearing and was undertaken because federal funds are involved in speed enforcement.

Since 1968, the U. S. National Highway Traffic Safety Administration (N.H.T.S.A.) has provided about $14,000,000 to help police departments buy speed-detection devices, mostly the 100,000-odd radar units that now account for 8,500,000 of the 12,000,000 tickets issued each year.

Radar, an acronym for Radio Detection and Ranging, has been used since the end of World War II, when security restrictions were lifted on the military technology that spawned it. Today's units bear little relationship to those first bulky radars with their open ink-wells and pens scratching out speeds on graph paper.

Computers and microcircuitry have made the devices more sophisticated, while allowing them to be smaller and more mobile. Nonetheless, all speed-radar works on the same principle—the Doppler shift, propounded in 1842 by the Austrian physicist Christian Johann Doppler.

TRIED-AND-TRUE PRINCIPLE

Doppler noted that sound coming from a moving object—a train whistle, for example—will change its pitch as it approaches or recedes from a stationary listener. The same sort of shift holds true for light rays and for the radio waves on which radar is based.

In police radar, a beam of microwave energy, oscillating at more than 10,000 megahertz, is emitted. When it strikes a stationary object, it is reflected back at the same frequency, showing no speed. When the radar beam hits a moving vehicle, however, the reflection will have a different frequency. The reflected beam will have a higher frequency if the car or truck is approaching the unit, and a lower frequency if it is going away. The frequency shifts are converted by computer into a speed reading in miles per hour.

"This is a tried-and-true principle, and radar does work," said Mr. Treado. "It is 99 and 44/100ths per cent accurate. In the hands of a neophyte, of course, something can always go wrong."

BUT . . .

That something, as detailed in the Florida hearing and elsewhere, includes radar units that have been confused by citizens-band radio transmissions, by heater and air-conditioner fan motors in the patrol cars, by the sheer size of objects rather than by their speeds, and by a phenomenon known as "cosine-angle error." (See page 347.)

A cosine error occurs because the Doppler shift is true only as long as the vehicle is coming directly at the signal source. When an angle is introduced, a component of the actual speed is undetected by the radar and a lower speed is registered. In an extreme example, a car speeding straight across the radar microwave beam will appear to the radar to be standing still, since there will be no frequency shift.

That, of course, works in favor of a motorist. The problem for drivers occurs in "moving radar," a type that allows a police officer to check the speed of oncoming vehicles while driving along the highway.

In moving radar, the unit emits "high" and "low" Doppler beams. The low beam is meant to look at the road and measure the patrol car's speed, while the high beam bounces off the target vehicles. The unit then subtracts the low Doppler from the closing speed of the two vehicles to give a reading on the target.

However, the low beam may "see" billboards or other unusually reflective objects at an angle along the highway, creating an error, known as a cosine error, and telling the radar that the patrol car is moving more slowly than it actually is. When that lower speed is then subtracted from the "high" beam reading, the target may appear to be travelling much faster than it is.

In the Florida case, the tree was shown to have been clocked at 86 miles per hour as a result of radio-frequency interference from a CB radio operated in proximity to the radar unit. And the house that radar showed to be loafing down the road at 28 miles per hour actually was an apparition that appeared when the radar unit read radio frequencies emitted by the blower motor in the police car's heater.

"The main thing is that radars should not have their antennas mounted on the dash," said Neal Sanders, a spokesman for Electrolert Incorporated, a company that makes a radio receiver designed to warn drivers of radar in time to avoid a ticket. The company also has become a clearing house for radar-arrest information.

"There are too many things that can cause a Doppler shift," Mr. Sanders said. "The thing to do is to get that antenna outside the window," as some units do.

Even then, according to Kustom Signals, one of the leading radar manufacturers, there are a great many electronic devices that operate on the same wavelength as police radar, which has been allotted two frequencies—X-band at 10.525 gigahertz and K-band at 24.150 gigahertz—by the U.S. Federal Communications Commission (F.C.C.).

In a sales memo, the company pointed out that K-band is better because radio-frequency interference can cause spurious readings, and X-band "is heavily polluted and getting worse every day." Among the items that operate on or emit the X-band frequency are security alarms, garage-door openers, microwave ovens, and even electric oyster shuckers, according to the memo.

Jay Schreiber, engineering manager for another of the major manufacturers, Decatur Electronics of Illinois, said there are additional advantages in K-band units. "Range is better, making it perform better on open highways," he said. "X-band has a wider beam, though, so it's more reliable when you have a situation of high clutter, such as a city environment."

GETTING SOMEONE ELSE'S TICKET

Beam width is, in fact, another problem for the government and the industry, whose current K-band units do not meet existing federal specifications, in the opinion of Mr. Treado. Width is prescribed by the F.C.C. as 10 degrees, but the narrowest now on the market measures 12 degrees.

"Essentially, they're measuring one way and we're measuring another," Mr. Treado said. "But I've been in radar for 25 years, and we've always measured it that way. The N.H.T.S.A. is the regulatory agency, though, and we'll take our report to them and let them do with it what they will."

What beam width means for the motorist, in the view of many experts, is that he may be getting someone else's speeding ticket. At its source, the beam typically has a width of only a few inches. At 5,000 feet, however, it can be more than 1,700 feet wide.

"The police say their radar can pick out specific lanes," said Electrolert's Mr. Sanders. "They can't do that, and if they think they can, then they're making mistakes. Also, the radar in use is too highly powered, meaning in some cases that it can pick up a vehicle a mile and a half away. A policeman can't even see a vehicle at that distance, much less tell how fast it's going."

Traditionally, courts have ruled that the closest vehicle to the patrol car is the one whose speed shows up on radar. But the tendency of radar to get the strongest reading from the largest object was demonstrated in a recent test by *Car and Driver* magazine. A Kustom Signals MR-7 radar did not "see" a Corvette until it was only 520 feet away, while it did register a tractor-trailer at a distance of 7,670 feet.

What this means in less exaggerated circumstances, say radar's critics, is that a law-abiding motorist who is closer to the patrol car may very well receive a citation deserved by a larger vehicle behind him.

HUMAN MONITORING

Mr. Schreiber agreed that, at any one instant, radar would read the stronger signal. But when the smaller car is closer, he said, it will be the one reflecting the stronger signal. "And, too," he said, "if you are speeding and a truck isn't, you'll open up space. You'll get close while the truck drops back, and the radar will read you."

One problem with that, according to Mr. Treado, is the capability of almost all police radars to automatically lock onto a target and sound an alarm, allowing an officer to go about other business.

"This is very bad," Mr. Treado said, "because he doesn't necessarily know which car the radar was pointed at."

The Bureau of Standards is going to recommend that new radars be built without the automatic lock capability, he said. In addition, he expects a requirement for an audio feature that would allow the operator to hear the Doppler shift, helping to pinpoint the culprit by indicating whether the vehicle is approaching or receding.

Meanwhile, a companion effort to improve training of radar operators is underway through a program being developed by the N.H.T.S.A.

Mr. Schreiber, like others in the industry, said his company is attempting to upgrade its own training program.

"I don't think the claims against radar have been overemphasized," he said. "Most times it's not going to be a problem—if a cop is looking at a target and the radar tells him it's coming at 260 miles an hour, he's not gonna write a ticket on that. But if you're coming along at 55 and the radar says you're doing 60, that's where it becomes critical" □

 SELECTED READINGS

"Dubious witness; police radar" by P. Bedard. *Car and Driver,* February 1979.

"Radar range" by P. Bedard. *Car and Driver,* October 1979.

HOW RADAR MEASURES SPEED

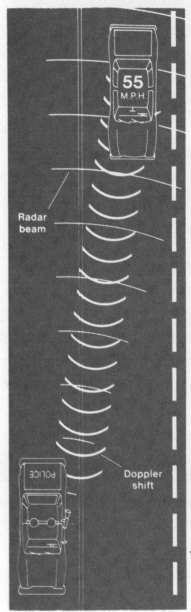

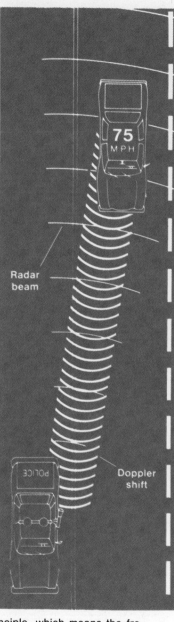

Police radar works on the Doppler principle, which means the frequency of a microwave beam alters as it bounces off a moving vehicle, indicating its speed. In the illustration, the speed of the vehicle effectively compresses the waves as it approaches the transmitter, and the frequency shift is converted by the unit into miles per hour.

COSINE ERRORS

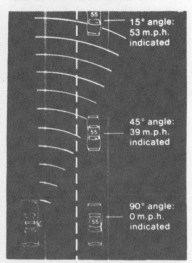

Trooper must allow for cosine angle error, which affects radar's perception of speed, progressively decreasing it to zero as the vehicle passes at a 90-degree angle.

TARGET SIZE

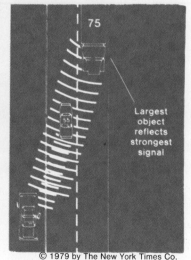

In the little-car/big-truck situation, radar tends to "read" the overpowering reflection from the larger vehicle, creating confusion about which speed is being registered.

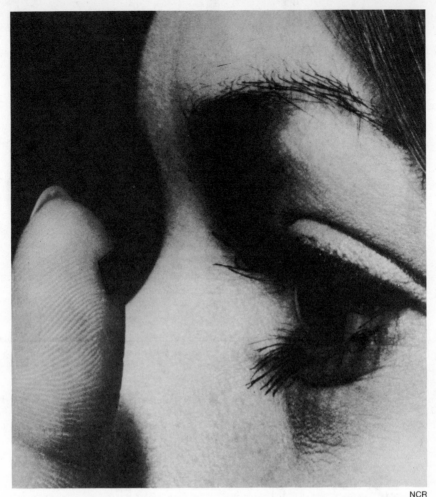

This microprocessor chip, on a fingertip, contains the equivalent of 2,000 transistors.

MICROPROCESSORS

by Marvin R. Gore

What do home TV games, programmable microwave ovens, hand-held calculators, digital watches, a modern jet aircraft, and the car in your future have in common? The answer to this question is that each contains one or more microprocessors. Microprocessors, often called "computers on a chip," affect us in many different ways at home, at work, and at play.

Microprocessors are a result of the miniaturization of electronic parts and circuits. A microprocessor is an important part of a very small digital computer, called a microcomputer. All computers, regardless of their size, have the same five elements: input, memory, control, arithmetic and logic, and output.

Figure 1 shows the relationship between these elements. Data and instructions enter the computer through the input unit. They are stored in the memory as combinations of the binary digits, 1 and 0.

BITS AND BYTES

Binary digits are called *bits*. Groups of bits, called codes, are used to store combinations of characters (letters, numbers, and special symbols) as data. Examples of binary-coded characters are: 11110001 an 8-bit code for the number 1, and 11000001 an 8-bit code for the letter A.

Any 8-bit code, such as the ones above, is called a byte. The codes for instructions

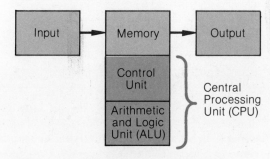

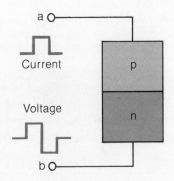

Figure 1 (*above*): Elements of a computer.
Figure 2 (*right*): Diagram of semiconductor diode.

are also made up of such bits and bytes. The sequence of instructions put into the computer to solve any given problem is called a *program*.

MANAGING INFORMATION ELECTRONICALLY

The control unit of a computer acts much like an officer directing traffic. It manages the operations of all of the other units of the computer. The control unit interprets the instructions that make up the computer program. Then it causes them to be executed in a correct sequence.

The arithmetic and logic unit, called the ALU, performs the actual operations upon the data. The control unit and the arithmetic and logic unit, together, are called the central processing unit, or CPU. Thus, the CPU causes incoming data to be processed and converted into usable information. This information can be recorded or displayed on suitable output devices.

A microprocessor (often called a microprocessor unit, or MPU) is a CPU miniaturized to fit on a single silicon chip. Such a chip is no larger than one-half centimeter square. Microprocessors are the most difficult circuits to design. In fact, their design and layout can take several years. The tiny microprocessor is the product of a new technology called microelectronics.

Microelectronics is the ability to design and to fabricate large numbers of miniaturized circuit elements. Current microelectronic techniques place thousands of elements on a small silicon chip. These techniques also combine the chips into complex electronic circuits. These electronic circuits are called *integrated circuits,* or IC's. Because they are low-cost, reliable, and re-producible, IC's are used in digital computers in large quantities.

THE AGE OF SILICON

The element silicon is a semiconductor that is used to manufacture microprocessor components. Silicon is classified as a semiconductor because it can be made to be electrically conducting or nonconducting. By adding impurities, a process called doping, scientists are able to give a small area in a silicon chip a lack of electrons. The lack of electrons makes the area electrically positive. This positive area is called a *p*-zone. By adding other impurities, or dopants, they are able to give an adjacent area a surplus of electrons. This addition makes it an electrically negative area, or *n*-zone.

The simplest semiconductor device is the diode, which acts as an electronic on-off switch. As shown in Figure 2, a diode is used by applying a voltage to adjacent *p*- and *n*-zones in a small region of silicon.

Transistors are the most important semiconductor devices. They are more complex than diodes because they are capable of giving the amplification needed in many electronic circuits. They can also act as on-off switches. As shown in Figure 3, a transistor can be formed by placing a *p*-zone between two *n*-zones. This is called a bipolar transistor.

One of the *n*-zones in a bipolar transistor is called the *emitter,* and the other is called the *collector*. The *p*-zone between them is called the *base*. When the base is at a higher positive voltage than the emitter, electrons move from the emitter, to the base. Most of these electrons also travel to the collector, causing an output current to flow. Small changes in the base input voltage can

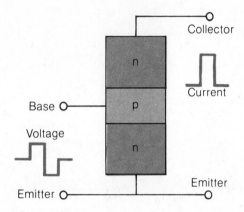

Figure 3. Diagram of an n-p-n transistor.

cause large changes in the output collector current.

The principle of operation is similar for a *p-n-p* transistor, which is made by placing an *n*-zone between two *p*-zones. There are also other types of transistors.

Chip manufacture is a high-technology process. About 250 chips are made from a razor-thin wafer of polished silicon about 75 millimeters in diameter. These wafers are sliced from crystal cylinders of 99.9 per cent pure silicon, which are grown in a laboratory.

The complex circuitry of chips is created a layer at a time on each silicon wafer. First, racks with wafers are placed in long cylindrical ovens at a temperature of about 1,000° Celsius. Here a hot oxygen-containing gas "rusts" the wafers, covering the surface with a thin electrically-insulating layer of silicon dioxide.

Then the wafers are coated with a photographic emulsion called the *photoresist* (Figure 4), which is sensitive to ultraviolet light. Next, a glass mask that contains 250 identical patterns for a single layer of an integrated circuit is placed over the wafer. These tiny circuit patterns have been placed on the mask by means of a photographic system that reduces them in size by a factor of ten.

When the wafers are exposed to ultraviolet light, the photoresist hardens, but the masked areas remain soft. The next step is an acid bath, which etches away the soft masked areas. The unmasked areas remain hard. These hard areas form the outline of the circuit for that particular layer.

Then the wafers are baked in the oven again in an atmosphere of gas loaded with a dopant such as boron or phosphorus. The dopant sinks into the underlying silicon creating a *p*-zone or an *n*-zone.

Since wafers usually contain as many as ten layers, all of these steps—rusting, photomasking, etching, baking, and doping—are repeated for each layer. Then the entire wafer is coated with aluminum conductor, which also must be masked, rusted, etched, doped, and baked. Finally after a computerized probe scans it for defective circuitry, the wafer is cut into numerous chips by means of a diamond cutter. These tiny microprocessor chips, in this case measuring about 50 millimeters on a side, have revolutionized the computer industry.

MICROCOMPUTERS

A microprocessor becomes a microcomputer with the addition of a memory unit and input/output (I/O) circuits, called *ports*. The ports connect the microcomputer with input and output devices. The *data bus* is the electronic path that links the two parts of the microcomputer.

The memory unit contains two types of storage made of semiconductor materials: random access memory (RAM) and read-only memory (ROM). RAM is high-speed memory on which the computer system can both store (write) or access (read) information. Typically, RAM is used as main memory for storage of up to 64,000 bytes. The MPU registers also are RAM.

ROM is memory that can only be read. It cannot be written on by the computer. ROM is useful for storing programs that should not be altered. For example, the instructions essential to the operation of the computer are stored in the ROM. So, too, are programs that translate human-readable instructions into the binary language of the computer. TV games, handheld calculators, and other items also use ROM's.

Initially, microcomputers used two separate chips, one for the MPU and another for the I/O ports and memory. Currently, sin-

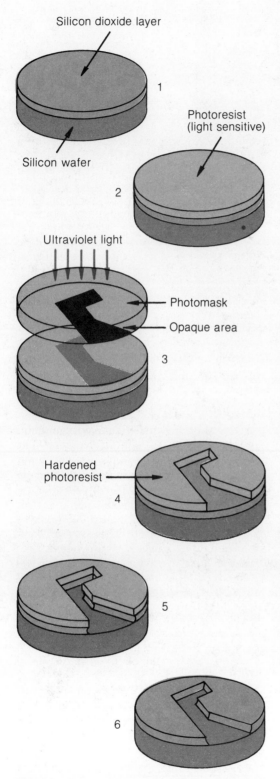

Figure 4. The making of tiny electronic circuits starts with a wafer of silicon using photographic procedures.

gle-chip microcomputers are available. With the addition of actual I/O devices, such as keyboards, cathode-ray tube (CRT) displays, printers, and soft (floppy) magnetic-disk storage units, the microcomputer becomes a microcomputer system.

THE FUTURE: SMART MACHINES

Approximately 30 years ago the transistor was developed as a replacement for the bulky, power-consuming vacuum tube. In the 1960's and 1970's, transistors were used in large quantities in digital computer design. Continual progress was made in reducing the size of integrated circuits. Microelectronics passed through three states of miniaturization: small-scale integration (SSI), medium-scale integration (MSI), and large-scale integration (LSI). The 1980's usher in a fourth stage, very-large-scale integration (VLSI). VLSI will increase greatly the number of logic circuits and bits of memory that can be placed on a single silicon chip.

Present LSI densities are less than 100,-000 devices per chip. By 1985 VLSI densities of at least a million devices per chip are likely. This means that a million bits of memory could be stored on a single chip. For example, a chip could contain a microcomputer complete with complex logic circuits, 250,000 bits of memory, and other supporting electronics. At the same time, chips will be even smaller in size than at present and will cost less.

We will soon be entering an era that will be dominated by smart machines—machines that contain one or more microprocessors. Smart machines will have increased use in the home, in the office, and in the market place. Our life styles and our standards of living will be altered to a greater extent than we now can imagine □

 SELECTED READINGS

"16-bit microprocessors" by H. Chamberlain. *Popular Electronics,* May 1979.

"Small talk; new processors with smaller circuit elements." *Scientific American,* April 1979.

The Japanese National Railway is testing a maglev vehicle for runs between Tokyo and Osaka. In one test, the vehicle reached 540 kilometers per hour.

Japanese National Railways

MAGNETIC LEVITATION

by John Tedford

IN 1853 Commodore Matthew Perry and a squadron of U.S. warships entered Tokyo Bay to encourage—by force if necessary—the Japanese to free their nation from feudal isolation. On his second visit, in 1854, Perry brought with him many gifts to tempt the Japanese to open their country to international trade. Among the gifts that Perry presented was a large model train with a steam locomotive run by an engineer perched on the roof of the cab, passenger cars big enough for an adult to ride as he would a horse, and a circular track.

In a country where even the horse was a luxury, and where there existed no system of roads for carriage travel, the train must have seemed miraculous and awesome despite its small scale. Nevertheless, the Japanese officials present set aside both fear and decorum, hitched up their kimonos, straddled the cars, and chugged off delighted. Soon they tired of riding and wanted to run the train themselves.

Today the Japanese operate the world's fastest train system. The "Bullet Trains" of the Shinkansen (New Trunk Line) zip between Tokyo, Osaka, and other major cities at an average speed of more than 200 kilometers per hour. On extensions of the system under construction, speeds will probably average as high as 240 kilometers per hour. But the most exciting development in Japanese railroading is the extensive testing of magnetic-levitation—maglev—train systems. The Japanese hope to have maglev trains in service between Tokyo and Osaka by the end of the 1980's, running the 500-kilometer distance in just one hour. The hopes were bolstered when, in December 1979, a test maglev vehicle reached a speed of 540 kilometers per hour.

WHAT IS MAGLEV?

Magnetic levitation is a system of locomotion that utilizes the basic properties of magnetism—attraction and repulsion—to lift a vehicle off the ground. Opposite magnetic poles attract one another; like poles repel one another. The application of these basic facts to propelling vehicles along a track is quite simple in principle, if not so simple in application.

In the maglev vehicle being tested by the Japanese National Railways (JNR) at Miyazaki, in Kyushu, repulsion is used to levitate the vehicle so that it floats freely in the air while in motion along a track, or guideway. The vehicle is equipped with special magnets, known as superconducting magnets, that conduct an electric current almost without resistance. These magnets in the vehicle induce currents in the aluminum guideway, thereby generating a magnetic field to oppose the vehicle's magnets, and thus—by repulsion—lifting the vehicle. (See Fig. 1.)

The JNR vehicle is propelled by means of a linear synchronous motor, which creates a flow of opposite and like magnetic fields between powerful superconducting magnets within the vehicle and ground coils in the guideway. The opposite fields pull the vehicle forward while the like fields push it. A linear motor may be likened to an ordinary rotary motor that has been sliced open and laid out straight on the ground. (See Fig. 2.)

Other maglev research is also being carried out. In Germany, a group called Transrapid–E.M.S. operated a maglev vehicle on a 900-meter long elevated guideway at the International Transport Exposition in Hamburg in the summer of 1979. Some 60,000 people rode on it. The system is now dismantled but Konsortium Magnetbahn Transrapid is constructing a new 22-kilometer test track in Emsland. In the United States, the Boeing Corporation is seeking funds from the U.S. Department of Transportation to test its design for a relatively low-speed maglev system.

WHY MAGLEV?

Why pursue magnetic levitation, a system that will require construction of all new guideways? Why not concentrate on achieving greater speeds from the more traditional system of running trains with wheels on rails? After all, the tracks already exist.

If speed is most important among the criteria for improving train service, then maglev is not a matter of preference but of necessity. As the Japanese found out in attempting to increase the speed of their existing Shinkansen system, several problems make much higher speeds impossible on a conventional wheel-and-track train.

Vibration and noise are two major factors. The slightest irregularity in the track produces extremely uncomfortable vibration within the train as higher speeds are reached. The noise produced by the contact between wheels and rails is difficult, if not impossible, to control. Maglev virtually eliminates both problems. Since the vehicle does not actually touch the guideway, but rather floats on an air cushion—except when starting and stopping at slow speeds—there is no more vibration or noise than on an airplane. And there is not the intense vibration encountered on an airplane during takeoff or landing.

Heavy maintenance cost is another major problem with conventional track systems. Constant friction between wheels and track and between overhead wires and their connections on the train causes damage which makes constant surveillance and frequent replacement of equipment necessary and costly. Maglev's no-contact system entails no such problem.

Fig. 1. In repulsive magnetic-levitation systems, magnets in the vehicle create a current in the guideway, thereby generating a magnetic field that opposes the vehicle's magnets and by repulsion lifts the vehicle.

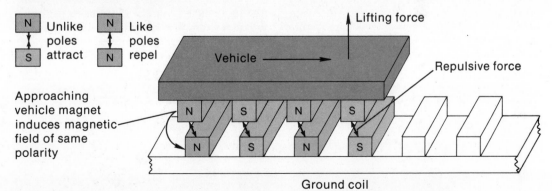

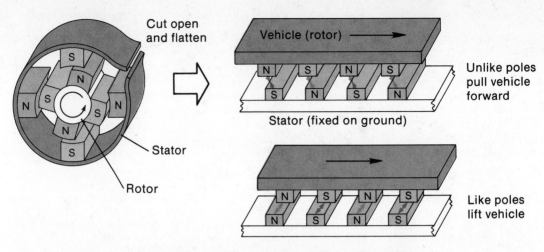

Fig. 2. The JNR vehicle is driven by a linear synchronous motor, which is like an ordinary rotary motor sliced open and laid out straight. The motor-produced magnetic field propels the vehicle, opposite fields pulling the vehicle forward, like fields pushing it.

Lastly, derailment is a major hazard of high-speed wheel-and-track systems. The faster the train goes, the greater the force becomes tending to push it off the tracks, especially on curves. In all maglev systems, however, the train "grasps" some kind of guideway in such a fashion that the possibility of derailment is virtually removed.

WHY FASTER TRAINS?

But why do we need faster trains anyway? After all, a 500-kilometer-per-hour train scarcely compares to airplane speeds for long distances. Convenience is one reason. A trip from New York to Chicago in 3 hours 10 minutes at 500 kilometers per hour offers the advantage of going from downtown to downtown. The approximately two-hour plane flight for the same trip is augmented by an additional hour or more at each end of the flight for the trip between the airport and home, a downtown hotel, or place of business. As cities grow, new airports are likely to be even farther from urban centers. At Tokyo and some European cities the bus or taxi trip to the airport is already often a matter of several hours. Moreover, trains can be boarded and evacuated more rapidly than planes, and they do not have to spend time taxiing and waiting turns for takeoff and landing.

Safety is also a major factor in the preferred use of high-speed trains. Both airplanes and automobiles have intensifying safety problems—overcrowded highways and air lanes, poor performance in bad weather, and reliance on the judgment of the individual pilot or driver. Since 1964, when the Shinkansen began operations, there has not been a single fatality on the line. The present system, or any future maglev system, nearly eliminates safety problems through centralized automation. A control center that can observe the positions of all trains at all times makes all operating decisions.

The principal reason, however, for building faster trains may prove to be fuel. A German study has shown that a 400-kilometer-per-hour maglev train would consume less than one half as much energy per passenger as would a jet airliner cruising at 950 kilometers per hour. And the energy expended for starting or takeoff would be considerably less for the train. Combine that with downtown-to-downtown service and maglev demonstrates its energy efficiency. The German study also concluded that above 350 kilometers per hour the maglev would use less energy than a conventional train.

Japan's Shinkansen has already shown the fuel efficiency of rapid trains *vs.* automobiles. A Bullet Train uses only 10 per cent of the energy required to move passengers the same distance by car—and the train is non-polluting.

ATTRACTIVE VS. REPULSIVE LEVITATION

The JNR system discussed earlier is based on repulsive levitation. Japan Airlines

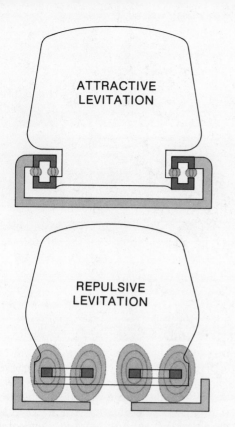

ATTRACTIVE
LEVITATION

REPULSIVE
LEVITATION

Fig. 3. In repulsive levitation, like magnetic poles repel each other and lift the vehicle. In attractive levitation, magnets on the vehicle are attracted to the guideway—but a small gap between vehicle and guideway must be maintained.

(JAL) has meanwhile been working on a system based on attractive levitation. The JAL system, called the High Speed Surface Transport (HSST) system, would be used to transport passengers swiftly between downtown Tokyo and the city's new airport. Electromagnets under the sides of the vehicle are attracted to the magnetic underside of a wraparound guideway. (See Fig. 3.) To keep an air cushion under the vehicle and prevent the magnets from clamping together, a gap of about one centimeter must be maintained between the track and the magnets. Maintaining this gap has been a major problem. Highly sensitive electronic controls are necessary to maintain a proper balance between gravity and the upward magnetic pull. These necessary controls make long-distance use of attractive levitation excessively costly. For the short runs intended by JAL, however, attractive levitation is both technically and economically feasible.

The German Transrapid vehicle is also based on attractive levitation. The designers seek to overcome some of the control problems described above by putting the primary power in the guideway and the levitation magnets on the vehicle.

There is not any problem of gap size between vehicle and track with repulsive levitation. The closer the vehicle and guideway get to each other, the greater the force trying to push them apart. There are other problems, however. One is the cost of maintaining the extremely low temperatures necessary for superconductivity. Cryogenic tanks are used to chill the on-train superconducting magnets in liquid helium to $-273°$ Celsius. Liquid helium is expensive and it boils off. JNR is now developing a way of condensing and recycling the vaporized helium.

Starting and stopping also present a problem. With repulsive levitation no lift is generated until the vehicle starts moving. This means that the vehicle must move on wheels until it reaches a speed of 30 kilometers or more per hour.

HOW SOON?

Although JNR seriously contemplates a maglev system in operation by the end of the 1980's, there is still no guarantee that such a system can become an economic and technical reality. Hope may lie, however, in the phenomenal success of the Shinkansen system: it operates at a consistent profit of over 50 per cent; it runs on schedule, in good weather and bad; and it is the fastest and most comfortable means of interurban travel from downtown to downtown. Maglev promises to become an even better system. In the United States, it would probably be most suitable for high-density corridors such as that between Boston and Washington, D.C.

Japan may, in time, repay its debt to Commodore Perry for his steam locomotive by providing the United States with the technology to revitalize its railroads ☐

 SELECTED READINGS

"Flying trains—whatever happened to magnetic levitation?" by Ben Kociver. *Popular Science*, August 1979.

General Motors

General Motors' new turbocharged cars—like this 1980 Buick Century Turbo Coupe—
have indicator lights on the instrument panel to show when the turbo is activated.

TURBOCHARGERS

by Chuck Nerpel

TO bring those of you who have been asleep since 1967 up to date, we are embarking on the decade of the turbocharger.

The reasons are simple: with a turbocharger, the car owner in a fuel-short age gets the best of about four worlds.

• He is able to buy a car with a small, relatively inexpensive engine.

• That engine, operating in a normally aspirated mode, returns optimum mileage.

• But when the boost kicks in, the small, flaccid motor turns into an Amazing Hulk—a fact Indy engine builders working with restricted piston displacement formulas have known for years.

• A factory-installed turbocharger is the cheapest way to add performance without jeopardizing reliability.

The turbo, a sub-genus of the supercharger, is no mysterious invention, no carburetor atomizer, no magic pill for the gas tank. It's been around awhile and not only on the race track. But if the turbo's been around for years, the conditions under which its use could be nurtured have only recently fallen upon us—principally the mandate for high fleet-average fuel economy without sacrifice of reasonable performance.

NOT NEW FOR PASSENGER CARS

Turbocharging is a term associated with the present generation of small in-line four and V-6 passenger-car engines. The system is not new for this application. It was available as an option on the Corvair and Oldsmobile over 15 years ago. In those days of low-cost high-grade fuel and large high-compression V-8 powerplants, few buyers were interested in making a little engine perform like a big one.

So, what is turbocharging? Plain and simple it is supercharging, a method of providing the engine with a high-density volume of air above normal atmospheric pressure, or in other words, with a pressurized charge of air/fuel mixture.

The theory of supercharging is simple. The air-to-fuel mixture ratio for internal combustion engines operating at existing atmospheric pressures is from about 15-to-1 to 17-to-1 by weight. The normal density of air is limited and varies with altitude and humidity. The best way to extract more energy per air/fuel charge is to squeeze the mixture as tight as possible without it detonating from its own compression heat, à la diesel engines.

Obviously, there is a limit to compression ratios and especially so today with lower-octane unleaded fuels. If the air density can be increased by compressing it, the amount of fuel burned per combustion cycle can be increased and more power produced on the firing stroke.

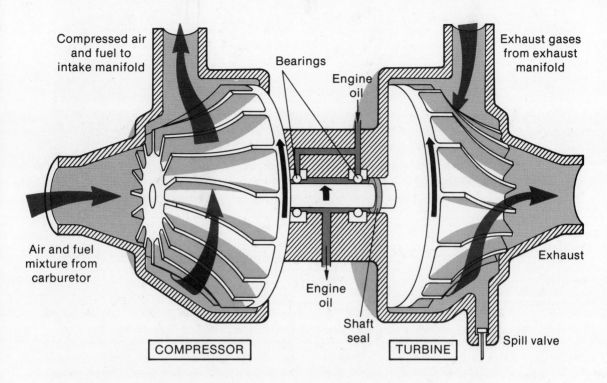

Compressed air
and fuel to
intake manifold

Bearings

Engine
oil

Exhaust gases
from exhaust
manifold

Air and fuel
mixture from
carburetor

Engine
oil

Shaft
seal

Exhaust

Spill valve

COMPRESSOR

TURBINE

Turbocharging is a method of providing an engine with a pressurized charge of air/fuel mixture. The heat of exhaust gases is used to turn a turbine wheel that drives an impeller that compresses the air/fuel mixture leaving the carburetor and on its way to the engine.

In addition, the air/fuel mixture is better dispersed, and exhaust gases are scavanged more completely from the combustion chamber. Also, pressure forces down the piston on the intake stroke rather than engine power having to suck in the charge.

SUPERCHARGERS

Supercharging is just about as old as the internal-combustion engine. Around the turn of the century, four-cylinder engines were designed with an extra cylinder that acted as an air pump. External belt—or gear-driven—systems soon followed. Others included vane pumps, axial flow, and centrifugal systems, usually belt driven.

Some racing applications used gear-driven centrifugal superchargers which really increased the horsepower, but quite a bit of horsepower was required to operate them. Besides, most of these so-called booster pumps were bulky and, in the case of the centrifugal types, difficult to control. The greater the speed, the higher the boost pressure.

BIRTH OF THE TURBOCHARGER

Searching for a method of driving a pump which did not use belts or other engine-driven couplings, engineers explored the possibility of using exhaust gases as a power source. Heat is energy, and plenty of it in the form of rapidly expanding gas pours out the exhaust ports of any internal-combustion engine. Here was the perfect power source: to conduct the gas through a small case which housed a turbine wheel; use the otherwise-wasted energy to turn the wheel; and hook the case to a centrifugal pump. Result: the birth of the turbocharger.

The advantages of such a system are many. First, the centrifugal pump takes no engine power to operate. Second, the power source can be controlled to limit the boost pressure. And third, the entire turbine and pump are combined in a very small but efficient unit.

On the hot—or exhaust—side is the driven turbine wheel turning on the same shaft as the impeller on the cool—or pump—side. These turbine wheels are not

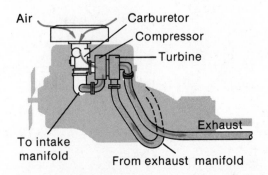

Air — Carburetor

Compressor

Turbine

To intake manifold

Exhaust

From exhaust manifold

This compact turbine-pump unit makes a small engine act like a big one—a big plus in terms of fuel efficiency.

just simple paddles spinning around. Constant research has improved their efficiency through blade design and housing shapes.

Turbocharging is not just a simple matter of bolting a turbine-driven compressor to the engine. Turbines are high-speed devices, as are centrifugal pumps. Both work best at high rpms, and the boost pressure increases four times if the speed of revolution is doubled. With engine-driven systems, boost pressure is almost impossible to control, but the exhaust-power drive can be governed to limit the pressure to any degree desired.

"TURN UP THE BOOST"

This is accomplished by the use of a waste gate—a method of bypassing some of the exhaust gases from the turbine. On passenger-car installations the waste gate control is fixed, but Indy cars have an adjustment in the cockpit so the driver can "turn up the boost" if an extra burst of speed is required. Of course, the higher the boost the greater the fuel consumption and strain on the engine.

The most popular means of installation is to place the turbocharger between the intake manifold and carburetor. Naturally, because of the greater air density, the carburetor jets must be changed to assure an adequate supply of fuel and prevent piston-burning lean mixtures.

There are also other limits to the amount of boost pressure that can be applied. As the air/fuel mixture is compressed,

it gets hot and its density is reduced. With light boost pressures, as in current passenger-car installations, this is not a serious problem. We mention it here to answer the question, why not extra-high boost for very high-horsepower output? There is first the inherent basic strength of a stock engine. It will only take so much without coming apart, and automakers want reliability more than ultra-high performance. If the engine were capable of such high pressures, some method of cooling the air/fuel mixture, such as an intercooler, would have to be placed between the turbocharger and the intake manifold.

Late-model passenger car engines are ideally suited to turbocharging. Lower compression ratios, mandated by the need to control emissions, can take the boost pressure nicely without water injection or intercoolers. Overall fuel economy remains about the same as that of a normal engine when running at cruising speeds in top gear, because the air pump is not putting out much pressure.

When a burst of speed is required and the throttle pressed, more exhaust gases enter the drive segment of the turbo. It speeds up, increasing the centrifugal impeller speed. Remember, as its speed doubles, the output increases four times and there is a very noticeable acceleration surge when the boost comes into the induction system. The new generation of turbocharged cars from General Motors and Ford have indicator lights in their instrument panels that show when the turbo is activated.

There is nothing mysterious or complicated about turbocharging. It is a very simple and reliable method that gives the engine extra power at the will of the driver. In this era of smaller engines, greater fuel efficiency and strict emission controls, we have come back to a process once ignored—making small engines act like big ones □

 SELECTED READINGS

"The world of turbos." *Motor Trend,* November 1979.

"Buick's turbocharged V-6," by E. F. Lindsley. *Popular Science,* September 1977.

"Taking care of a turbocharger," Tom Tappett. *Mechanix Illustrated,* January 1979.

Toni Angermayer/Photo Researchers

Members of an endangered species—the vicuña llama.

WILDLIFE

REVIEW OF THE YEAR

UPI

U.S. House Majority leader Thomas O'Neill looks on as oil drilling begins in Georges Bank, off Cape Cod, Massachusetts, amid mounting concern about possible damage to fisheries there.

Canada and the United States are jointly protecting the migration route of the porcupine caribou.

Charlie Ott/Photo Researchers

There was a lot of good news for wildlife in 1979. It seemed like years of effort and large cash expenditures for wildlife management, habitat protection, and pollution abatement were finally beginning to pay off in some areas. But there was bad news too—and some ominous forecasts.

Wildlife _vs._ Energy Production. There were significant conflicts between energy production and wildlife issues in the United States during 1979. The U.S. Congress lowered clean-air standards so that more coal—and therefore less oil—could be burned. A major problem was then recognized: acid rain. Coal burning increases acid levels in rain and this, in turn, has serious consequences for life forms. The old notion of "getting rid" of power-plant pollution by building tall smokestacks has been thoroughly discredited as studies show that high-altitude dispersal merely sends the pollutants eastward with the prevailing westerly winds to fall in raindrops hundreds and thousands of kilometers away from the source. As acid rain increases, some lakes are becoming more and more inhospitable for fish and other life.

Some oil operations may also endanger wildlife. Late in 1979 the U.S. Department of the Interior gave the go-ahead for oil operations on the Georges Bank off Cape Cod, Massachusetts, one of the ocean's most productive fisheries. At the same time, cleanup crews were mopping up oil on the Texas coast from the largest off-shore well blowout in history.

Increased strip-mining may pose an additional threat. During 1979 the Carter Administration pushed for the necessary technology to strip-mine shale deposits under vast tracts of public lands. At the same time conservationists produced evidence that the reclamation of strip-mined lands—and thus help for wildlife habitats—was almost at a standstill.

Virtually all national conservation groups and many segments of the public want the U.S. government to encourage more research on energy sources that don't have such high impact on wildlife habitat. They want emphasis on solar, wind, and geothermal energy rather than on boosting fossil-fuel use.

Habitat Destruction. Vast areas of public lands in the western United States are still overgrazed by cattle ranchers. Poor irrigation practices are wasting underground water, causing less to be available for wetlands upon which many species of wildlife depend. And continued urban and suburban sprawl, plus fence-to-fence intensive agriculture, ate up more than 400,000 hectares of wildlife habitat in 1979.

The most celebrated defeat of wildlife, however, came at the hands of the U.S. Congress. After a judge ruled that the Tellico Dam could not be completed because it would destroy the last known habitat of the endangered five-centimeter snail darter fish, the legislators gave the go-ahead for the dam's completion.

Bright Spots. There were several noteworthy bright spots on the international wildlife scene. The Phoenix Zoo in Arizona, which has for years been propagating a small herd of Arabian oryx, was at the end of 1979 preparing to transport several dozen animals back to their natural habitat on the Arabian peninsula. Completely killed off in the wild in the 1960's, the Arabian oryx was saved from extinction by the captive breeding program. Special programs to guarantee protection for the graceful animals have been in the works for years, guided by the wildlife-minded Sultan of Oman in whose country the first animals will be released. ■ Canada and the United States agreed to protect the migration routes of the 10,000-strong porcupine caribou herd that travels between Alaska and the Yukon. ■ The International Whaling Commission lowered limits on the killing of sperm whales and a few other species. ■ New tuna netting techniques have greatly reduced the accidental killing of porpoises.

Encouraging signs on the U.S. wildlife scene included a federal government crackdown on dredging and draining of wildlife-rich wetlands for suburban and agricultural development. Some endangered species, including bald eagles, peregrine falcons, and alligators, continued their comeback. And some rivers, notably the Merrimac and the Connecticut, showed significant improvements, and fish began returning as pollutants decreased.

Public Attitudes. Continued habitat protection and the preservation of wildlife depend on the public's good will and understanding of the issues. In what may later be seen as a benchmark study, the U.S. Fish and Wildlife Service released some surprising results of a three-year study of public attitudes toward wildlife. One section of the survey showed that the public does not think of all living things as deserving protection when necessary. The survey showed that the public overwhelmingly supported the protection of bald eagles and mountain lions. On the other hand, less than a majority favored protecting endangered species of plants, snakes, and spiders if it increased costs for an energy project. Public understanding of sport hunting proved limited as 85 per cent said they approved of hunting for meat, but only 40 per cent said they approved of hunting for recreation and sport. The public may not realize that sport hunters eat their game.

Public support of wildlife's right to its own home came up strong on questions about the number of campers and hikers in back-country areas. Most—39 per cent—of those surveyed thought human access to areas where bears are present should be restricted. Slightly fewer—38 per cent—thought the bears should be relocated. A surprising number—16 per cent—would limit the number of people visiting, and only 5 per cent thought killing some bears was a good idea.

And so, a decade ends. The 1970's demonstrated that special programs on behalf of wildlife can be effective. The decade also showed that in most cases wildlife still comes second to economic issues. The fate of wildlife depends to a large extent on how the U.S. population responds to the energy challenge. All the major conventional sources of energy production disrupt wildlife habitat. The other major threat to wildlife lies in the "development" of habitat. In these cases the problem is not so much the gigantic oil refinery or chemical plant as the millions of small conversions of wasteland into areas for housing and commerce. It may not be possible—or desirable—for the U.S. government to protect all land, but unless wildlife values can compete with economic factors, wild creatures will probably find their living space shrinking a little more each year.

Bob Strohm

Dick George, Phoenix Zoo Photo

The graceful Arabian oryx has been saved from extinction by a captive breeding program.

Another bright spot: the Connecticut River has been cleaned up and fish are returning. Here the first salmon caught in several years.

John Ligos

C. G. Maxwell/Photo Researchers

FOOD FOR THE BIRDS

by Alan Pistorius

PROBABLY nobody has lived through a cold, snowy winter without occasionally wondering, as night falls in the grip of a raging blizzard, how the birds make it. It's different, after all, with the mammals. They grow fur, put on fat, store food, den up. Some avoid the whole problem by sleeping through the winter.

Of course, most of our breeding birds migrate. But what about our winter residents? Birds generally do not store food. Neither do they den up, although woodpeckers will excavate winter roost holes, and several other species will roost in hollow trees or boxes made for the purpose.

It's curious that birds, the master nest builders, don't make winter nests, while many mammals do. Indeed, some small mammals simply roof over a last-summer's bird nest for cozy winter quarters. Putting on fat isn't much of an option, either; birds, like other flying machines, cannot tolerate excess weight. Besides, an adult chickadee weighs less than 30 grams.

Many wintering birds have few options when it comes to coping with winter weather. They take advantage of protective cover, especially for roosting purposes. Year-round residents of regions with seasonable climate extremes have perhaps half again more feathers in the winter than they do in summer. They will fluff these out in extreme cold to maximize their insulation value.

Birds protect unfeathered body parts to reduce heat loss. Every feeder watcher is familiar with a bird's cold-weather habit of drawing the legs up alternately into the body plumage. And it is the extra measure of brain-protecting heat in its head that the bird conserves at rest and in sleep by tucking its head "under its wing" (into back feathers, actually).

These anatomical and behavioral strategies are directed at conserving heat, heat that originates as a waste product of metabolism. Birds (especially small birds) metabolize more rapidly than we do, to maintain geared-up life-support systems. Birds' respiratory and heart rates are higher than ours. (A starling's heart beats 600 or 700 times a minute *at rest.*) Birds maintain a higher internal body temperature (about 41° Celsius) than we do.

Small wonder that, to support this high metabolic rate, birds have large hearts. Small wonder, too, that birds require relatively large amounts of food. For it is food that fuels the metabolism that produces the heat that keeps the bird alive. Thus food is the an-swer to the original question of how birds make it through a hostile northern winter.

All birds must eat regularly. Small birds must eat frequently during cold weather. A healthy hawk or large game bird can fast for a week, even in bitter-cold weather. Under such conditions a chickadee must feed well every day, or it will not survive the following night. The northern winter simply leaves songbirds no margin for error.

WHEN TO START FEEDING

October is the month to line up feed and hang feeders. If you start feeding by the end of October, resident birds will have plenty of time to locate your feeders before weather becomes a serious factor. Once a program has been established, it is important that it not be interrupted or suspended early.

If you mean to spend February in Florida, either find someone reliable to stock your feeders or don't start to feed at all. And it is a mistake to call it a season in March, when the snow cover recedes, the jays thin out, and the grackles begin to take over. Natural food, especially insect food, does not magically appear with the disappearance of the snow. Every northern feeding program should be continued through April.

A slate-colored junco fluffs up its insulating feathers to keep its body warm in the snow.

Gregory K. Scott/Photo Researchers

Northern feeding programs must continue through April to help small birds like this chickadee.

Russ Kinne/Photo Researchers

Courtesy, Nature Center Associates

A cracked-corn-based birdseed mix requires storage care, but it is the best all-around feed.

William J. Jahoda/Photo Researchers

Wintering birds like this nuthatch need water, but can get by with what they derive from their food.

FOOD FOR THE BIRDS

What to feed is the single most important question a bird feeder can ask. Most people don't ask it at all. They simply pick up a bag of wild birdseed mix at the local store, assuming the compounders know what's best for the birds. The typical commercial mix contains, in order of decreasing amounts, red millet, white millet, milo, sunflower, and wheat. A four-year Delaware study attempted to determine what seeds birds actually prefer. In decreasing order of preference, they were sunflower, peanut hearts, cracked corn, white millet, and canary seed. Red millet, milo, and wheat, which comprise about 60 per cent of the typical commercial mix, amounted to less than 2 per cent of the birds' diet.

It is unfortunate that most commercial mixes are based on millets and milo rather than on cracked corn. Of the many high-carbohydrate cereal grains available, corn combines all the most important advantages. It is cheap, readily available, and attractive to birds. Its only real disadvantage is that it requires some storage care. It must be kept cool and dry to avoid moths and mold. Be certain you're getting *fine*-cracked *yellow* corn; fine-cracked is more palatable to the smaller birds. Yellow corn, unlike white, is a good source of vitamin A.

The cereal grains, while rich in carbohydrates—and hence good energy-suppliers—are poor sources of protein, fat, and some vitamins and minerals. Probably the best sources of protein for birds are sunflower seed and peanuts, usually fed in the form of peanut hearts or peanut butter. The remarkable popularity of sunflower is well deserved. Very similar nutritionally to peanuts, it gets the nod for providing three times as much iron, twice as much calcium and phosphorus, half again more potassium, and a better vitamin complement. Every bird feeder will want to provide either sunflower or peanuts; anybody who can afford to will feed both.

The other high-fat, high-protein seed popular among northern bird feeders is niger, or black thistle. Thistle seed, as it is usually called, is cultivated for its oil, as are the peanut and sunflower. Long fed to cage birds, thistle has in recent years burgeoned on the wild-bird food market, having proved a favorite of goldfinches, pine siskins, and redpolls. Most ground feeders, from doves to juncos, relish it also. Recently the problem with thistle has been getting it.

In addition to various seeds, beef suet has long been a standard feeder item. Suet is pure fat; as such it is extremely high in calories. A winter insect substitute, it is very popular among woodpeckers, chickadees, nuthatches, and titmice.

Must we provide water and grit in addition to food? The birds will get by without artificial sources of water. They derive more water from their food than you would imagine, and they will supplement that source, if necessary, by eating snow.

Birds do need grit all year long, and grit, like food, is less generally available in the winter. It is not really necessary to provide it, however.

Leonard Lee Rue III/Photo Researchers

Choose protected areas facing south to scatter grain for ground-feeding birds like this grosbeak.

Russ Kinne/Photo Researchers

Sunflower feeding from clear plastic tubes is very popular with both birds and their suppliers.

Many people are more concerned about, and pay more for, their feeders than the food they put in them. While this is obviously illogical, some thought should certainly be given to the dispensing of various foods. In the old days a feeder meant a simple shelf or box, the food placed directly on the floor or gravity-fed from a hopper. Then box feeders became more elegant, utilizing glass, adding weather vanes. Often suet holders were positioned on either end, and the resulting structure was called a feeding station.

Many such feeders are still built and bought, but they have a serious flaw. By putting everything under one roof, the feeding station in practice tends to deny most birds access to anything. A couple of jays or gray squirrels munch away all day while the other birds look on. Feeding stations are now available, for example, with plastic-coated wire grids protecting the open sides. The wire openings are sized to exclude large birds and squirrels. This expensive feeder can be duplicated easily. Knock together a box feeder, and tack plastic-coated chicken wire across the open sides. But make it 1½-inch mesh. Jays, grackles, even gray squirrels will squeeze through standard 2-inch chicken wire.

It is perfectly possible and proper to feed your ground feeders (doves, sparrows, some finches, grosbeaks, cardinals, blackbirds) where they prefer to feed—*on the ground.* Choose protected areas near cover along the south wall of your house, along a tree line or fencerow, under low-growing evergreens or large bushes, and simply scat-

ter your cereal grain, along with some thistle if you can afford it. Feeding on the ground requires some clearing work during and after snow storms, but it is a practical, flexible, and effective way to feed small grains.

Sunflower feeding has been revolutionized in recent years by the use of clear plastic tubes. These are designed to dispense seed through feeding ports or simply through small holes stamped out of the plastic. The genius in this design is that the interior of the feeder is reserved for the food, requiring the birds to feed from outside. Birds much prefer this arrangement as many of them are reluctant to enter a box to feed, even if two sides are open. The feeder keeps the food dry and clean without itself being soiled by the birds. In addition, these feeders lack a horizontal feeding surface. This automatically accommodates the smaller clinging birds while discouraging the larger, less agile birds.

Most bubble feeders are small and lack perches altogether. A variation on the bubble feeder is a small plastic tray with a dome-shaped top, which can be raised or lowered to admit whatever sized birds you choose.

However you feed sunflower, you will sooner or later attract squirrels, which provide a more rigorous challenge than many people care to deal with. A squirrel will jump three meters from tree trunk to hanging feeder. Then, when you have re-hung the feeder from a long horizontal wire, the squirrel proves adept at wire-walking. Probably you will have to buy or rig up a baffle of some sort. Most commercially available feeder baffles are aluminum or steel discs

G. Carleton Ray/Photo Researchers
Squirrels are adept at getting into feeders, but may be discouraged by baffles or careful scheduling.

about 30 centimeters across. Some people use phonograph records, which they place above a hanging feeder or below a post-mounted feeder, hoping to foil the approaching squirrel.

While most squirrels are indifferent to suet, the odd one will take a liking to it. Partly for this reason many people feed suet in netted bags or variously shaped wire cages made for the purpose; these can be hung—and, if necessary, baffled—just as you would a sunflower feeder. (And remember, the minimum height for any suet feeder is several centimeters above the top of the jump of the biggest dog in your neighborhood.)

What does one do about feeder pests? Of course, not everyone agrees on what constitutes a pest. Evening grosbeaks, where common, will outconsume the jays and squirrels together. But few people attempt to discourage them.

Whatever you wish to discourage, your two best approaches are the decentralization of food sources and the use of selective feeders. Spread your small cereal grain in several places. Hang a couple of sunflower feeders and a couple of suet feeders, one of each near the house where you can more easily discourage unwanted birds or squirrels. This applies especially to the suet, which cannot easily be fed selectively. Few jays or squirrels like it, but starlings may consume it.

A DAILY FEEDING SCHEDULE

You can minimize feeding competition from squirrels and large birds through simple feeding scheduling. Squirrels and jays, for example, retire for the night well before the smaller birds (probably, again, because of the advantageous heat-retention factor of their larger bodies). Starting in late fall, I feed once a day, about an hour before sunset. As the winter progresses, I back the feeding time up as far as I can, noting the retiring times of jays and squirrels. By midwinter I'm feeding at about 2:30 P.M., after which I never—well, hardly ever—have a jay or a squirrel. This is two full hours before the last of the small birds retire.

In the morning, as one would expect, the order is reversed, but the lag time is far shorter. Selected arrival times for last February 23 at my Vermont feeders, for example, were: tree sparrow, 6:09; redpoll, 6:19; chickadee, 6:30; goldfinch, 6:39; first blue jay, 6:44.

It's interesting that, among birds of a given size, ground feeders are earlier than tree feeders; they are also later in the evening.

The advantage of this feeding schedule is clear. By the time the jays and squirrels hit my feeders in the morning, the smaller birds have had two uninterrupted sessions with the new food supply. This is just when they need it most—immediately before and after the long winter night. My cereal grain, sunflower, and thistle are likely to peter out about midday, after which most of the birds drift away to forage elsewhere. But the small birds know to return for their undisturbed late-afternoon feeding.

PREDATORS

If most birds come with an eye to suet and seeds, a few will come with an eye to your feeder birds. We had visits, this past winter, from a kestrel, a sharp-skinned hawk, a Cooper's hawk, and two northern shrikes, representing every species of bird predator likely to visit a New England feeder except the goshawks and merlins.

Their visits were typical, consisting of a day or two of intermittent attention to our feeders. The feeder watcher learns to look for a hawk or shrike when a preternatural quiet prevails about his feeders, for at the appearance of a predator, feeder birds will typically dive for cover and sit tight. As far as we could tell, the total predator kill at our feeders was one jay and one sparrow. Native birds handle avian predators pretty adeptly, and most of us welcome the opportunity to study a hawk or shrike at close range.

Several mammalian predators may, on occasion, visit feeders. Three winters ago I was surprised to find a freshly killed evening grosbeak under a sunflower feeder. We left it where it had been killed, and an hour later my wife was a lucky witness when an ermine returned to claim its kill. Among all the predatory mammals, however, only the domestic cat poses a serious threat to feeder birds. You can bell your own cat, of course, or keep it indoors. Strays, barn cats, and other people's house cats are another story. Problem strays can be delivered to the nearest SPCA if you can catch them.

Non-predatory animals will visit your feeders, too, providing more opportunity for behavior study than you had perhaps imagined. Unfortunately, most mammal activity takes place at night, making some sort of artificial lighting and/or stealth necessary to observe it. But don't be surprised to find rabbit pellets collecting under your sunflower feeders. Tired of chewing prickly ash bark,

the rabbits are gathering to munch your sunflower hulls. With a flashlight and some patience under a tree-hanging suet bag, you may be able to catch a glimpse of a flying squirrel, one of our most beautiful and least-known common mammals.

Probably anyone who has read this far is either feeding birds already or is thinking about starting. But how much does a feeding program cost? As for the feeders themselves, the sky's the limit. You can easily pay $100 for three or four feeders, or you can make all your feeders yourself for next to nothing. You may want to do some of each, as I do. I use five purchased feeders: two suet feeders (one netted bag, or one cage-type), two plastic tubetype sunflower feeders, and one nylon thistle feeder. Total cost, about $30.

Feed costs can be halved by buying in bulk, either from feed stores or through cooperative buying programs sponsored by local conservation organizations. A brief account of my own requirements will give you an idea of quantities and costs for a modest but adequate winter feeding program.

I feed 100 pounds of fine-cracked corn; cost, about $12. I need perhaps 30 pounds of suet to sustain two hanging feeders; cost,

Country Journal

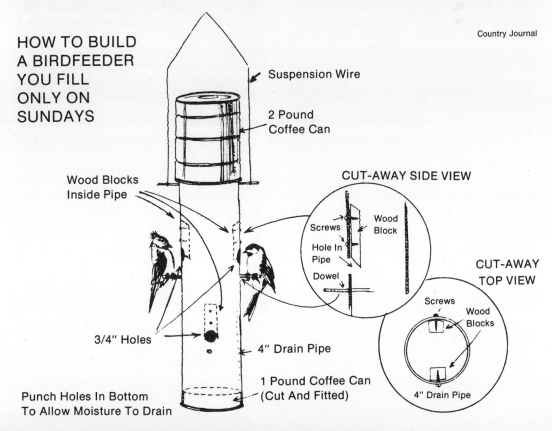

HOW TO BUILD A BIRDFEEDER YOU FILL ONLY ON SUNDAYS

Suspension Wire

2 Pound Coffee Can

Wood Blocks Inside Pipe

CUT-AWAY SIDE VIEW

Screws

Wood Block

Hole In Pipe

Dowel

CUT-AWAY TOP VIEW

3/4" Holes

4" Drain Pipe

Screws

Wood Blocks

1 Pound Coffee Can (Cut And Fitted)

4" Drain Pipe

Punch Holes In Bottom To Allow Moisture To Drain

A house finch perches on a birch stump; most finches are ground feeders, winter or summer.

An open-sided feeder will attract larger birds, like this cardinal, than will the hanging kind.

about $8. (Suet may bring as much as 49 cents in the supermarket; your local butcher may give you all you want.) I feed 200 pounds of sunflower (in hull) through two standard-sized tube feeders; cost, about $50. It is very difficult to anticipate quantity requirements for thistle. I scatter some with my corn and feed it in one small net feeder.

Demand varies according to the unpredictable flights of a few species—especially redpoll, pine siskin, and goldfinch. If you have flocks of these birds all winter, you can feed an enormous amount of thistle. (I communicated this past winter with a Midwesterner who had converted a stovepipe into a 2-meter-long, 10-centimeter-diameter thistle feeder. It was a good year there for small finches, and he was putting $100 *a month* through that feeder.) During a winter when these birds are scarce, you won't need much thistle. Let's say you will need about 25 kilograms (used sparingly) for an average winter; cost, at last winter's going rate, $50. If the supply loosens up, the price should come well down.

Total food cost for a basic feeding program of moderate pretensions, then, comes to something more than $100. Adding some white millet, peanut hearts, and grit will not add substantially to the bill; adding safflower seed, halved pear, and fried fish will.

Can't you save a lot of money by growing your own sunflowers? I once thought so. After all, sunflowers, in addition to being a visual delight, are easy to grow, easy to harvest, and a pleasure to feed right in the heads. But drying the things—there's the

rub. You cut the heads in the fall when the jays begin to wreak havoc with them (before the seeds are fully ripened), and then what?

My brief career raising sunflower for seed got off to a promising start. I brought the heads in after a dry spell and lined them up to dry along the keeping-room walls. A week or so later we noticed that the seeds proceeded to ripen nicely. But my wife and I couldn't agree on the appropriate response to the new night sounds. I found the muffled munching of the deer mice soothing from the upstairs bedroom, but she chose to resent it. We later discovered that, in addition to eating the seed, the mice had been storing it in the most unlikely places. They even managed to ascend the brass stand of an old floor lamp to fill the empty light bulb sockets.

In short, I am grateful to get sunflower at $25 a hundred pounds—which is up, amazingly enough, only 20 per cent over the last twenty-five years. But if you have found a convenient way simultaneously to dry and mouse-proof sunflower heads, by all means carry on. And please, let me know how you do it □

SELECTED READINGS

"Attract more birds to your backyard" by G. Harrison. *National Wildlife*, August 1976.

"Backyard feeders for your feathered friends" by S. Smyser and R. Weintsleiger. *Organic Farming*, October 1976.

"A tightwad's guide to feeding birds" by J. Dennis and E. Van Kesteren. *National Wildlife*, April-May 1979.

WILDLIFE FILMS

by Peter Steinhart

JUST a few years ago, there were nearly a dozen animal programs to watch on television each week. They ranged from "Safari to Adventure," "Last of the Wild," and "Animal World" to "Audubon Wildlife Theater," "The World of Survival," and "Wild Kingdom." Today, most of these programs are off the air. A few are in reruns and, of them all, only Marlin Perkins' "Wild Kingdom" is filming new programs.

The sudden demise of creature features on television has created a void in the nation's living rooms. That's because televised films have become, for most of us, our chief means of seeing animals. "The vast majority of people live in cities," notes Carol Taylor, film producer for the National Audubon Society. "Very few get out into the field to learn about wildlife themselves. Television takes the rest of us out." Films have even changed the way we view animals. Says filmmaker David deVries: "Because of wildlife films, the average American is more aware of the environment and concerned about wildlife."

Is it possible the public has lost interest? Not at all. The occasional wildlife television specials still get about the same ratings. "Most positively there's an audience for them," says Jerry Infantino of the A.C. Nielsen Company, which measures the popularity of television programs. "I think there is another reason for the decline."

Indeed, there are several reasons. For one thing, the cost of making wildlife films has increased while the cost of some competing forms of entertainment has gone down. For another, the ratings game has become more serious. Perhaps most important, wildlife films are so good and have increased the audience's sophistication so much that it is harder and harder to produce new and interesting material.

DISNEY—THE REAL START

Most wildlife filmmakers will tell you the modern era of wildlife films began in the late 1940's with Walt Disney. In 1948, Disney released a short subject about the life of

Wildlife films taken in an animal's natural habitat help assure accuracy. Here photographer Wolfgang Bayer films elephants in Kenya.

Candice Bayer

Films depicting the yearly life cycle of animals such as these monk seals have an audience—but not enough to compete with other programs.

fur seals on Alaska's Pribilof Islands. No New York distributor would handle the film, so Disney booked it himself into a Pasadena, California, theater. There, it drew good audiences. It ended up winning the Academy Award for best short subject in 1949.

Convinced that audiences were interested in animals, Disney set up his own distribution company, Buena Vista, and followed each year thereafter with another True Life Adventure. *Beaver Valley, Nature's Half Acre, Water Birds,* and *Bear Country* each in turn won short-subject Academy Awards. In 1953, Disney released a full-length nature film, *The Living Desert.* He followed in 1954 with *Vanishing Prairie.* Both of them won Academy Awards, too, and each turned a profit. Disney proved that audiences would pay to see animal films.

Disney's were not the first wildlife pictures. In the 1920's and 30's, Frank Buck and Osa and Martin Johnson brought back photographic records of African safaris and South Seas adventures. The early Tarzan pictures were full of wildlife. Travel films often stripped in purchased film of animals to add authenticity.

There were lecture films, generally random scraps held together by the personality of the lecturer and the special interest of the audience. Recalls Karl Maslowski, a lecture filmmaker for many years: "In the old days, if you had a red bird, a yellow bird, and a sunset, all in color, people stood up and cheered." There were educational films. Disney bought much of his True Life Adventure film from independent photographers who had gone out to make instructional films.

HOLLYWOOD TECHNIQUES

But if Disney's wildlife films were not the first, they were the first to apply Hollywood studio techniques. Says N. Paul Kenworthy, who filmed several Disney True Life Adventures: "We were using standard dramatic filming techniques that apply to actors, but for animals. You have two cameras recording two points of view. You have close-ups. You set up the action and have control over it. Often, you can repeat the action for the camera."

Disney photographers were inventive. They took viewers inside beaver lodges and down prairie-dog burrows. They gave the animals' point of view. Ants appeared on the screen as big as locomotives. The Disney revolution was a revolution of intimacy. Film was taking us into the deeper relationships of animal life, just as 30 years earlier it had begun to explore human emotions.

Disney quietly bowed out of the True Life Adventure series in 1960. Paul Kenworthy guesses that "having used up the more dramatic film on hand, Disney probably didn't want the expense of keeping a crew in the field for months with uncertain results." It is much less expensive to film in a studio. So, after 1960, Disney's animal movies were strictly storybook affairs, filmed indoors with rented animals trained to perform on the lot.

Television then took Disney's interest in animals and started its own boom in animal cinematography. "Wild Kingdom," now in its 18th season, took a lesson from Disney and moved its cameras outdoors.

In the early 1970's, the U.S. Federal Communications Commission (FCC) ruled that at least one hour of early evening television had to be reserved for non-network programming. Wildlife films and other educational programs were exempted. That precipitated a rush of syndicated wildlife shows to fill the "prime access time" openings. All at once, the American home became livelier than the Bronx Zoo.

MORE SCIENCE

But the new television fare differed from the old Disney films. The biologists called for more science. One could tell the intimate story of the animal in its environment. Or one could study its reproduction or explain how it copes with human encroachment on its habitat. It was not necessary to make animals behave like people. In any case, the filmmakers, limited by their budgets and by the film they had in their cutting libraries, found it easier to produce scientific documentaries than to try to do what Disney had done.

So, the half-hour programs began to strike a new balance. They treated the animals with more respect. For action, they put in people: Marlin Perkins chasing a kongoni in a Land Rover or biologist John Craighead sedating a grizzly bear.

The debate between education and entertainment has continued to this day. At one extreme are the scare movies about killer whales, murderous grizzlies, and marauding bees. "This is the animal-vs.-people fantasy you can't put on television, the blood-and-guts violence you can only show in a movie theater," Smith says. At the other extreme is the purely scientific film. Most of the examples seen in America have been on educational television and come from England. These range from microphotography of the life in a drop of water to dramatized stories of the search for a disease cure, as in the "Nova" series.

VIEWERS BECOME CONSERVATIONISTS

There has not been much pure science on commercial television. Producers have long held that the average viewer won't sit still for it. The television wildlife boom of the early 1970's, however, did move dramatically in that direction.

By investing a lot of money, filmmakers found that science was as interesting as the biologists said it was. *National Geographic* led the way, in part because it had already funded such scientists as John Craighead and Jane Goodall. Others, including Jacques Cousteau and the Survival Anglia Company in England, soon followed. They sent crews out into the field for months, even years at a time. The filmmakers they hired were generally trained in biology and had the insight needed to get close to their subjects. The photographers were inventive and persistent. They designed remote-control cameras for shy subjects and special gear for filming in small places.

Alan Root spent a year climbing about the branches of an African baobab tree to record the variety of life in and around it. Dieter Plage camouflaged his camera inside a stuffed seagull and swam underwater to film waterflow from an unusual angle. Soon, viewers were seeing "womb to tomb" stories, intimate hour-long portraits of whales, hippos, wolves, octopuses, snow geese, sea otters, and caribou. The films were accurate and scientific. The often poignant truths and tragedies they revealed converted millions of viewers into avid conservationists.

SOPHISTICATED AUDIENCE

The films were so good that audiences became used to seeing something new and startling in each one. Explains deVries: "A couple of years ago, I could have had film of a cheetah killing a gazelle and had the audience on the edge of its seat. They've seen that a half dozen times now, and they want something more. Now, you have to examine subtle relationships."

Filmmakers found it necessary to develop more stunning ideas and to get even closer to the animals. That effort produced

Wildlife photographers must be inventive—to catch natural shots such as this of a newt in underwater vegetation.

Long hours of costly filming are necessary to produce specials like those of Jacques Cousteau (red cap).

even more spectacular films, but it also created problems for the filmmakers. Alan Root was bitten by a puff adder and thrown bodily from Kenya's Mzima Springs by an angry hippo. He ran out of gas twice in the same day while filming from an airplane. Lee Lyon, a young American camerawoman, was killed by an elephant while filming for Survival Anglia. John Pearson, filming another Survival Anglia production in East Africa, was killed in a shooting accident.

In a way, those tragedies were portents of what lay ahead for wildlife films. Beginning in 1976, the weekly series began to disappear. Suddenly, game shows and reruns of old comedies were knocking them out of the early evening time slots. Today, wildlife television films are almost extinct. "Wild Kingdom" is filming only 12 new programs for the 1980 season. National Geographic, Jacques Cousteau, Survival Anglia, and a few other producers once delivered a dozen wildlife specials to the networks each year. In 1980, few if any specials are under contract to the major networks.

It's not that the weekly series have run out of film. Bill Burrud reports that he still has a large amount of unseen film in his library, yet he is not putting any of it into half-hour programs. "You just can't make 26 shows a year," says Burrud.

BIOLOGIST FILMMAKERS

What has happened is that most of that library film was shot a few years ago and, in the light of more recent achievements, has grown commonplace. "You're not going to get very exciting films just cutting out of libraries," says deVries. A wildlife filmmaker must go out and shoot new film. But that is becoming more and more difficult to do. The filmmaker must find an interesting animal, study it, and find in its natural history an interesting story.

Before going out to shoot a film about caribou for Survival Anglia, deVries spent "bits and pieces of three years talking to Eskimos and scientists—everybody who knew about caribou—finding out where they were, when they would be there, how I could get my crew in." Then, he wrote a 20-page treatment organized on the basis of the story his research had suggested. Then he drew up a shopping list of the scenes he hoped to film: a mother dropping her calf; wolves hunting caribou; a bull standing in front of the sinking sun. All this preparation, says deVries, "is the difference between being a filmmaker and a photographer."

To get all those ideas on film requires time. Alan Root spent two years filming the story of the wildebeest migration and another two on the life of the termite. DeVries spent most of two years filming caribou in the Arctic. There are always unforeseen delays. DeVries had trouble recording the birth of a calf. "I was all primed up. I knew where they should be having their calves and when. So we helicoptered in. There were no caribou and we got weathered in. After six days, my pilot came in and said, 'They're not here. They're in Canada.' We spent days getting the equipment out and getting into Canada. Once we set up the equipment and just missed a caribou giving birth by 20 minutes. We didn't finish the film that year."

Wolfgang Bayer has seen more expensive projects go wrong. Once, he waited for months beside an African termite mound for the first rains to bring on the annual swarm of winged ants. But it never rained. It was a year of drought and there was no swarm. Bayer also worked on a Disney television film that was to be called *Clyde, the Kootenay Ram*. After months of shooting, the principal actors, two bighorn rams, died. It would take years to raise and train two more, so the project was shelved.

Wildlife films have brought the life history of even the smallest members of the animal kingdom—such as the red mite—into the living room.

EXPENSIVE TO MAKE

The uncertainty of working with wild animals and the time it takes to record a life cycle make the films "incredibly expensive," says "Wild Kingdom" executive producer Dick Reinauer. Robert Dickson has filmed for Disney and now makes instructional films for the University of California. A whole year of filming to get an animal's yearly life cycle—feeding, mating, birth, everything—could easily run $250,000, he says. That may be more than the competing dramatic programs and celebrity specials cost. According to independent filmmaker Marty Stouffer, the networks pay from $225,000 to $285,000 for wildlife specials. "So," says Stouffer, "you'll sell a film for just about what it cost you to make it."

AND THEN . . . . RATINGS

The high costs make it necessary to sell wildlife films as prime time programs. That plunges them into the rough-and-tumble of the ratings game. The ratings competition has stiffened in recent years, so that now, according to Victor Simpkins of Survival Anglia, "this kind of program is a luxury on the network. Our material is fairly competitive, but it is never going to score like 'Charlie's Angels.' Quality programs to the wind, the name of the game is numbers, and wildlife programs just don't make the numbers."

Television is, above all, an entertainment medium. Wildlife programs have a broad appeal, but not the mass appeal that pure entertainment has. Stouffer says most wildlife films receive ratings of 20 or less. His own film, *The Predators,* which aired opposite David Frost's Nixon interviews in 1977, got a rating of 26. Stouffer believes the rating was unusually high because the film was narrated by Robert Redford and there had been much publicity about Redford's participation.

In the television ratings game, wildlife

There's danger too: here a snake is captured and held for closeup filming.

specials are not positioned opposite such phenomenally successful series as "Mork and Mindy." The networks cannot afford to preempt a lucrative program like that for a relatively low-rated wildlife show. Instead, they will pit wildlife against similarly rated programs—usually celebrity specials like "Cher Bono Goes to Hawaii" or "The National Cheerleading Finals." Network executives believe about three fourths of their entertainment specials will get ratings in the high teens or low twenties, which is where wildlife programs usually score. "In other words," says Marty Stouffer, "we're running neck and neck with Cher."

Well, not quite. Because the network executives also know that about one fourth of their entertainment specials will score over 30, they are not pre-disposed to gamble on a wildlife show that they "know" will be lucky to score 20. Not when a single ratings point is worth millions of dollars in advertising revenue. "It is engraved in stone in the network halls in New York," sighs Stouffer, "that wildlife films do not rate."

AND FOR THE ANIMALS

So it looks like the cost of making a wildlife film has just about gone beyond the limits of the rating system. Does this mean wildlife films will vanish altogether from our television screens? The filmmakers themselves don't think so. "If anything," says filmmaker-biologist Jeff Foott, "I think there is more public interest in wildlife films now than there has ever been." Stouffer believes wildlife films can score higher ratings. Even if they can't outscore the most popular of the entertainment specials, he says, there will always be some market for them.

While that may be so, there's no question the market is shrinking. And that bodes ill for the makers of wildlife films. Educational films and public service efforts sponsored by corporations are not likely to fill the gap. "It's pretty hard to make any money on an educational wildlife film," says Foott.

There may be fewer wildlife filmmakers in the future. And fewer of the spectacular wildlife films we have grown used to. That could be important. After all, wildlife programs have brought animals into our lives and made us eager to fight for their protection. Conversely, does the demise of wildlife fare on television mean wildlife will be put onto some back burner in the public's mind? Given the precarious plight of wild creatures all over the world, that is a grim prospect to consider □

SELECTED READINGS

"First learn to think like a bear" by P. Shankle, Jr. *Popular Photography,* September 1978.

"Masterpieces of wildlife photography from the Audubon Society" by P. Caulfield. *Popular Photography,* August 1978.

"Up close and personal." *National Wildlife,* December, 1978.

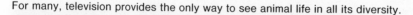

For many, television provides the only way to see animal life in all its diversity.

Peace River Films

Dr. E. R. Degginger

Its old skin cast away, the scarlet king snake displays its new brightly-colored skin.

TAKING IT ALL OFF

by Leonard G. Appleby

ECDYSIS, or shedding of the outer epidermis, is one of a snake's most remarkable habits. It so impressed the ancients that they believed the snake to be immortal, being reborn each time it casts its skin. This is understandable to anyone who has seen a snake just after it has sloughed. Its colors then have the appearance of fresh paint. The snake itself is then active and alert, in striking contrast to its drab appearance and lethargic behavior just prior to skin shedding.

Why does a snake shed its skin? For much the same reason we do (although in scarcely noticeable fashion): to renew the outer epidermis as it becomes worn. Once it has formed, a snake's outer epidermis, or stratum corneum, keratinizes. This is a process that makes it tougher and more resistant to wear. This is important in view of a snake's close contact with the ground and the considerable friction that results. Keratiniza-

tion not only makes a snake's skin resistant to abrasion but also prevents too much loss of moisture from the body. In addition, it forms a barrier to ultraviolet rays, which can be harmful if overabsorbed.

Snakes do not always wait for the stratum corneum to become worn before growing a new one. For an adult snake to follow one sloughing with another within a few weeks is by no means unusual. Just why it does this is not known for certain. With captive snakes, skin shedding in rapid succession usually occurs after a snake has consumed large quantities of food following a period of fasting.

As a rule, an adult snake sloughs three to four times a year, at intervals that are sometimes fairly regular, but often vary widely. Skin wounds can cause frequent sheddings, one following close upon another in order to hasten healing. Skin lesions,

This gopher snake is shedding its dull old skin, alternately contracting and expanding small sections of its body to help loosen and move the skin toward the tail.

Leonard G. Appleby

whether due to injury or disease, show marked improvement—sometimes disappearing completely—when the outer epidermis is renewed. But frequent shedding also occurs in snakes that show no sign of skin injury.

METABOLISM AND SHEDDING

The more rapid a snake's metabolism, the more frequently it will shed. Generally, the higher the temperature, the more rapid is its metabolism. There are a number of tropical snakes, however, such as pythons and boas, that are capable of regulating their metabolic rate regardless of temperature. Their metabolism does not necessarily become more rapid as temperature rises. By varying the secretion of certain hormones they can retard their physiological processes and estivate (become dormant during the summer).

During estivation shedding is either minimal or nonexistent. Snakes in temperate climates experience temperature-induced high metabolism only during very warm spells. On the other hand, they usually demonstrate a slowed metabolism after a sharp drop in temperature.

When the temperature becomes low enough, they hibernate. Skin shedding does not occur during hibernation. In the case of a snake that is preparing to slough when it enters hibernation, the process is halted by the prevailing low temperatures and will not recommence until warmer weather returns in the spring.

A MATTER OF FOOD INTAKE

While its metabolism is dictated by temperature and hormone secretion, a snake cannot operate at full capacity until there is a substantial intake of food. A snake that begins to feed after a lengthy fast usually eats ravenously. A sudden reawakening of appetite is also likely after shedding. The rapid intake of a large quantity of food results in such an abrupt acceleration of the snake's metabolism that a second shedding of the skin follows a few weeks later.

Nearly 40 years spent studying snakes has brought me to the conclusion that the major influence on the frequency of skin shedding is the amount of food consumed. A snake that feeds greedily sheds its skin more often than does an indifferent feeder. But the subsequent rapid growth in a snake that feeds readily is not the prime cause of frequent sheddings.

An aged snake grows very little, if at all, yet it will shed more often when it is feeding well than when not interested in food. For example, an aged royal python in my possession, which measured 145 centimeters when captured, and which has grown scarcely at all in the seven years since then, will shed twice a year if it has fed well over a period of several months. But during fasting, the interval between one shedding and the next has been as long as eighteen months. Like most royal pythons, it is an erratic feeder and frequently fasts for long periods.

SYMPTOMS OF SHEDDING

In most cases, a sudden lack of interest in food signals that a snake is preparing to shed its skin. Gradually, colors dull and markings become less distinct. The ventral scales and the skin between the dorsal scales may take on a milky gray color. Not all snake species exhibit this graying phase, and it is often difficult to determine whether they are preparing to shed until the eyes become obscured by a grayish white opacity. All snakes exhibit this symptom. When its eyes begin to cloud over in this manner, a snake is said to be entering an "opaque."

The eye shield's opaqueness is caused by a thickening of the outer layers of skin and occurs as the new stratum corneum starts to form beneath the old one. The thickening epidermis also obscures the colors and markings of the snake, most of which are in the deeper layers of skin. The Brazilian rainbow boa is one snake that does not become drab as ecdysis draws near. Instead, its beautiful reddish orange color is transformed

Leonard G. Appleby

The Brazilian rainbow boa becomes a milky silver-white (above) before shedding its old skin to reveal its usual beautiful reddish-orange colors and distinct markings (below).

Leonard G. Appleby

to a striking silvery white. The length of time the eyes remain obscured varies by species. For most it lasts five to six days, although total opacity is only half that time.

While its vision is impaired, a snake is generally inactive and prefers to remain hidden since it is particularly vulnerable to attack by other predators then. A cool-climate snake, however, will often emerge to bask in the sun if insufficiently warm in its hiding place. As a rule, a snake that is preparing to shed will not feed. Others will feed immediately after the eyes have cleared and before the skin has been cast. Most will not feed for several days before entering the opaque stage and will only recommence feeding when the old skin has been completely removed.

TAKING IT OFF

When the moment arrives for the skin to be cast—between two and five days after the eyes have cleared—the snake awakes from its torpor and becomes restless. To loosen the old skin, it rubs its nose and the sides of its jaws against rough surfaces. Some snakes yawn frequently, sometimes causing the skin to break free from the edges of the mouth.

Small snakes will often burrow just below the surface of loose soil and thus start the skin peeling. Normally, shedding begins at the head, and getting the skin to break free at this point often takes the snake longer than ridding itself of the whole skin.

Once it has started to peel, the old stratum corneum usually unfurls rapidly. Sepa-

Temperature-sensitive organs in the lips of this emerald tree boa, and similar sense organs in other snakes, help control metabolism and frequency of shedding.

Tomsich

ration of the new epidermis from the old is assisted by a secretion exuded by the underlying layers of skin tissue. As the old skin comes away, the presence of this secretion, which also gives some snakes an oily appearance, is revealed by the moistness of the snake's body and the inside surface of the old skin. This sticky secretion causes particles of foreign matter to adhere to the skin that has been cast. Where there is adequate separation between the two layers of skin, removal of the outer one can be completed within ten to twenty minutes.

As the skin comes away from the head, the snake reduces its head rubbing and begins to push its way through dense vegetative growth, where available. The loosened skin catches on twigs and branches, which help to pull it free as the snake moves forward. Any narrow gap through which the snake can squeeze itself will assist in removing unwanted skin. It is not unusual to find the cast skin of a snake draped in a forked tree branch. While such aids to shedding help to speed the process, they are not necessary.

Once the skin is free of the head and forepart of the body, a snake is capable of removing it through muscular action involving alternate contraction and expansion of a small section of the body at a time. This not only loosens the skin, but also pushes it backward toward the tail. The muscular action is, however, only possible up to a point just anterior to the vent. The snake accomplishes removal of the skin covering the tail by moving forward and allowing the drag of the trailing skin to pull it free.

Nearly all snakes can, under favorable circumstances, shed the outer epidermis in one piece. This occurs commonly among the smaller species, but the considerable weight of the large phythons and boas often prevents them from shedding in one piece. Their skin often tears and must be shed piecemeal. Many snakes require a certain degree of humidity to be able to achieve a perfect shed. Nevertheless, desert-dwelling snakes and others accustomed to a fairly dry habitat are able to remove the integument easily and completely no matter how dry their surroundings.

THE CAST-OFF SKIN

The cast skin possesses none of the colors of its former owner, but may show the markings quite distinctly. Nearly all cast skins are either transparent and colorless or semiopaque and a dirty brown. Depending on the species, some are very fine and delicate; others are coarse and rough. Pythons and boas, which have claws at the vent position, cast the outer casing of the claws along with the skin. On a perfectly cast skin every scale, including the eye shields, can be seen.

In all cases the cast skin is longer than the snake itself because the connecting skin tissue between the scales, which underlaps them, becomes unfolded and extended during shedding. But the amount by which the cast skin is longer than the snake depends largely on the skin's elasticity. This in turn depends on the conditions in which it was removed.

A skin cast in a very damp atmosphere will stretch considerably more than one that is shed under dry conditions. Consequently, the cast skin of a desert-dwelling snake may be only slightly longer than the snake itself, whereas that cast by a water snake in its natural habitat may be longer than the snake itself by as much as one-fifth the snake's length.

One of the snake's first actions after it has released itself from the unwanted skin is to take a drink of water, if possible. Many snakes not only stop feeding while the new stratum corneum is forming, but also do not drink. There is considerable loss of moisture through evaporation from the body during the actual casting of the skin, and this must be replaced.

Shedding is an important event in the life of a snake. Not only does it acquire a new and roomier integument, but also minor skin wounds are healed and unwelcome parasites such as mites are left behind with the shed skin that lies discarded on the ground ☐

 SELECTED READINGS

Reptiles by Angus D'A. Bellairs. Humanities Press, 1975.

A large female wasp drags her paralyzed tarantula victim across the grass.

THE SPIDER AND THE WASP

by Peter D. Capen

IT is late summer. Dawn breaks over the rolling hills of California's upper Carmel Valley, sending brilliant shafts of light cascading across the short, withered grass and bouncing too among the leaves and heavy gnarled limbs of the oaks. As the sun's rays shorten and warm, the last chill of night loses its grip. The hillsides turn a rich golden hue. It promises to be another hot day.

Sitting on a small knoll, breathing in the fragrance of the dried grass mixed with the scent of sage and chaparral, I look around me and see the day's activities are already well under way. A myriad of insects and other creatures small and large are busily crawling, scurrying, or flying about in their daily and unending search for food. Some are gathering seeds, pollen, or nectar. Others are predators in search of prey.

Two adversaries that will have a fateful encounter this summer morning are a spider and a wasp. Only one will survive. The other will play a unique role in the renewal of the victor's life cycle.

ENTER THE COMBATANTS

Off to one side of the knoll, not far from where I sit, a large, hairy tarantula spider is making its way home to its burrow after a successful night's hunt. It is about five centimeters across the body, excluding the long, sturdy legs. It moves over the clods of dirt and dried stubble at an unhurried, but steady pace. Although its eyesight is poor and it has little or no hearing or sense of smell, the tarantula has a highly developed sense of touch.

Unexpectedly bumping into a stiff blade of grass, the spider rears backwards on its four hind legs, raising high its four front legs and slowly opening its fangs. There is no doubt about its warning signal. Provoked further, it suddenly lashes out with blinding speed and awesome force, grabbing viciously at the offending grass barring its way. Even the most agile beetle or grasshopper that makes the mistake of blundering across the path of a tarantula—especially a hungry one—cannot escape its lightning attack.

After two or three minutes in its raised defensive stance, the spider, sensing the danger has passed, slowly lowers its front legs to the ground. Moving off, it resumes its unhurried journey towards its burrow.

On the other side of the knoll on which I am sitting, a large female wasp is just emerging from her underground home. Metallic-blue to greenish black in color, with fiery orange wings that turn a dusky hue at their tips, she is a striking and formidable-looking creature. She is about to begin her search for the nectar on which she feeds. Yet on this day she is motivated by another urge as well, an urge every bit as compelling as her need for food. In her ovary she carries an egg that is ready to be laid. But before she can lay it, she must first find a live victim that will provide nourishment later on to her developing young. She must find a tarantula. She is the spider's deadliest enemy and, appropriately, is called the "tarantula hawk."

Although the tarantula hawk's movements seem slow and deliberate, she is able to dart away at great speed when menaced. She has very good eyesight, and an extremely painful sting. She produces but few eggs, which are laid singly at intervals of two or three days. For every egg she lays the wasp must provide a live, but paralyzed, tarantula. Since the adult spider lays 200 to 400 eggs at a time, producing as many as several thousand young, there is little likelihood the wasp will be unsuccessful in her hunt, or upset the delicate balance that exists between predator and prey.

THE BATTLE BEGINS

Hesitating at the entrance of her hole, the wasp takes a few moments to clean herself, then lifts off and flies out low over the knoll. After flying back and forth for several minutes, she spots the spider and immediately alights. The spider, having not yet sensed its deadly foe, is still plodding along.

Peter D. Capen

The wasp is about to deposit the tarantula in the grave she has carefully chosen and prepared.

Showing neither fear nor hesitation, the wasp walks up to the much larger spider and gently taps its legs with her feelers. The spider rears back in its posture of defense. Yet, strangely, it does not strike. The wasp walks away, noses around, cleans herself a little, and returns to the spider. Once more she taps its legs with her antennae. Then lightly she touches the tips of the tarantula's legs with her own. She taps its jaws with her feelers, apparently totally unconcerned by the menacing fangs that are now fully extended. Although obviously alarmed, the spider still does not strike. The wasp quickly slips underneath the tarantula and emerges out the other side. Her inspection complete, she flies off.

The tarantula hawk does not go far, however. Landing a short distance away, she begins digging in the loose dry dirt. She is preparing the spider's grave. Using her front legs, she digs rapidly. She grasps bits of soil in her jawlike mandibles and passes them back between her legs. When the hole is about four centimeters in diameter and perhaps eight centimeters deep, the wasp stops digging, backs out of the hole, and flies off. She skims over the ground and lands about five meters away. Furiously, she starts digging another hole. Finally, the new grave is completed and the wasp takes off to search for the spider, which in the meantime has continued on its way. She quickly locates it.

The paralyzed tarantula, tucked away in its grave, becomes food for the wasp's young.

Peter D. Capen

IN FOR THE KILL

Wasting no time, she walks right up to the tarantula and begins feeling it all over again with her antennae. Despite the wasp's persistent molestation, the spider makes little attempt at resistance. It is almost as if it were already resigned to its inevitable fate. Slowly the wasp maneuvers her hapless quarry into a corner, while all the time searching for the vital spot in the soft membrane at the point where the spider's leg joins its body. It is the only place her sting can penetrate the horny skeleton. She grabs one of the tarantula's legs in her powerful jaws and bends her abdomen, distending her sting, ready to deliver the final blow, at the same time giving off a strong, pungent odor.

The tormented spider at last makes a desperate but vain attempt to save its life. Locked in deadly combat, the two roll over and over on the ground, until the wasp finally manages to plunge in her sting and hold it there a few seconds while pumping in the poison. The tarantula falls over on its back, paralyzed. Its "heart" has stopped beating, but it is not dead.

The wasp, none the worse for wear, begins busily cleaning herself, after which she sucks up the "blood" oozing from the wound in the spider's abdomen. Grabbing hold of the tarantula's leg with her jaws, she begins hauling it on its back across the ground to the grave she has prepared.

LIFE FROM DEATH

As I sit watching in fascination, the wasp loosens her powerful grip on the spider. She enters the hole and immediately sets to work inspecting it. She moves rapidly around the prospective grave, touching the walls continuously with her antennae. Shortly, she re-emerges. But rather than dragging the spider down into the hole, as I expect her to do, she instead flies away. Having apparently decided this hole is not the one she is looking for, she hurries off in search of the right one.

Crisscrossing the knoll, the wasp finally pauses at another burrow, carefully examines it, and seeming to find it satisfactory, flies off to retrieve the spider. Yet the grisly drama is still not over. After pulling her heavy burden over more rough terrain to the new location, and with difficulty depositing it inside, she again changes her mind. Slipping on the loose dirt, the wasp labors to drag the spider back out into the open. Once done, she takes to the air to resume her search.

The wasp's puzzling behavior continues unabated for almost an hour. By now it is nearly mid-day. Eventually, the tarantula hawk's painstaking efforts are rewarded. The long-sought grave is found. Lingering not even a moment to rest, the wasp returns to the spider and hauls it over to the hole. Quickly tugging it inside, she disappears from sight.

Once the spider has been carefully tucked away in its grave, the wasp lays her egg on the side of its abdomen, securing the egg in place with a sticky secretion. Then she fills in the hole, obliterating all traces of its whereabouts.

Her young safely secured on the road to life, the tarantula hawk flies away. Later, when the tiny larva hatches, all the fresh food and liquid it will require to reach adulthood is right at hand. In the end, the spider will be reduced to little more than an indigestible chitinous skeleton and the young wasp will leave the burrow to begin the cycle anew □

INDEX

CONTRIBUTORS

LAWRENCE K. ALTMAN, M.D., *Medical reporter, The New York Times*
REVIEW OF THE YEAR: HEALTH & DISEASE

LEONARD G. APPLEBY, *ophiologist, writer, and sculptor*
TAKING IT ALL OFF

JOEL E. AREM, *crystallographer and curator of the Smithsonian Institution's National Synthetics Collection*
SYNTHETIC CRYSTALS

ISAAC ASIMOV, *Associate Professor of Biochemistry, Boston University School of Medicine; well-known science writer, author of more than 200 books*
THE 1980's

GINA BARI KOLATA, *staff writer for Science magazine; frequently writes about new developments in mathematics*
PROBLEMS TOO HARD FOR COMPUTERS

J. KELLY BEATTY, *staff member, Sky and Telescope*
SATURN

TRUDY E. BELL, *Science writer and editor*
co-author AN AMAZING GALAXY IS FOUND

EDWARD M. BRECHER, *Free-lance writer on science and medicine*
SMOKING ADDICTION

JANE E. BRODY, *Free-lance writer*
ASPIRIN

CHARLES G. BURCK, *Associate Editor, Fortune magazine*
SOLAR PHOTOVOLTAIC ENERGY
CANCER AND THE DIESEL CAR

LAURIE BURNHAM, *Research associate, Museum of Comparative Zoology, Harvard University*
AMBER

GENE BYLINSKY, *Associate Editor, Fortune magazine*
THOSE SMART YOUNG ROBOTS

GENE ELLE CALVIN, *Collects and photographs seeds and plants.*
co-author FUEL FROM PLANTS

MELVIN CALVIN, *Awarded the Nobel Prize in 1961 for his work in photosynthesis; at the Laboratory of Chemical Biodynamics in Berkeley, California, he is finding ways to convert plants to useful energy sources.*
co-author FUEL FROM PLANTS

PETER D. CAPEN, *Free-lance writer and underwater photographer*
THE SPIDER AND THE WASP

MARK R. CHARTRAND III, *Director, Hayden Planetarium*
co-author AN AMAZING GALAXY IS FOUND

JAMES CORNELL, *Publications manager of Smithsonian Astrophysical Observatory; author of several books on popular science.*
THE MULTIPLE-MIRROR TELESCOPE

WILLIAM J. CROMIE, *Director, the Council for the Advancement of Science Writing; former oceanographer*
EL NIÑO

JOEL DAVIS, *Science writer; contributor to Astronomy, Futura, and Omni magazines.*
THE SUN-GRAZERS

TREVOR FISHLOCK, *Journalist: fellow of World Press Institute, Macalester College*
CLEANLY FLOWS THE THAMES

DAVE FOREMAN, *Southwestern regional representative, The Wilderness Society*
ORV'S THREATEN A WILD CANYON

KENDRICK FRAZIER, *Free-lance writer, formerly of Science News*
THE ANASAZI SUN DAGGER

ROBERT GEBALLE, *Free-lance science writer*
EPILEPSY

MARVIN R. GORE, *Dean, School of Business Administration, Mt. San Antonio College*
MICROPROCESSORS

JOEL GREENBERG, *Behavioral Sciences Editor, Science News*
REVIEW OF THE YEAR:
BEHAVIORAL SCIENCES

KATHERINE HARAMUNDANIS, *Research Associate, Smithsonian Astrophysical Observatory; co-author, "Introduction to Astronomy"*
REVIEW OF THE YEAR: ASTRONOMY

ZSOLT HARSANYI, *Member of the faculty, Cornell Medical College; project director, genetics research, U.S. Congressional Office of Technical Assessment.*
co-author USING GENES TO PREDICT DISEASES

ANNABEL HECHT, *Staff writer, Food & Drug Administration, Office of Public Affairs*
LASER LIGHT SHOWS

JOHN F. HENAHAN, *Free-lance science writer*
FIRE

HUGH F. HENRY, *Head, Department of Physics, DePauw University*
co-author REVIEW OF THE YEAR:
PHYSICAL SCIENCES

GLADWIN HILL, *Free-lance writer; former environment editor, The New York Times*
REVIEW OF THE YEAR: THE ENVIRONMENT

KEITH HINDLEY, *Free-lance science writer*
ARIANE: EUROPE'S SPACE LAUNCHER

RICHARD HUTTON, *Author "Bio Revolution" and co-author "Life-Spans"*
co-author USING GENES TO PREDICT DISEASES

RICHARD JAYNES, *Geneticist, The Connecticut Agricultural Experiment Station*
THE AMERICAN CHESTNUT

CAROL KAHN, Free-lance science writer
GROWING OLD

JOHN G. KEMENY, Former president, Dartmouth College; chairman of President's Commission on The Accident at Three Mile Island
THE KEMENY REPORT

RICHARD M. KLEIN, Professor of Botany, University of Vermont; columnist Garden magazine
THE LEAF'S PLUMBING

CORLISS KRISTENSEN, Science writer, Bio-Science Laboratories Representative, National Audubon Society
SYNTHETIC FUELS

SARA LAZAROFF, Free-lance science writer
STUTTERING
NIGHTMARES AND NIGHT TERRORS

BENEDICT A. LEERBURGER, Free-lance science writer
GASOHOL
MOUNT ST. HELENS ERUPTS

DAVID LEFF, Senior writer, Medical World News
DIABETES IN THE EARLY 80's

BRUCE MARGON, Astronomer, University of California, Los Angeles
SS 433: A PECULIAR STAR

WILLIAM MATTHEWS III, Regent's Professor of Geology, Lamar University; Director of Education, American Geological Institute
REVIEW OF THE YEAR: EARTH SCIENCE

BARBARA MCDOWELL, Free-lance writer
THE 1979 NOBEL PRIZES IN PHYSICS
AND CHEMISTRY

MARTIN MCLAUGHLIN, Senior Fellow, Overseas Development Council
co-author REVIEW OF THE YEAR:
MAN & HIS WORLD

WILLIAM D. METZ, Editor, Science magazine
MEXICAN OIL

JULIE ANN MILLER, Life Sciences Editor, Science News
PROTECTING YOUR TEETH
REVIEW OF THE YEAR: BIOLOGY

CHUCK NERPEL, Executive Editor, Motor Trend magazine
TURBOCHARGERS

HOLCOMB B. NOBLE, Editor, The New York Times Magazine
THE AIR: UNSAFE AT ANY SITE

JEANNE O'NEILL, Associate Editor, Science World
REVIEW OF THE YEAR: COMPUTERS
AND MATHEMATICS

THOMAS W. PEW JR, Free-lance writer
BIOFEEDBACK AS BEHAVIORAL THERAPY

MAYA PINES, Free-lance writer; author "The Brain Changers: Scientists and the New Mind Control"
DRUGS AND THE MIND

ALAN PISTORIUS, Contributor to several birding magazines
FOOD FOR THE BIRDS

JANET RALOFF, Policy/Technology Editor, Science News
REVIEW OF THE YEAR: ENERGY

ARTHUR L. ROBINSON, Research News Department, Science magazine
TALKING TO COMPUTERS

KATHRYN KARSTEN RUSHING, Former assistant editor, National Parks & Conservation magazine; co-author, bicentennial series on historical topics of significance to the National Park System
THE ESKIMO AND THE BOWHEAD

CARL SAGAN, Astronomer; educator; author "The Dragons of Eden," "Broca's Brain"
GROWING UP WITH SCIENCE FICTION

EDWIN R. SAGE, Author "Problem Solving with the Computer"
BASIC

MARSHALL SCHUON, Assistant to the Science News director and automotive editor, The New York Times
POLICE RADAR

ANNE K. SHELLY, Free-lance science writer.
WINNING THE BATTLE AGAINST HEART DISEASE

DAVA SOBEL, Free-lance science writer; contributing editor, Harvard magazine
JOVE'S THUNDERBOLTS

PETER STEINHART, Free-lance writer
WILDLIFE FILMS

BOB STROHM, Managing Editor, National Wildlife magazine
REVIEW OF THE YEAR: WILDLIFE

WALTER SULLIVAN, Science Reporter, The New York Times
LOW-LEVEL RADIATION

STEVEN R. TANNENBAUM, Professor of Food Chemistry, MIT; author "Nutritional & Safety Aspects of Food Processing"
NITRITES IN YOUR BODY

JOHN TEDFORD, Free-lance science writer
MAGNETIC LEVITATION

JENNY TESAR, Free-lance writer
SPLIT GENES

LANSING P. WAGNER, Free-lance science editor
SCIENCE BOOKS OF THE YEAR

EUGENE J. WALTER JR, Editor, Animal Kingdom; curator of publications, New York Zoological Society
ANIMAL BEHAVIOR

SUSAN WEST, Earth Sciences Editor, Science News
DINOSAUR HEAD HUNT

VITA WEST-MUIR, Free-lance science writer
WOOD STOVES

JOHN NOBLE WILFORD, Director of Science News, The New York Times
REVIEW OF THE YEAR: SPACE SCIENCE

GURNEY WILLIAMS III, Science & Engineering Editor, Popular Mechanics
MICROSURGERY

J. TUZO WILSON, Sc.D., F.R.S., Director, Ontario Science Center, Toronto
PLATE TECTONICS